CATALYST SUPPORTS AND
SUPPORTED CATALYSTS

Catalyst Supports and Supported Catalysts

Theoretical and Applied Concepts

Alvin B. Stiles
University of Delaware

Butterworths

Boston   London   Durban   Singapore   Sydney   Toronto   Wellington

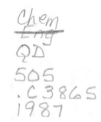
Library of Congress Cataloging-in-Publication Data

Stiles, Alvin B., 1909–
  Catalyst supports and supported catalysts.
  Bibliography: p.
  Includes index.
  1. Catalysts. 2. Catalyst supports. I. Title.
QD505.S74 1987   660.2'995   86-18858
ISBN 0-409-95148-X

Butterworth Publishers
80 Montvale Avenue
Stoneham, MA 02180

10 9 8 7 6 5 4 3 2 1

Printed in the United States of America

CONTENTS

PREFACE

Over the years, a better understanding of the cofunctioning of catalysts and their supports has been achieved. Pre-1940 publications usually referred to the support as a carrier, and this is exactly what researchers thought was occurring. The catalytic material, usually thought of as the more expensive of the ingredients, was distributed over a carrier in order to decrease the cost per unit volume of the catalyst. This was particularly true of the precious metals but was similarly true with vanadium pentoxide promoted with potassium sulfate, quickly recognized by the reader as sulfuric acid, synthesis catalyst for the oxidation of SO_2 to SO_3 invented in both Germany and the United States in the period 1916 to 1919 [1, 2, 3]. Reference to the supports described in those days revealed a hair-raising array of materials—blood char, bone char, chamotte, cement, and kaolin, as well as common clay. For those who are concerned about asbestosis, asbestos was one of the most common carriers.

As the years passed, an understanding of the carrier increased. The term *support* came into more common use, and it was recognized subsequently that the support quite often was a promoter. In fact, one reference describes the difference between a promoter and a support as being the difference in quantity. If the support exceeds the quantity of the catalyst, it becomes a support; otherwise it is a promoter. This view, of course, was rather simplistic, but presumably in future years much that we publish now will be thought of also as quite simplistic or, worse, erroneous.

Considering clays, a substantial increase in understanding of their fundamental characteristics is emerging. First, we recognize that there are many types of clays; second, the clays have ion exchange properties; and, third, by certain treatments of the clays, one can develop silico-aluminate crystallinity with enhanced ion exchange properties closely resembling the zeolites.

In many of the early references to alumina, there was no differentiation between the types of alumina species that were present. Usually they were defined as corundum or activated alumina. As our knowledge of alumina has increased and different species have been isolated and identified, it has become recognized that catalysts supported on the different species of alumina have different catalytic properties [4]. This led to the observation that the aluminas that were highly reactive, such as gamma and eta, could react with the catalytic component in a solid-state reaction at comparatively low temperatures (with oxides such as nickel) to form spinels [5]. On the other hand, if the catalytic metal was put on the support as a salt or as a precipitate, which could orient on the support and assume lattice dimensions similar to that of the type of alumina on which it was supported, then an epitaxial relationship could develop, altering the catalyst's spatial dimensions so the catalyst again could be strongly altered from its inherent characteristics [6].

In this same time frame, observations were made that the catalyst and the support were sometimes cooperating to produce two simultaneous and mutually beneficial reactions. This was called the dual-functioning catalyst and was observed in hydro-denitrogenation, hydrodesulfurization, and reforming catalysts, to name only a few.

The purpose of this book is to try to bring to this rather unclear and complex picture a better understanding of the catalyst-support interaction, whether it be solid-state reactions, in which an element moves into the lattice of the support and becomes totally lost to the reaction, or whether the catalytic material either during the manu-facture of the catalyst or during its use orients in a manner referred to technically as epitaxial orientation. This book brings into one volume a recognition of the effects on the resultant catalyst of such diverse forms of crystalline structure as the spinel, wurtzite, perovskite, and the pseudomorphs that can be developed intentionally or unintentionally. Inasmuch as alumina is one of the most common of supports, many of our reference and experimental data will refer to the many forms and catalytic examples involving alumina as a support or ingredient.

Strong effort has been made to bring into this publication the vast knowledge of experts in the field. In addition to the contributing authors who have labored long and ungrudgingly to combine their own research with the literature, I want to thank Sandra Grim, who knows so well the tremendous effort that was necessary to assemble this book.

REFERENCES

1. Kozlowski, R., et al. 1983. X-ray absorption fine structure investigation of vanadium (V) oxide, titanium oxide (IV) oxide catalysts. *J. Phys. Chem.* 87:5172–6.
2. Wachs, Israel E.; Saleh, Ramzi Y.; Chan, Shirley S.; and Chersich, Claudio C. 1985. The interaction of vanadium pentoxide with titania (anatase): Part I. Effect on o-xylene oxidation to phthalic anhydride. *Appl. Catal.* 15:339–52.
3. Wachs, Israel E.; Chan, Shirley S.; and Saleh, Ramzi Y. The interaction of V_2O_5 with TiO_2 (anatase) II. Comparison of fresh and used catalysts for o-xylene oxidation to phthalic anhydride.
4. U.S. patent 3,244,644 (4-5-66) "Method of Preparing a Catalyst Composition Consisting of Eta-Alumina and the Product Thereof."
5. U.S. patent 3,186,957 (6-1-65) "Method of Preparing a Nickel Oxide Alumina Composition and the Product Thereof."
6. U.S. patent 3,317,439 (5-1-67) "Catalyst Aggregates of Crystallites."

INTRODUCTION AND SCOPE

The purpose of this book is to cover as completely as possible all ramifications of support types and support-catalyst relationships. The definition of the support will be broad, including granular, powdered, colloidal, coprecipitated, extruded, pelleted, spherical, wires, honeycombs, and skeletal supports such as diatomaceous earth. The inorganic supports will also be defined as refractory oxides or metals whose melting point is above 1000°C. This temperature has been arbitrarily chosen. Catalysts to be considered will be the oxides, mixed oxides, metals, mixed metals, and mixed oxides and metals. A further consideration will be that it is unlikely under any circumstances that an absolutely pure metal will be present or a stoichiometrically true oxide or mixed oxide comprises the support. The organic supports will in general be resins or plastics usually having ion exchange properties.

A further purpose of this book is to elucidate the relationship between the catalyst and the support. In the past, it was believed that the support or carrier was simply a platform on which the catalytic metal or oxide was disposed as broadly and uniformly as possible. Even researchers in the early twentieth century had some understanding of the chemical relationship between the support and the catalyst and spoke of it in publications. However, over the years with the more sophisticated instruments, purer gases with which to work, and more definable reaction environments, it has been possible to pinpoint to a greater degree the relationship between the support and the catalytic material [1–9]. In *Catalysis* (Berkman et al. 1940), the relationship between a support and a catalyst was defined rather crudely. If the support was present to the extent of less than the catalytic material itself, it was stated to be a promoter, but if it was present to a percentage greater than the catalytic material, it was a support. This implies the recognition even at this early date that the support was a catalytic component in the broadly construed catalytic composition.

The purposes of the support have been varied. An early purpose was to obtain a solid granular material on which a catalytic component could be coated so as to derive a sufficiently hard and stable structure to withstand disintegration under gas or liquid flows. Later it was observed that a precious metal such as platinum would serve as well on a support as in a wire screen in many cases. As a consequence, platinum was supported on asbestos, alumina, diaspore, corundum, and many other types of support. The purpose in this case was to make it possible to fill a large volume with a catalyst comprising precious metals diluted to perhaps 0.01% of that which would be necessary if wires or screens were used as the precious metal. Another purpose has been identified over the years as a stabilizer to prevent agglomeration of lower-melting-point materials. As an example, aluminum oxide, magnesium oxide, or thorium oxide, in finely divided dispersion prevents the agglomeration of metals such as copper, platinum, or oxides such as zinc, molybdenum, and those comprising the heteropoly acids. A still further use for the support was as a refractory sponge such as that typical of diatomaceous earth, which is the siliceous residue of the skeletons of freshwater diatoms. This spongy refractory serves as a reservoir for semimolten salts such as potassium vanadate, potassium sulfate, iron, cobalt, and nickel sulfate mixtures. The melting point of this catalyst mixture is approximately the same as or slightly below the operating temperature of the reaction in which it is used—the oxidation of sulfur dioxide to sulfur trioxide in the sulfuric acid process. Thus we have some of the physical functions of the support.

As stated, we are learning that the support may and should be considered an active part of the catalytic composite. A case in point is methanol synthesis catalysts. A few of the various types of methanol synthesis catalysts are

Zinc oxide $\cdot$ $ZnCr_2O_4$,

Zinc oxide $+$ Cr_2O_3,

$ZnO + CuOx$,

$ZnO \cdot CuO \cdot ZnCr_2O_4CuCr_2O_4$,

$ZnCrO_4$(reduced),

$ZnO + CuO + Al_2O_3$,

$ZnO + CuO + Cr_2O_3$.

Methanol synthesis catalyst can be made by various methods. The first involves the reaction of zinc oxide with chromic acid, as shown in the reaction

$$ZnO + H_2CrO_4 \rightarrow ZnCrO_4 + H_2O.$$

This catalyst is identified after reduction of the chromate to chromite as the high-temperature, high-pressure methanol synthesis catalyst. This catalyst has specific methanol synthesis properties under specific temperature and pressure conditions. It will produce large quantities of by-products if not operated under the optimum conditions. This catalyst can also be made by the following technology: $Cu(NO_3)_2 + Zn(NO_3)_2 + H_2CrO_4 + NH_4OH \rightarrow CuOH \cdot ZnOH \cdot 2(NH_4)_2CrO_4 + 4NH_4NO_3$, which on heating to 400°C becomes basic zinc copper chromate. The decomposition product of this basic chromate, $CuO \cdot ZnO \cdot CuZn(Cr_2O_4)_2 + H_2O + N_2$, which is known as copper-zinc chromites is produced from hexavalent chromium. Still another method of producing a methanol catalyst with stabilizers is $Cu(NO_3)_2 + Zn(NO_3)_2 + Cr(NO_3)_3 + 7NH_4OH$ gives $Cu(OH)_2 + Zn(OH)_2 + 2Cr(OH)_3 + 7NH_4NO_3$. This on calcining becomes $CuO + ZnO + 2Cr_2O_3$, which is not a chromite inherently but a mixture of copper, zinc, and chromium oxides. This mixture, however, on calcining, will go through a solid-state reaction, which produces the chromite identifiable as such by X-ray diffraction. This chromite is derived from trivalent chromium.

Copper-zinc oxide methanol synthesis catalysts can also be produced in the following precipitation:

$$Cu(NO_3)_2 + Zn(NO_3)_2 + Al(NO_3)_3 + 7NH_4OH \rightarrow$$
$$Cu(OH)_2 + Zn(OH)_2 + Al(OH)_3 + 7NH_4NO_3.$$

On calcining, the hydroxides are converted to the oxides of zinc + copper + Al_2O_3.

There are many other ways of producing methanol synthesis catalysts, which are simply variations of those already presented, one of which is the use of sodium aluminate to precipitate copper and zinc from their respective nitrates or the use of sodium chromate for the precipitation of basic copper and zinc chromates using the same fundamental scheme of precipitation. In both cases, the sodium must be removed by ion exchange after the precipitation and calcining processes are completed. Although the alkali can be essentially completely removed to less than 50 parts per million, the catalysts produced by this scheme have a decidedly different methanol synthesis character than do the catalysts described, and furthermore each behaves differently from the others in the group. Still a different method of preparation involves the slurrying of finely divided alumina hydrate in the copper nitrate, zinc nitrate solution, and the precipitation of the copper and zinc carbonates or hydroxides using ammonium hydroxide, ammonium carbonate, or sodium carbonate. These precipitates must also be carefully ion exchanged to remove the sodium.

The point being made here is that, although the compositions of the catalysts and the stabilizers used are similar to another one in the group, the performance of each one of these is individual to its composition and especially the methods of preparation.

In the equations of the preparative reactions, the chromium oxide and aluminum oxides can be represented either as the mixed oxides with the catalytic materials or as the aluminates or chromites, which are spinels, ionic crystal compounds. A structural relationship in a spinel is illustrated in Figure 1. One of the important points being established is that in this case, spinel (sharing of oxygens of the catalytic metal with

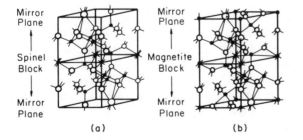

Figure 1   Simplest spinel unit crystal: (a) $MgAl_2O_4$, (b) Magnetite $FeFe_2O_4$.

Note: The Fe ion is such that it fits into either the A or B site of a spinel. γAl_2O_3 is also a spinel structure.

the support) is formed in the precipitation step when the salts have the chromium in the anionic location ($NH_4)_2CrO_4$ or $Na_2Al_2O_4$. This same spinel is formed but under solid-state reaction conditions when all the oxides are precipitated in the cationic location. For example,

$$400°C$$
$$Cu(OH)_2 + Zn(OH)_2 + 4Cr(OH)_3 \rightarrow CuO \cdot ZnO \cdot 2Cr_2O_3.$$

X-ray pattern of this mixture fails to detect spinel. However, if the $CuO \cdot ZnO \cdot 2Cr_2O_3$ is heated further to 500°C, the X-ray pattern shows the incipient (50%) spinel, and as the temperature increases, the quantity increases and the crystallite size increases.

These various raw material salts and reactions are presented to demonstrate the following:

1. If precipitated under favorable conditions, spinel formation and support-catalyst oxygen sharing is inherent.
2. If precipitation conditions are not favorable for the formation of the spinel by methasis, heating will, in the cases cited, form the spinel by solid-state reactions.

This eventual formation of the spinel despite varying preparative conditions is to show that chemical union of the catalyst and support is more likely to occur than not to occur either under preparation conditions or operating or regeneration conditions for the catalyst. The foregoing spinels are a rather simple representation of much more complex reactions (oxygen sharing in ionic crystals) such as copper zincate or, even more likely, copper aluminate or chromite spinels with an oxygen removed from the spinel lattice by reduction prior to use. These component interactions will be considered more fully subsequently, but the purpose is to prepare readers for the major thrust of the book: to elucidate catalyst-support relationships and thereby offer explanations for some apparent aberrations of supported catalysts.

At one time, the zinc oxide itself was considered to be simply a support for the copper in the copper-zinc oxides methanol catalyst. We now know that there is an optimum ratio for the copper and zinc, and neither the Cu nor Zn should exceed a range of values. Does the interaction produce an incipient zincate? It would be helpful to know.

This introduction will not describe the variations caused by the degree to which the solid-state reaction product is formed; this will be discussed in greater detail in Chapter 2. It has been shown already that the copper and aluminum or chromium of a spinel actually share oxygens. This is a point that must be carefully considered as one of the characteristics of a support: the sharing of oxygens (or other ions) with the catalytic material. It is obvious that this sharing makes a substantial alteration in the catalytic properties of both, particularly when one of the shared oxygens can be removed by reduction, leaving a vacancy, as is the case with copper, zinc, and nickel spinels.

Perovskites ($CaTiO_3$ model) have received much attention recently in the open as well as the patent literature but have failed to live up to their initially reported excellence. Although much effort has been exerted to reproduce their earlier reported

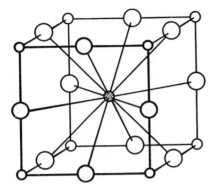

Figure 2 Perovskite structure.

equivalence to precious metals, the precious metals producers and processors have not lost either any business or sleep. A. W. Sleight reported good activity with the non-stoichiometric perovskites, and Alan Lauder has patents on perovskites as shells containing and immobilizing Ru when used in three-way catalytic automotive fume abatement service. These also have not stimulated reported further development or commercial adopting or adapting.

A glance at the perovskite unit crystal in Figure 2 reveals its twelve central ion coordination and the obvious chemically and physically stable structure.

It will be a further objective of this book to describe alumina exhaustively as a support because it is probably the most frequently used support material. It is described in sufficient detail and as a model so that it can be shown that different species react with the catalytic entity in a specific way, and each species has a marked effect on the catalytic properties of the resultant composite. For example, alpha alumina is a much less reactive alumina than is gamma or eta and thus interacts with the catalytic compound with greater difficulty. Because of these differences in reactivity of different species, aluminas will be discussed with respect to species because it would tend to serve as a model of other types of support materials that also have many species whose characteristics vary widely.

Coprecipitated supports have already been considered in the discussion of the methanol synthesis catalyst. Colloidal silica is obtainable as spherulites of various diameters and can be coprecipitated. It is frequently used in oxidation catalysts such as those used for the synthesis of acrylonitrile from ammonia, oxygen, and propylene. The interaction of the silica and other components has been a subject of extensive research and reporting. On coalescing, the colloidal silica forms clustered spheres producing a sponge-like reservoir for the catalysts of the heteropoly acid series; the coalescing colloid thus produces another effect, providing a "sponge" with specific pore openings between the spheres. Other types of oxides such as zirconia, titania, chromia, and ceria can also be obtained in colloidal form.

Molecular sieves will be considered to be supports. Chapter 10 is devoted to their manufacture, ionic exchange, use, and characterization after use.

Organic resins and fibers also can be used as catalyst supports. They will be considered separately in Chapters 7 and 8.

Activated carbon presents an interesting subject because it is so difficult to specify and ensure that one lot of carbon is equivalent to the next lot. Although the use of carbon presents specific problems, there are characteristics of activated carbon that are valuable and are not attainable in any other support. For example, carbon is completely resistant to acidic or basic medium, which is not true of other supports, and if one is conducting a reaction in a corrosive medium harmful to other supports, it becomes essential that activated carbon be resorted to. Activated carbon also has a very high melting point and as a consequence minimizes metals' or oxides' agglomeration or sintering on the surface. Activated carbons can also be produced with ion exchange properties, and this subject also will be considered in Chapter 5.

In comparatively recent work, the sharp differences in catalyst performance have been documented when the catalytic component has been supported on such widely diverse types of oxides as lanthanides, titania, zirconia, alumina, chromia, magnesia, silica, or zeolites. These will be reviewed in Chapter 3.

Dual functioning of a supported catalyst attributable to catalyst-support interaction will also be considered in Chapter 11, as will hydrogen spillover, which is a function also of the support in Chapter 9. Finally, an activated metals support derivable for the surfaces of tubes, wires, heat exchanger sheets, and the like also will be dealt with (Chapter 6). It is hoped that the subject matter will be sufficiently broad yet in substantial depth to provide a good understanding of the diversity of supported catalysts and their characteristics.

REFERENCES

1. Kozlowski, R., et al., 1983. X-ray absorption fine structure investigation of vanadium (V) oxide, titanium oxide (IV) oxide catalysts. *J. Phys. Chem.* 87:5172–6.
2. Wachs, Israel E.; *Saleh, Ramzi Y.; Chan, Shirley S.; and Chersich, Claudio C. 1985. (Corporate Research-Science Laboratories, Exxon Research and Engineering Company, Annandale, NJ *Intermediates Technology Division, Exxon Chemical Company, Baton Rouge, LA.) The interaction of vanadium pentoxide with titania (anatase): Part I. Effect on o-xylene oxidation to phthalic anhydride. *Appl. Catal.* 15:339–52.
3. Wachs, Israel E.; Chan, Shirley S.; and Saleh, Ramzi Y. (Exxon Technology Division, Baton Rouge, LA.) "The Interaction of V_2O_5 with TiO_2 (Anatase) II. Comparison of Fresh and Used Catalysts for o-Xylene Oxidation to Phthalic Anhydride."
4. U.S. patent 3,244,644 (4-5-66) "Method of Preparing a Catalyst Composition Consisting of Eta-Alumina and the Product Thereof."
5. U.S. patent 3,186,957 (6-1-65) "Method of Preparing a Nickel Oxide Alumina Composition and the Product Thereof."
6. U.S. patent 3,317,439 (5-1-67) "Catalyst Aggregates of Crystallites."
7. Henrich, V. E., and Sadeghi, H. R. 1985. Studies of the strong metal-support interaction (SMSI) in rhodium/titanium dioxide model catalyst. *ACS Division of Petroleum Chemistry* 30:153–54.
8. Marcelin, G., and Lester, J. E. 1985. The effect of supports on the chemisorphive properties of catalysts. I. Magnetic studies of nickel catalysts. *J. Catal.* 93:270–78.

9. Spencer, M. S. 1985. Models of strong metal-support interaction (SMSI) in platinum on titanium dioxide catalysts. *J. Catal.* 93:216–23.
10. Brumberger, H., et al. 1985. Investigation of the SMSI catalyst platinum/titanium dioxide by small angle X-ray scattering. *J. Catal.* 92:199–210.
11. Akubuiro, E., et al. 1985. Dispersion and support effects in carbon monoxide oxidation over platinum. *Appl. Catal.* 14:215–27.
12. Shapiro, E. S., et al. 1984. Study of the nature of strong interaction between metal and supports. *Kinet. Katal.* 25:1505–7.
13. Resasco, D. E., and Haller, G. L. 1983. A model of metal-oxide support interactions for rhodium catalysis. *J. Catal.* 82:279–88.
14. Arakawa, H., et al. 1983. The effect of support in catalysis of metal supported catalysis. *Petrotech* 6:859–64.
15. Erdohelyi, A., and Solymosi, F. 1983. Effects of the support on the adsorption and dissociation of carbon monoxide and on the reactivity of surface carbon on rhodium catalysis. *J. Catal.* 84:446–60.

CHAPTER 1

Getting the Catalyst and the Support Together

Alvin B. Stiles

This book is intended as a reference for those interested in preparing supported catalysts. For this reason, each chapter will be self-supporting on the subject matter, and there may be some duplication of material that is presented in one or more other chapters. However, the information in a given chapter will be that necessary for a complete picture of the subject matter of that chapter. In this chapter, the support is added for a number of reasons. The primary reason is to stabilize the catalyst against agglomeration and coalescing, usually referred to as a thermal stabilizer [1, 2]. The support may also be added to introduce resistance to poisons or a resistance to by-product formation. In this case, the support is referred to as a component enhancing directivity or poison resistance. Poison resistance may also refer to the minimization of carbon deposition [3]. A third purpose for a support can be the decreasing of density of the catalyst and also the diluting of costly ingredients by less costly ingredients. A fourth reason is to prepare the catalyst in such a form that its resistance to breakage and minimization of pressure drop is accomplished. This latter effect is generally introduced by the placing of the catalytic materials on such supports as massive honeycomb, saddles, rings, and the like.

COPRECIPITATED SUPPORTS

This classification likely represents the largest grouping of catalysts that we will be considering in the realm of supported catalysts. Of the four objectives of using promoters, three can be attained by the coprecipitation procedure. Coprecipitation can take on many forms and procedures, as Table 1.1 shows. The table lists only those catalysts in which the promoter is added as a coprecipitated oxide, carbonate, or the like. Those materials added as colloids will be dealt with in the next section.

Table 1.1   Examples of Coprecipitated Catalysts on Support

Metals-Oxides	Supports in Solution or as Colloids
Nickel	Al_2O_3
Cobalt	SiO_2
Copper	Cr_2O_3
Silver	CeO_2
Gold	Pr_2O_3
Platinum	Nd_2O_3
Ruthenium	MgO
Palladium	CaO
Rhodium	SrO
Iridium	BaO
Osmium	ZrO_2
Cerium	TiO_2
Manganese	LaO_2

Mixed Oxide or Compounds	Supports in Suspension
Metal chromites	Kieselguhr
Metal molybdates	Clays (attapulgite and others)
Metal tungstates	MgO
Metal aluminates	CaO
Metal manganates	SiO_2
Metal vanadates	$Al_2O_3 \times H_2O$
Metal ferrates	Carbon (many types)
Heteropoly acids	
Metal Cerates	Zeolites (many types)
Metal stannates	Metal antimonates
Metal arsenates	

COLLOIDAL-INTERSPERSED SUPPORTS

Somewhat general statements should be made with regard to a comparison of coprecipitated supports derived from soluble salts and those derived from colloidal materials. First is the fact that the colloidal dispersion is much less reactive toward the catalytic material, and, as a consequence, solid-state reactions are slightly less likely to occur with the colloidal materials than with the coprecipitated materials from soluble salts. Second, the particles of the colloid are larger than the particles of the coprecipitated salt. This has the feature of making for larger pores and a more open structure for the final catalyst. Third, colloids usually are prepared with some type of added stabilizing agents such as an alkali sulfate or an acidic medium derived from hydrochloric or nitric acids. If these agents are objectionable in the catalyst, it is well to be aware of the fact that there is a possibility they would be present in the colloid and consequently in the catalyst.

Table 1.2   Catalytic Materials and Colloidal Supports

Catalysts	Colloids Available
Elemental	SiO_2 (many types)
Ni, Co, Pt, Pd, Cu, and others	TiO_2
Oxide	ZrO_2
Mn, Cu, Co, and others	CeO_2
Mixed oxides or compounds	Al_2O_3
Chromites	Cr_2O_3
Molybdates	MgO (CO_2)
Tungstates	CaO (CO_2)
Heteropoly acids, and others	BaO (CO_2)

Note: Special colloids are available from Nyacol Products, Inc., Ashland, Massachusetts, and Magnesium Elektron Company, Farmington, New Jersey.

The most common form of colloid is silica. It can be purchased in many different grades and many different particle sizes. It can also be purchased as a dry fumed silica, which can also be slurried into a catalyst preparation in such a way as to derive a final catalyst which is similar to a preparation made from an aqueous dispersion of the colloid. Although silica is the most common of the colloidal materials, essentially all other refractory oxides can be obtained from various vendors. Nyacol is prominently represented in this industry; others are listed in *Chemical Week Buyers' Guide*.

It is possible to produce a silica sol simply by dissolving sodium silicate in distilled water so that a 4% concentration of the sodium silicate is obtained. The next step is the adding of a small amount of indicator such as phenolphthalein, which gives a red color to the solution, and then quickly adding hydrochloric or nitric acid to the solution so that the pH is reduced to 1 or 2 and the phenolphthalein changes from pink to water white. This sol is very stable and can be held in storage for long periods of time without gelling. This stock solution can be used to add to the precipitations. Table 1.2 lists a large number of catalysts and a large number of supports derivable from colloids with the type of finished catalyst eventually derived. The purpose of this table is not to give explicit instructions on how these catalysts are prepared but to show the compatibility of various catalytic materials with various supports.

CATALYTIC COMPOUND-SUPPORT SOLID-STATE REACTIONS

This subject is the essence of the purpose of this book. Solid-state reactions occur between catalysts and support under many conditions. Probably the most prominent factor for solid-state reactions is for an intimate mixture of highly active oxides to be prepared. This means coprecipitation in such a way as to produce a precipitate encompassing both constituents as a compound. The basic chromates are an example of this type. The second classification in this general grouping is the highly reactive oxides. For example, nickel oxide is the catalytic component and silica or alumina the support materials coprecipitated with the nickel. The nickel can be coprecipitated as the hydroxide, carbonate, oxalate, or other anion that is insoluble and appropriate for the catalytic composition under investigation or preparation.

Hydrothermal reaction can also cause the catalytic and support materials to interact. The hydrothermal effect ordinarily is produced in an aqueous solution, which may be modified with alkalis or acid to facilitate the formation of the catalyst-support composite or compound. The interaction in this case can be thought of largely as the conversion of both to the hydroxides, with the hydroxides being amphoteric and interacting one with the other, with the least basic serving as the acid and the most basic as the cationic ion.

The reaction conditions that are probably the most understandable are those that occur during heating of the components of a catalyst. The effect of the heating varies with the temperature, but probably the other most important factor is the fine state of subdivision and intimacy with which these subdivided particles are mixed with one another [4]. The chemical composition of each of the components is important, but this is not the sole factor that controls the activity. Aluminas in different species vary substantially in their reactivity toward the catalytic component [5]. For example, freshly precipitated gamma alumina will react extremely rapidly with nickel oxide at about 400°C; alpha alumina reacts much more slowly and requires a temperature in the range

Table 1.3   Factors Retarding or Enhancing Catalyst Support Interaction

Retarding Interaction

Low-temperature catalyst fabrication and use
Large-particle size
High-melting-point catalyst or support
Support that is neither acidic (such as Cr_2O_3) nor basic (such as Al_2O_3)
High purity (that is, absence of fluxes or mineralizers such as alkalis or low-
   melting-point oxides such as some sulfates, phosphates, or borates
Absence of H_2O, or H_2^+, CO_2, Cl^-, SO_2^-, etc., at elevated temperatures
   and pressures

Enhancing Interaction

High-temperature fabrication or use
Small particle size of all components
Intimate association of finely divided components
Compression of components so as to decrease distance between intimately
   associated finely divided particles
Low melting point of one or more ingredients
Prolonged exposure to coalescing conditions
Presence of flux or mineralizers in catalytic components or in environment
   where catalyst is used. Mineralizers are alkalis, alkali sulfates, phosphates,
   borates, or hydrothermal conditions including Cl^-, SO_2^-, CO_2^-

of 600 to 800°C, in contrast to the 300 to 400°C required for a freshly precipitated γ-alumina and nickel oxide.

An additional factor, which is less likely to be considered by catalyst scientists than it is by ceramists, is the fluxing action of certain low-melting-point oxides such as the alkalis. Inasmuch as ceramists are accustomed to making frits and enamels this way, they consider alkali-enhanced fluxing (melting) as second nature. But catalytic scientists must take into account that low-melting oxide such as potassium or sodium, antimony, lead, or tin oxides can sharply reduce the sintering or melting point of the catalytic and support components to the point where solid-state reaction products and objectionable sintering may occur at relatively low temperatures.

It becomes evident that the interaction between catalysts and supports is complex. Those who want to avoid it, employ the least reactive oxides or carbonates as the support material. They also avoid any fluxes or low-melting-point oxides that could assist in the interaction between the components. They avoid high temperatures during the preparative conditions in a hydrothermal environment or during calcining or reduction during the preparation for the operating conditions. Table 1.3 shows some of the things to do or to avoid when considering beneficial or adverse effects of interreaction between the catalyst and the support material.

EPITAXIAL RELATIONSHIP BETWEEN CATALYTIC COMPONENT AND SUPPORT

This is perhaps the most subtle of the relationships between a catalyst and a support material [6]. That it occurs there can be no doubt because it occurs in the mineral kingdom in a most magnificent display of chalcopyrite ($CuFeS_2$), which is normally in the tetragonal form but in this example appears as isometric tetrahedra on a single crystal of sphalerite (ZnS), which is also in the isometric form.

Figures 1.1 and 1.2 show a mineral depicting this orientation of chalcopyrite on sphalerite. Figure 1.3 shows the two unit crystals, one of sphalerite and the other of chalcopyrite, showing the fact that the dimensions truly are different one from the other, but they are not so greatly different that the distance can be modified in the epitaxial structure without excessive strain.

It becomes evident, however, when epitaxial conditions of this type are shown on the scale that the mineral kingdom permits us to see that the spacings in the epitaxially oriented entity are under strain, and consequently the bonds are modified and the bond energies are different from those in a normal crystal. This implies that the catalytic properties of the supported material are different because bond energies are modified, making for a more labile compound.

At times it is difficult to explain differences in performance of catalyst supported on different species of alumina or silica, for example. That these species have different lattice spacings or different crystal forms gives credence to the fact that epitaxial structures are a major factor in catalytic performance, although in many cases the epitaxial nature cannot be established by available instrumental surface techniques.

Figure 1.1   Photograph of oriented chalcopyrite mineral on single crystal of sphalerite.
Note: Tetrahedra faces are evident but not mirroring because of the angle of the single source light.

The implication is that the epitaxial factor is a critical and a frequently encountered factor affecting catalytic performance. There are many examples, which are cited in the reference list at the end of this chapter.

HONEYCOMB-TYPE SUPPORTS AND WASH COATING

In services in which pressure drop is an important factor, such as automotive exhaust abatement and other fume abatements in industry, honeycomb-type structures are a popular method of supporting catalysts. The honeycomb can be fabricated from alumina, cordierite, mullite, and other non-metals, as well as various temperature-resistant metals. The surfaces of all honeycomb-type structures are usually glassy or relatively smooth and do not offer a good anchor for catalytic materials. As a result, it is necessary to coat these smooth surfaces with an undercoater or a prime coat onto which the

Figure 1.2   Photograph of oriented (same mineral specimen as Figure 1.1) chalcopyrite on single crystal of sphalerite.

Note: Tetrahedra faces both large and small now reflect single-source light because those faces are all in the same parallel planes. This is a striking example of epitaxial growth in the mineral kingdom.

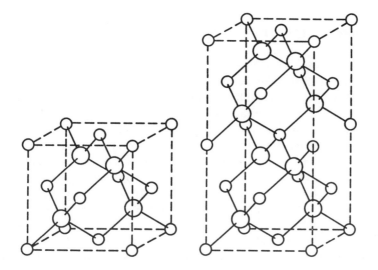

Figure 1.3   Sphalerite (left) and chalcopyrite (right).

catalytic material is eventually placed. These prime coats (also referred to as wash coat) offer a better anchoring for the catalytic material and also have extremely high surface area and tend to stabilize a catalyst placed thereon thermally and impart resistance to chemical poisons such as sulfur and halide, which are relatively common in automotive abatement.

The degree of interaction of the wash coat with the honeycomb is a factor primarily related to the temperature at which the wash coat is processed after being placed on the honeycomb. The degree of interaction of the catalytic material with the undercoater or wash coat is a factor closely related to the conditions previously reported in this chapter (temperature of exposure, state of subdivisions, uniformity of inter-mixing, and proximity of particles).

Wash coats that can be applied are colloidal alumina, colloidal silica, and other colloids. These colloids are mixed with finely dispersed oxides of the same composition as the colloids themselves or with other compositions: a solution of magnesium nitrate in which is suspended aluminum oxide or aluminum hydroxide, aluminum nitrate in which is suspended magnesium oxide, or magnesium hydroxide. The concept of the mixed oxides, hydroxides, and nitrates is that the nitrate on decomposition acts as an adhesive, the oxide tends to establish high surface area, and the combination of the two provides a porous layer that would otherwise be brittle, with a comparatively low surface area and relatively nonadherent. The general principle involves usually a nitrate or a colloid, either of which is a good film former, to which is added an oxide or a hydroxide, which tends to break up the film in such a way that it becomes thicker, nonbrittle, more adherent, and of higher surface area. The final requirement is that this solution-slurry of nitrate oxide must be dilute enough that when the honeycomb structure is immersed in it and the excess drained off, the openings in the honeycomb will not be closed off by the excess dried wash coat.

LOSS OF CATALYTIC ELEMENT ION INTO SUPPORT LATTICE

A rather infrequent but distressing event that can occur when an element such as platinum is supported on alumina and that catalyst is operated at a higher temperature —say, about 800°C—is that the metal ion is so mobilized and so small that it will move into the lattice of the alumina in such a way that it becomes completely submerged in the lattice and therefore catalytically unavailable. Inasmuch as the platinum group metals are frequently supported on alumina and used at very high temperatures for fume abatement, this occurrence may happen under these operating conditions.

A solution to this problem involves the reaction of the alumina with an elemental oxide that will produce a denser unit crystal than that of the aluminas, even alpha alumina. Reacting the alumina with magnesium oxide produces a spinel onto which precious metals can be placed, and the catalyst thus derived is operated at a higher temperature than is possible with alumina alone. Other oxides, some of which may have desirable catalytic properties, particularly in the disposal of gaseous effluents, are those of manganese, nickel, cobalt, copper, or cerium. All of these react to produce relatively dense unit crystals into which elemental metals cannot enter until extremely high temperatures are attained and the lattices become larger and accommodate small, metallic ions.

This loss of catalytic ion into the support lattice is not a frequent occurrence, but it can be avoided or at least minimized by the proper treatment of the support with oxides that tend to produce compact lattices [7].

REFERENCES

1. U.S. 4,323,482 4-6-82. "Catalyst and Method of Preparation."
2. Arnoldy, P., et al. 1985. Temperature-programmed reduction of Al_2O_3-, SiO_2- and rhenium oxide (Re_2O_7) catalysts. *J. Catal.* 93:231–45.
3. Marcelin, G., and Lester, J. E. 1985. The effect of supports on the chemisorphive properties of catalysts. I. Magnetic studies of nickel catalysts. *J. Catal.* 93:270–78.
4. U.S. 3,186,957 (6-1-65) "Method of Preparing a Nickel Oxide Alumina Composition and the Product Thereof."
5. U.S. 3,244,644 (4-5-66) "Method of Preparing a Catalyst Composition Consisting of Eta-Alumina and the Product Thereof."
6. U.S. 3,317,439 (5-1-67) "Catalyst Aggregates of Crystallites."
7. Chan, Shirley S.; Wachs, Israel E.; Murrell, Lawrence C.; and Dispenziere, N. C. 1985. Laser raman characterization of tungsten oxide supported on alumina: Influence of calcination temperatures. *J. Catal.* 92:1–10.

CHAPTER 2

Alumina

Regis Poisson
Jean-Pierre Brunelle
Patrice Nortier

It is difficult to know where to begin a discussion of alumina. It encompasses all of the interesting features of a satisfactory support and also represents many of the problems encountered in the selection of a support. A few of the features of alumina can be tabulated that reveal the chemical and physical characteristics that are its attributes as a satisfactory support. First, it is amphoteric, which means that it can act as an acid in a basic medium or as a base in an acid medium. Sodium aluminate, in which the alumina is in the anionic form, is familiar to all of us, and aluminum chloride, in which the aluminum is in the cationic form, is equally familiar. These characteristics are relevant to alumina reactions with magnesia (a base) to form a magnesium aluminate spinel or with flurosilicate (acidic) to form topaz.

Alumina has a high melting point—slightly over 2000°C—which is also a desirable characteristic for a support. The high melting point identifies it as a refractory oxide, which means that it has excellent characteristics for separating particles of a finely divided catalytic material from each other in such a way that they (usually having a lower melting point than aluminum oxide) will be prevented from agglomerating or coalescing. In this service, the alumina as a support serves also as a catalyst thermal stabilizer.

Alumina in the hydroxide form can also be a voluminous gel. This makes possible the production of alumina in the form of a high-surface-area, highly porous, comparatively low-density oxide. This hydroxide in aqueous form can also be slurried and suspended in alcohols such as methyl, ethyl, or propyl and as such becomes an alcogel, which on drying can have controlled pore dimensions (simulating the alcohol) and a tendency for lower density than is the characteristic of the hydrogel.

The most striking property of alumina is its transition phases that exist over a very large temperature range. These phases, which for the most can be described as a spinel network (Figure 2.1), distinguish themselves by the existence of crystalline defects in their structures. The formation of the condensed alpha-alumina phase (Figure

Note: Valuable discussions with J. Caillod, R. Fourre, M. Le Page, and E. Trebillon are acknowledged.

11

Figure 2.1   Alpha alumina close packing. (Photograph courtesy of Klinger Educational Products, Jamaica, N.Y.)

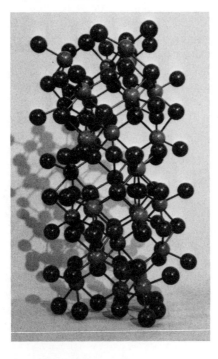

Figure 2.2   Gamma alumina, loose packed. (Photograph courtesy of Klinger Educational Products, Jamaica, N.Y.)

2.2), although thermadynamically possible at a low temperature, becomes effectively possible only after a certain reordering of these transition alumina phases, which requires a high temperature. This explains the fact that a high surface area still exists at temperatures as high as 1000°C and even 1200° C.

Aluminum oxide can be derived from many sources. The purest form is derived from the element itself, either by dissolving the metal in acid as in the UOP process or by dissolving it in alcohol as in the CONOCO and the CONDEA processes. However, the majority of alumina is produced from the hydrate of the Bayer process, either by dissolution in soda followed by precipitation (the so-called gel processes) or by flash calcination as in the Rhone Poulenc and Kaiser processes.

An additional pure form is derived from the element itself by oxidation of the metal, such as that used in the formation of honeycomb structures as described in Patent Talsma U.S.3,255,027. In this Talsma process, metallic aluminum is coated with a small amount of sodium or potassium silicate as an oxidation catalyst and heated in 100°C increments to 800°–1000°C in a mildly oxidizing atmosphere over a 72- to 120-hour period until rigid porous structure is obtained. The final product is alpha alumina with about 1% SiO_2 and with low alkali, most of which has been sublimed at the very high surface temperature. As the aluminum is oxidized, it migrates towards the surface forming the oxide and leaving voids and thereby creating a rigid ceramic form with high porosity and many reservoirs in which the catalytic material may locate. Though expensive, the advantage is formations into which aluminum sheet, wire, or rods can be formed. Honeycomb is a particularly interesting form. Since the chemical composition is alumina, the physical characteristics will be those of alumina, with one characteristic being that of poor thermal shock resistance.

Because the alumina so readily forms a gel, and also because aluminum nitrate has a strong coalescing effect when it is calcined to form the oxide, alumina or aluminum salts are highly amenable to extrusion or are formable into granules or spheres. Alumina is not unique in this respect, but it is admirably adaptable to these techniques and perhaps to a degree exceeding all other oxides or hydroxides.

Because of this gel-forming or cohesive characteristic, alumina can be developed into a film-forming "paint," making it possible to put an aluminum oxide layer on the surfaces of otherwise impervious materials, such as metal or ceramic rods, sheets, tubes, honeycombs, or other types of smooth-surfaced structures.

Also, probably attributable to the gel-forming characteristics of alumina, the oxide is susceptible to the formation of different types of porosity and pore structures. Materials can be occluded in the alumina in such a way as to be extractable or combustible from the final product, with the result that a void remains after this extraction or combustion, which is in itself a controlled-size pore. These can vary from the size of cellulose crystals to rather large diameter fibers or even cotton linters.

Another characteristic of alumina is that in the form of alpha alumina, it is an extremely hard material. It is the next hardest material to diamond and as a result has two characteristics: it is extremely stable under high temperature, high pressure, and extremely abrasive conditions and is an excellent grinding medium in a reactor or in pumps, valves, or transfer lines.

The uses of special aluminas have experienced considerable growth over the last thirty years. Today, they enjoy an annual market of several hundred thousand metric tons, a market that excludes the manufacture of metallurgical alumina. This concerns such highly diversified fields as ceramics, polishing agents, refractories, fillers, pigments, adsorbents, and catalyst supports. The markets for adsorbents and catalysts alone represent annual quantities of approximately 120,000 metric tons. The economic importance of special aluminas no longer needs to be demonstrated.

Many of the basics of our present knowledge concerning the structure of aluminum hydrates and transition aluminas go back more than twenty years; however, considerable progress has been made over the last twenty years to improve purity and optimize the texture and mechanical properties of alumina pellets as a result of the development of a large number of new processes.

This chapter deals only with the use of alumina in adsorption and catalysis and shall try to demonstrate the main features concerning the structure, synthesis, and forming processes of alumina pellets, as well as their uses in the field of catalysis.

Many of the basics of our present knowledge concerning the structure of aluminum hydrates and transition aluminas go back more than twenty years; however, considerable progress has been made over the last twenty years to improve purity and optimize the texture and mechanical properties of alumina pellets as a result of the development of a large number of new processes.

This chapter deals only with the use of alumina in adsorption and catalysis and shall try to demonstrate the main features concerning the structure, synthesis, and forming processes of alumina pellets, as well as their uses in the field of catalysis.

STRUCTURES OF ALUMINAS

Numerous authors have approached the problem of alumina structures; a thorough bibliographic review is not specifically included, but such bibliographies may be found in references [1] and [2]. Nevertheless, it is fitting to mention three publications by Stumpf et al. [3], Tertian and Papee [4], and Lippens [5, 6], which founded the bases of our present knowledge in the field of structures of aluminas [3–6].

The term *aluminas* refers to three classes of compounds:

1. Aluminum trihydroxides with the formula $Al(OH)_3$,
2. Aluminum oxyhydrides whose formula is close to $AlO(OH)$,
3. Aluminum oxides, in which it is necessary to distinguish further between transition aluminas and alpha alumina or corundum.

Table 2.1 Packing Order of the Different Hydroxides

Gibbsite	Bayerite	Nordstrandite
B	B	A
A	A	B
A	B	B
B	A	A
B	B	B
A	A	A

Aluminum Trihydroxides

Three crystallized forms that meet the formula $Al(OH)_3$ may be distinguished: *Gibbsite*, *Bayerite*, and *Nordstrandite*.

The Bayer process leads to Gibbsite, of which the major part is calcined to corundum destined for the manufacture of aluminum. The crystallized trihydroxides may generally be obtained by amorphous hydroxide synthesis under well-defined conditions of pH and temperature. Only Gibbsite and Bayerite are used in industrial applications.

The structures of these two products can easily be described by visualizing that two layers, A and B, of oxygen yield a quasi-compact hexagonal packing. Aluminum ions occupy two-thirds of the octahedral sites generated by oxygen packing. The three structures (Gibbsite, Bayerite, and Nordstrandite) can be described by the packing order of layers A and B, as shown in Table 2.1.

Table 2.2 shows the crystallographic characteristics of these trihydroxides. As an example, Figure 2.3 shows a model of the Gibbsite structure.

Aluminum Oxyhydroxide

Corresponding to the formula $AlO(OH)\cdot xH_2O$, we have two known structures: *boehmite*, an isotype of iron lepidocrocite, and *diaspore*, an isotype of iron goethite. It is useful to distinguish a third form, called *pseudoboehmite* or *microcrystalline boehmite*, which is structurally derived from boehmite but with specific properties.

Van Oosterhout [8] derived an easy method to describe the structure of the corresponding iron compounds, which we can use for aluminum compounds. In the direction of the a-axis there are HO-A1-O chains, which are shown schematically in Figure 2.4. Two of these chains can be placed in positions antiparallel to each other in such a way that the O atoms of the second chains are at the same level as the Al atoms of the first chain. The chains give both modifications a repetition distance of 2.85 Å in the direction of the a-axis. The difference between the two modifications

Table 2.2   Crystallographic Characteristics of Crystallized Aluminum Trihydroxides

	Gibbsite	Bayerite	Nordstrandite
Lattice	Monoclinic	Monoclinic	Triclinic
a (A°)	8.67	5.06	8.75
b (A°)	5.07	8.67	5.07
c (A°)	9.72	4.71	10.24
(n°)	(90)	(90)	109°20′
p (n°)	94°34′	90°16′	97°40′
(n°)	(90)	(90)	88°20′
Density	2.42	2.53	
A1(OH)3/cell	8	4	8

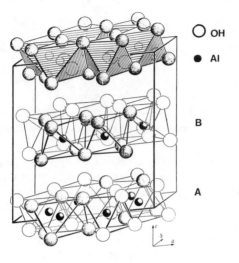

Figure 2.3 Structure of the Gibbsite Al(OH)₃.

is due to a different arrangement of the double molecules, as shown in Figure 2.5, where the a-axis is perpendicular to the plan of the drawing. Another representation of the boehmite structure is shown in Figure 2.6.

The characterization of *gelatinous boehmite* has been a matter of controversy. The principal features are an excess of water and a shift and broadening of the (020) peak, which are irreversibly reduced by drying or hydrotreating. Lippens [5] and Papee [9] interpreted this as extra water bound with strong H bridges between the layers of the boehmite. Baker and Pearson [10] proposed that this was due to extra water bound to Al atoms on the border of the sheets.

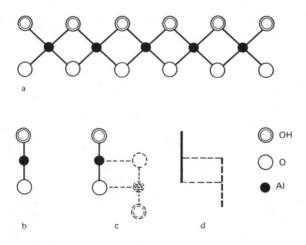

Figure 2.4 Schematic representation of boehmite: (a) Al-O-OH chain; (b) Profile of one chain; (c) Profile of two antiparallel chains; (d) Schematic representation of c.

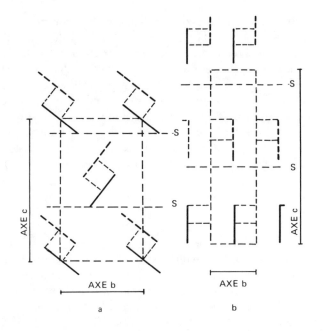

Figure 2.5   Schematic representation of structures: (a) Diaspore; (b) Boehmite.

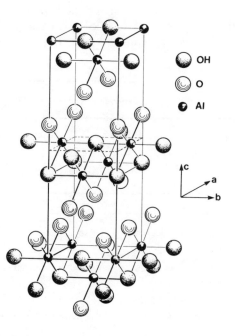

Figure 2.6   Structure of the boehmite AlO(OH).

Since neither of these interpretations is consistent with the experimental result, this problem has been recently reanalyzed [11]. A model of stacking defects with a certain probability of existence is proposed. An excellent agreement may be observed between the calculated and measured values for a defect amplitude of about 1 Å. This distance between blocks of normally spaced sheets is big enough to allow intercalation of water—2 moles for a mole of AlO(OH)—and the excess water content can be well correlated to the shift of the (020) peak (through the probability of existence of this defect). Nevertheless, even if we think this is the best crystallographic model for pseudoboehmite, we are aware that some specific properties of these products are related to more sophisticated parameters, such as the presence of anions and alcoholates.

Transition Aluminas

The partial dehydration of aluminum hydroxides and oxyhydroxides leads to compounds with the crude formula Al_2O_3 x H_2O with $0 < x < 1$, which generally are poorly crystallized. These compounds are those used in such applications as catalyst supports, Claus catalysts, and adsorbents, which explains the interest shown in them. There are six principal phases designated by the Greek letters *chi*, *kappa*, *eta*, *theta*, *delta*, and *gamma*. The nature of the product obtained by calcination depends on the starting hydroxide (Gibbsite, boehmite, and others) and on the calcination conditions. In effect, there exist several sequences during dehydration (Figure 2.7 and Table 2.3). In all cases, the ultimate product of dehydration is *corundum* (αAl_2O_3).

An excellent bibliographical review of transition *alumina* has been compiled by Leonard [12]. The situation can be reduced to a simple one on the basis of crystallographics, once one becomes aware that there are only two types of structures: *spinel*, for eta, gamma, delta, and theta and *hexagonal*, for chi and kappa. In chapter 4, we

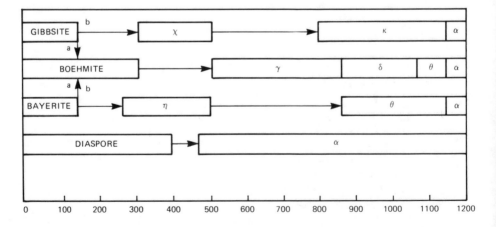

Figure 2.7   Decomposition sequence of aluminum hydroxides.

Note: Enclosed area indicates range of occurrence; open area indicates range of transition (see Table 2.3) [13].

Table 2.3   Decomposition Sequence of Aluminum Hydroxides

	Conditions favoring transformations	
Conditions	Path a	Path b
pressure	> 1 atm	1 atm
atmosphere	moist air	dry air
heating rate	> 1 K/min	< 1 K/min
particle size	> 100 μm	< 10 μm

Source: ALCOA Technical paper No. 19 by K. Wefers and G.M. Bell [13].

shall see that the differences find their origin mostly in the presence of defects or in the nature of the planes contributing to the surface area and that both are related to the nature of the starting hydroxide and the *pseudomorphosis* laws governing the structural change from the hydroxide to the oxide.

PREPARATION OF ALUMINA

There are four main processes leading to catalyst carriers relying on the main possible ways to obtain alumina, as shown in Figure 2.8. Beginning with the simplest, we have

1.   Flash calcination of hydrate,
2.   Acidification of aluminate,
3.   Neutralization of aluminum salts,
4.   Hydrolysis of alcoholate.

It may be observed that since the general procedure is to prepare a gel and then dry and granulate it, there are two processes where the order of operations is reversed (UOP and flash calcination processes). In fact, in both cases, there is taken into account a particular facility of making beads that enables a very high crushing strength to be obtained, with the concomitant factor being a lesser ability to vary structure and texture.

Bayer Process

It is impossible to speak of alumina without taking into account the Bayer process [14], by means of which the majority of alumina and aluminum is extracted and processed (40.10^6 metric tons per year).

Schematically, bauxite ore, a mixed hydroxide of iron and aluminum, is solubilized by soda. The solid impurities are eliminated, and alumina is separated by crystallization of trihydroxide, the *Bayer hydrate*, which is in fact Gibbsite. The alkali solution is regenerated, reconcentrated, and reused in the resolution. The process is conducted so as to recover an easily filtrable (and calcinable) product, which explains why this hydrate is an aggregate of crystallites more than 20 μm in diameter. This

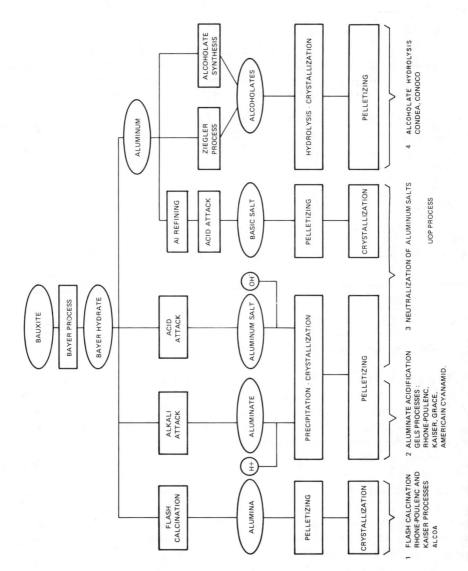

Figure 2.8 Main processes for alumina support preparation.

product is relatively pure except for occluded Na. A typical analysis is shown in Table 2.4. The main uses of this hydrate are

- Electrometallurgy (alumina and also cryolite),
- Fillers such as hydrates,
- Refractories and ceramics as corundum powder,
- Sulfate salt (water treatment),
- Adsorbents and catalyst carriers.

Flash Calcination

The thermal decomposition of Bayer hydrate (Gibbsite) should proceed through the reaction

$$2 \, Al(OH)_3 \rightarrow Al_2O_3 + 3H_2O \tag{2.1}$$

leading to a very high surface area when performed at temperatures of 250°C and higher. But according to the size of the crystallites of Gibbsite produced, it must be recognized that inside the grain, there is a high partial pressure of water, and there exists the possibility of a hydrothermal treatment inside the crystallites according to the equations

$$Al(OH)_3 \rightarrow AlO(OH) + H_2O; \tag{2.2}$$

$$Al_2O_3 + H_2O \rightarrow 2AlO(OH). \tag{2.3}$$

This treatment leads, consequently, to well-crystallized boehmite of low surface area. Flash calcination was discovered by the French researcher Sausol [15], who observed that the calcination of Bayer hydrate with a very short residence time leads to a unique high surface area and very reactive powder without interference of reactions 2.2 and 2.3. This great reactivity makes possible a simple process of making beads in a rotating plate delivering high surface area and high-crush-resistant beads used mainly as desiccants and Claus catalysts.

A further hydrotreating according to equation 2.3 gives rise to alpha alumina carriers again, characterized by their high crush resistance [16, 17]. This exceptional quality enabled the introduction of beads in catalytic fume abatement, where they still find extensive application.

Table 2.4 Typical Chemical Composition of Bayer Hydrate

Impurities	Na_2O	SiO_2	Fe_2O_3
%	0.2	0.015	0.02

Acidification of Aluminate

This is the most common way of producing alumina gel for catalysis. Every catalyst manufacturing company has several patents in this field. This situation is easily understandable because it is the most economical gel process, and it offers the possibility of preparing a large variety of products of fairly good purity.

In the case of the Bayer hydrate used as a starting material, the process may be pictured by the equations

$$Al(OH)_3 + OH \rightarrow AlO_2^- + 2H_2O; \tag{2.4}$$

$$AlO_2^- + H_2O + H^+ \rightarrow Al(OH)_3. \tag{2.5}$$

This means that the consumption of reactants is only a mole of alkali and a mole of acid for a mole of aluminum. In fact, due to the stability of aluminate, more than one mole of alkali must be added because the lower limit corresponds to the ratio

$$\frac{Na^+}{AlO_2^-} = 1.1 \text{ to } 1.25.$$

On the other hand, the price of acid, which increases with the same ratio, is often lower than expected due to the disposal of low-value residual acid or aluminum salt. In the latter case, the neutralization can be written as

$$3AlO_2^- + Al^{3+} + 6H_2O \rightarrow 4Al(OH)_3. \tag{2.6}$$

This process has been studied extensively [18]. By regulating the various parameters, such as pH, temperature, and type of anion, it is possible to obtain a great variety of structures (Bayerite, boehmite, and pseudoboehmite) and texture, such as surface area and pore distribution (Figure 2.9). Purity can be fairly good, depending on the purity of the starting hydrate and the possibility of additional purifying of the aluminate solution. In fact, the only limitation is the cost of removal of sodium, which is related to the difficult washing of the gel. This explains the existence of the UOP and alcoholate processes.

Neutralization of Aluminum Salts

In this section we include the alumina gel obtained by the reaction

$$Al_2(OH)_{(6-x)}^{x+} + {}_xOH^- \rightarrow 2Al(OH)_3$$
$$\text{with } 1 < x < 6. \tag{2.7}$$

Starting from Bayer hydrate, this process is more expensive than the aluminate process because the attack of hydrate by an acid is difficult and will need more than one mole of acid per mole of aluminum and thus more than one mole of base afterward. Never-

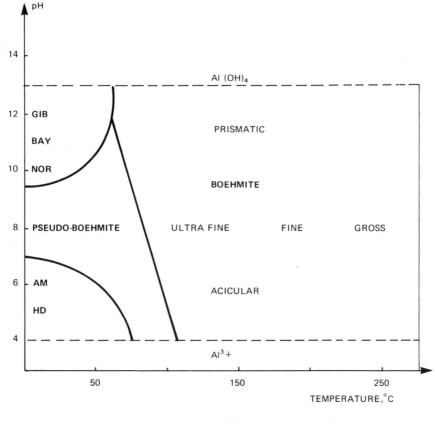

GIB = GIBBSITE; BAY = BAYERITE; NOR = NORDSTRANDITE; AM = AMORPHOUS
HD = MICROCRYSTALLINE GIBBSITE.

Figure 2.9 Simplified two parameters phase and morphology diagram [18].

theless, with respect to the recent growth in interest in sol-gel technology, it is worth reporting existing processes of this type because it was the second use of the sol-gel concept after the silica process [19] to produce "homodispersed" particles.

The first known example, though of limited use, is the UOP process [20]. It starts from a basic salt of aluminum $Al_2(OH)_5Cl$ obtained by attack of aluminum metal using hydrochloric acid, which is mixed with hexamethylene tetramine (HMT). This solution is poured through dies in a column of hot combustion products, which effects the formation of beads and their gelification while decomposing the HMT according to the equation

$$(CH_2)_6N_4 + 4H^+ + 6H_2O \rightarrow 6CH_2O + 4NH_4^+. \tag{2.8}$$

Translucent beads are recovered at the base of the column, which are further treated for crystallization. The homogeneous gelification and crystallization inside the bead allow a close distribution of crystallites and consequently a monomodal pore distribution. The resulting pore diameter and pore volume can be easily regulated by the conditions of crystallization. This enables manufacture of high-strength, high-pore-volume pellets.

The second known example is Baymal alumina made by du Pont [21]. By hydrothermal treatment of basic salts according to equation 2.7, there result concentrated sols of oxyhydroxide, with the solid particles having a surface area as high as 600 m^2/g. The same result can be obtained by autoclaving amorphous gel [22]. These acicular products are an astonishing example of a perfectly crystallized hemicolloid of 2.5 nm size.

Alcoholate Hydrolysis

The starting point of this process is the Ziegler process [23]. When petrochemical products were cheap, this method was developed to produce long-chain linear alcohols [24]. Starting with aluminum of current grades, hydrogen and ethylene, we have the following steps:

Synthesis of triethyl aluminum
$$Al + \tfrac{3}{2}H_2 + 3C_2H_4 \rightarrow Al(C_2H_5)_3; \tag{2.9}$$

Growth of the chains
$$Al(C_2H_5)_3 + 3nC_2H_4 \rightarrow Al[(C_2H_4)_nC_2H_5]_3; \tag{2.10}$$

Oxidation of the trialkylaluminum
$$AlR_3 + \tfrac{3}{2}O_2 \rightarrow Al(OR)_3; \tag{2.11}$$

Hydrolysis of the alcoholate
$$Al(OR)_3 + 3H_2O \rightarrow Al(OH)_3 + 3ROH. \tag{2.12}$$

The end result is alcohol with aluminum hydroxide as a by-product. Because reaction 2.9 is selective, the impurities of Al are left in the shape of an insoluble mud, which is eliminated by filtration and centrifugation. So except for the mineral impurity TiO_2 necessarily introduced by the polymerization catalyst, it provides a high-purity alumina, which, moreover, has a high surface area. These two conditions and the fact that it could be delivered at a low price as a by-product have allowed an increasing use of this type of alumina in catalysis.

Recently the Condea company developed a similar type of alumina processed through an alcoholate obtained by direct reaction of aluminum and alcohol, with the alcohol being further recycled. In this case, most of the metallic impurities remain insoluble in the alcoholate solution and can be eliminated by filtration before hydrolysis. This leads to a relatively pure alumina but without reaching the low level of the preceding one. The problem is knowing whether the added price of this process as compared to the aluminate process is worth the low level of alkali impurities.

Miscellaneous Processes

In order to be complete, we shall mention the processes related to the production of double salts and their thermal decomposition leading to high-surface-area products [25, 26].

ALUMINA FORMING

Several agglomeration techniques allow the production of adsorbents or alumina supports of size, shape, type, and strength that meet the requirements of the catalytic processes in which they are used. This basically concerns *disc-pelletizing*, *extrusion*, and *oil-forming* techniques. Out of the worldwide market of approximately 120,000 metric tons of alumina pellets used in adsorption and catalysis applications, about 40, 50, and 10% are, respectively, prepared using the three techniques previously mentioned. *Tableting* and *spray drying* are, respectively, mainly used for the forming of bulk catalysts and fluid-cracking catalysts. Let us also mention the special *wash-coating* process used to deposit a layer of alumina of a few tens of microns inside the channels of ceramic monoliths for automotive exhaust-gas purification. This section describes the first three techniques: disc pelletizing, extrusion, and oil forming.

Disc Pelletizing

Disc pelletizing corresponds to an agglomeration in the form of pellets via progressive humidification of a powder. This operation is carried out using a granulator, which rotates about an inclined axis. This alumina powder is introduced continuously and moistened. Alumina seeds are also continuously introduced into the pelletizer and progressively take on a coating of the moistened powder under the influence of capillary forces to give increasing diameter to the bead. As it grows, the bead gradually moves away from the center of the pelletizer and then is ejected beginning from a certain size under the effect of centrifugal force (Figure 2.10). The granulation operation is followed by an activation operation for the alumina pellets.

The quality of granulation, as well as the characteristics of the resulting alumina pellets, will depend on a large number of factors. Among these are the physicochemical characteristics of the alumina powder that is to be agglomerated, the feed rate of the alumina powder, seeds, water, the type and quantity of binder, the rotational speed and inclination angle of the granulator, and the location of water and powder supplies.

The disc-pelletizing technique is particularly well adapted to agglomeration of flash alumina. In effect, the high rehydration and crystallization speed of this reactivated alumina immediately, at the moment of granulation, sets up, as in the case of cement, by the formation of very fine alumina hydrates. This phenomenon provides the pellet with important strength, which is then increased at a later aging stage. Such aluminas constitute excellent adsorbents or precursors for catalyst supports.

Figure 2.10 Disc pelletizers.

Extrusion

Extrusion is the most frequently used forming process for agglomerating alumina gels. One very widely used application of alumina extrusions is for catalyst support for hydrotreatment of petroleum refinery process streams. This forming process generally features two stages: an alumina compound mixing stage, followed by extrusion of the compound itself.

Mixing consists of blending an alumina powder generally made up of pseudo-boehmite or boehmite with water, a small quantity of peptizing agent (usually an acid such as nitric or acetic acid), and, if required, a plasticizer. The purpose of this operation is to disperse the peptizing agent in the most uniform manner possible and to transform the mixture into a compound with rheological behavior, which is generally of the *pseudo-plastic* type with a finite flow threshold.

The paste is then extruded (for example, in a single- or twin-auger extruder) and then dried and calcined. The most common extrudates are 1.2 mm diameter cylinders. Recently some manufacturers have proposed extrudates with different cross-sectional shapes (multilobes), which lead, in theory, to better performances in some applications [27, 28].

The generally pseudo-plastic nature of alumina paste is very interesting (decrease in viscosity with shear forces). It enables, in effect, the creation of conditions favorable for flow of the paste in the extruder die while retaining a certain solidity upon emerging from the extruder, particularly if the relaxation time is short. During mixing, the microcrystalline particles that constituted the initial alumina gel break down by mechanical (shear) and chemical (peptization) processes and then reagglomerate under the action of chemical bonding and physical attraction forces to give substantial strength to the extrudate.

The mixing-extrusion conditions have a great influence on the textural and mechanical characteristics of the calcined extrudates. Several parameters, such as the alumina-water ratio, quantity of peptizing agent, mixing time, and type of mixer, have to be optimized to obtain the required characteristics [29–31].

Oil Forming

The principle of manufacture of alumina pellets using the oil-forming technique, most often the oil drop, consists of generating drops of an aqueous sol of alumina using a sprayer. These drops fall in a column containing a solvent nonmiscible in water. The superficial tensions exerted on the sol droplets in this column result in perfectly spherical alumina pellets, which are neutralized and, if required, crystallized, then dried, and calcined.

This forming technique includes several processes that differ, either in the nature of the starting sol or in the method of hardening the alumina pellet (Figure 2.11). A first type of process consists, for example, in generating drops of an amorphous sol of aluminum basic oxychloride and hexamethylene tetramine (HMT). Under the influence of the temperature of the oil column, approximately 90°C, the HMT decom-

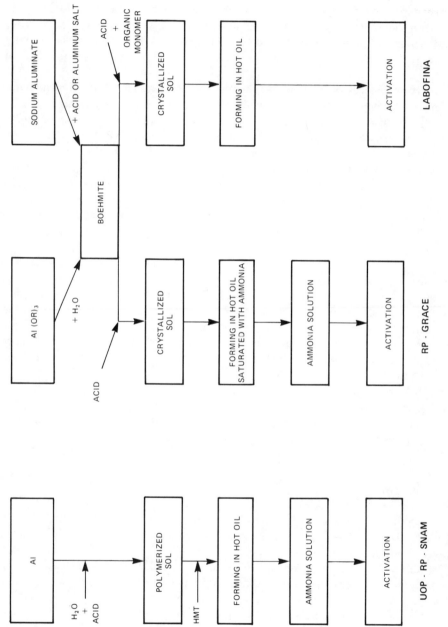

Figure 2.11 Different alumina beads oil drop processes.

poses into formal and ammonia. Then the ammonia neutralizes the aluminum basic sol and leads to gelling of the pellet. The product is then crystallized, dried, and calcined [32–34]. Another type of process consists of letting drops of an alumina-crystallized sol (boehmitic sol, for example) fall in a column of ammoniated oil, with the ammonia contained in the oil used to solidify the periphery of the drop before its complete coagulation in a second column containing an ammonia solution [35, 36]. A third type of process consists of generating drops of an alumina-crystallized sol containing an organic monomer, which solidifies the alumina pellet in a hot-oil column by polymerization of the organic monomer [37].

Oil-drop carriers are used, for example, in the manufacture of regenerative catalytic reforming catalysts, which require high flow and, in turn, high strength.

Forming Comparison

The three forming processes described may be distinguished by the alumina concentration of the alumina-water system formed. The percentage by weight of alumina, being equal to approximately 60% in the case of disc pelletizing, decreases to approximately 45% for an extrusion and to 25% for an oil-drop forming. Moreover, the extrusion of the boehmitic gel as well as the oil-drop process for coagulation of a crystallized alumina sol consists in forming an alumina powder that already has the characteristics required for final application. On the other hand, the oil-drop process for gelification-crystallization of aluminum basic salts, as well as the disc-pelletizing process for flash alumina, corresponds to processes whose forming step precedes the final crystallization step of the alumina.

Regarding the characteristics of the alumina pellets, the main interest in the disc-pelletizing technique is the higher productivity that it can reach and, consequently, the relatively low-cost price of beads. However, it offers the disadvantage of leading to alumina pellets of varying size distribution, requiring that the product be sieved later. The oil-drop technique has the advantage of leading to beads with good symmetry and equivalent size. However, it is generally more costly than the disc-forming procedure. As for extrusion, it is well adapted to manufacture of supports that do not require exceptional properties of flow or attrition resistance.

TEXTURE

By *texture*, we mean the description of particles constituting the pellets and the porous system related to them. This section will examine the morphology of particles, microporosity, macroporosity, and control of porosity.

Morphology of Particles

During calcination of the hydrate, the resulting oxide normally keeps the shape of the starting crystallite or aggregate of hydrate and, most of the time, even that of the

Table 2.5 Tabulation of Crystalline Species

	SHAPE	SIZE	SPECIFIC SURFACE AREA (m²/g)	PROCESS	REFERENCES
BAYERITE	SOMATOID RODS	L > 1 μm Thickness > 0.1 μm	< 10	SCHMÄH	
GIBBSITE	AGGLOMERATE OF MICRON SIZE PARTICLES		0	BAYER	
	PLATELETS	L ≃ 1 μm	0 - 20	SEEDING	
	Idem	0.01 > e > 0.05 μm	5 - 70	GEL EVOLUTION	BF 1667 553
	VERY THIN HEXAGONAL PLATELETS		90 - 140	GEL EVOLUTION	BF 1371 808

Note: Main morphologies of hydroxides.

porous agglomerate. Thus, to describe the morphology of oxides, we need only describe the morphologies of the hydrate.

Trihydroxide

Bayerite and Nordstrandite are rather difficult to obtain, as may be seen in Figure 2.9. This figure clearly shows a limited range of conditions required for this result. But once obtained, they always appear in the form of large crystallites measuring 0.1 μm and larger with consequent low surface area.

Under the conditions of the Bayer process, the decomposition of aluminate leads to large micron-size crystallites of Gibbsite aggregated in particles of 20 to 120 μm. But using better decomposition control, platelets as thin as 0.05 μm may be prepared. Employing variations in the preparation procedures for the gel, it is possible to obtain small hexagonal platelets with surface area as large as 140 m^2/g^- [38]. The various possibilities for trihydroxide morphologies are shown in Table 2.5.

Boehmite

In the case of boehmite, a large variety of morphologies and sizes are available. The two extreme shapes are that of the acicular, as may be seen in Figure 2.12, in which crystallization takes place in the direction of the a-axis only, and the rhombohedral tables, which feature isometrical growth along all axes (Figure 2.13). In between,

Figure 2.12   Acicular boehmite.

Figure 2.13 Isometrical boehmite.

practically all of the intermediary shapes may be found, among them chain-type and boat-like boehmites, as shown in Figures 2.14 and 2.15. The different morphologies of boehmite are summed up in Figure 2.16. Surface-area range goes from a few square meters per gram to 600 m^2/g in the case of acicular products [21, 22].

As for pseudoboehmite, implying imperfect crystallization, it appears typically as very thin wrinkled sheets (Figure 2.17).

Microporosity

The transformation of hydrates into oxides is governed by the laws of *pseudomorphosis*. This physically means that the oxide network is constructed according to simple laws, starting from the hydrate network. For example, plane (001) of Bayerite becomes plane (111) of the spinel eta alumina. This derives a specific structure of pores. This topic has been thoroughly studied by Lippens and Steggerda, and much of what is said here is extracted from their work [5, 6].

There are two main types: crystalline trihydroxide and microcrystalline boehmite. In the case of crystalline trihydroxides, which have no porosity and which feature small surface area most of the time (large crystallites), on thermal decomposition lose 3 water molecules, creating, as expected, a fairly high-pore volume in the range of

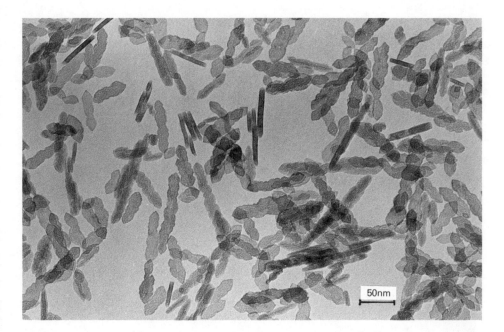

Figure 2.14   Chain-type boehmite.

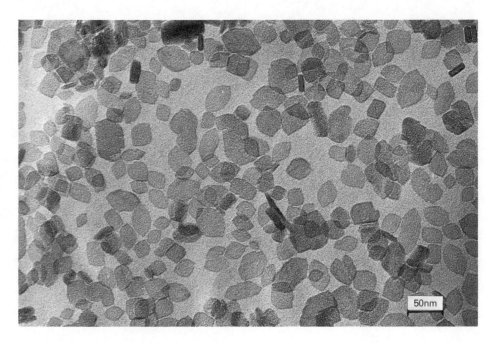

Figure 2.15   Boat-like boehmite.

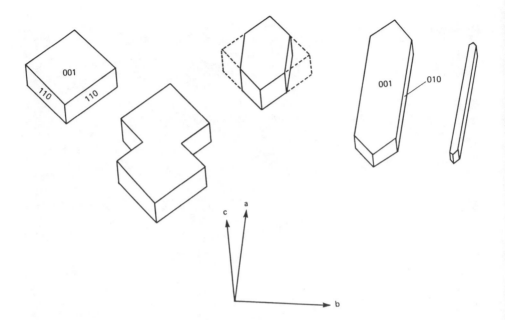

Figure 2.16 Boehmite morphologies.

Figure 2.17 Pseudoboehmite wrinkled sheets.

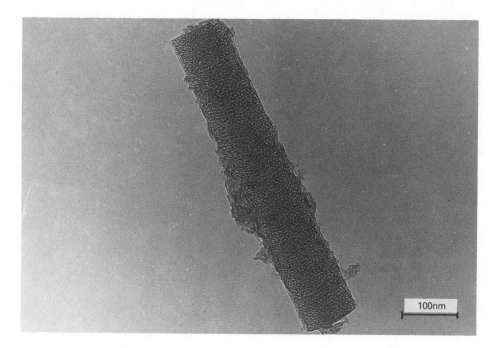

Figure 2.18 Calcined bayerite.

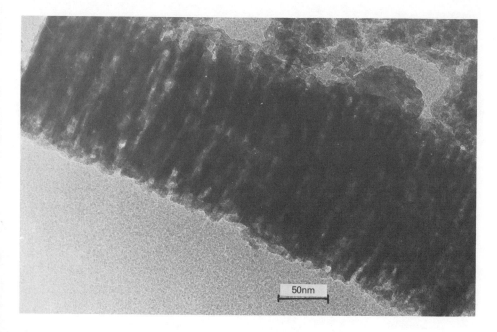

Figure 2.19 Calcined bayerite shown at higher magnification.

0.2 to 0.3 cm^3/g^{-1}. At low temperature, the micropore system is constituted of planar parallel pores (corresponding to the (001) cleavage plane of trihydroxide). As shown in Figures 2.18 and 2.19, these pores are no wider than 2 mm, which results in surface areas as high as 500 m^2/g^{-1}. This gradually disappears with heating, giving rise to a rod-like system with the same orientation, parallel to plane (001).

In the case of microboehmite or pseudoboehmite decomposition, due to the small size of particles and to the lesser interference caused by the loss of only one mole of water, a crystallite of boehmite leads to a nonporous particle of gamma alumina with the same morphology as the starting particle.

In the first case there is creation of an intraparticle porosity, whereas in the second case there is created an interparticle porosity, with no addition of porosity

Table 2.6　Texture of the Different Transition Aluminas

ALUMINA SEQUENCE		OXIDE DESCRIPTION
GIBBSITE → HEXAGONAL STRUCTURE (CHI, KAPPA)		Porous particles mpV = 0.2 - 0.3 cm^3/g S.A. ≤ 500 m^2/g
	BIG CRYSTALLITES	L = 0.1 to 10 μm
	SMALL CRYSTALLITES	L = 0.01 to 0.1 μm
BAYERITE → SPINEL STRUCTURE (ETA, THETA)		Porous particles mpV = 0.2 - 0.3 cm^3/g S.A. ≤ 500 m^2/g L = 0.1 to 1 μm
BOEHMITE → SPINEL STRUCTURE (GAMMA, DELTA, THETA)		
	BIG CRYSTALLITES (GAMMA T)	Slightly porous particles mpV = 0.02 - 0.05 cm^3/g S.A. ≤ 100 m^2/g L ≤ 0.1 μm
	FINE CRYSTALLITES	Non porous particles
	. Ultra fine table like (GAMMA T)	L > 5 nm S.A. ≤ 300 m^2/g
	. Acicular (GAMMA C)	L > 2.5 nm S.A. ≤ 600 m^2/g
	. Wrinkled sheets (pseudo GAMMA)	L > 2.5 nm S.A. ≤ 600 m^2/g

mpV　: microporous volume

S.A.　: surface area

L　: length

during the thermal decomposition. As for the mechanism of microporosity generation, it does not make any difference. In both cases, porosity is a consequence of the packing of transition alumina crystallites. The only difference is that in the second case, the microporosity is designed during the crystallization step of boehmite, while in the first case, during the crystallization step, there is no effect on microporosity but rather on macroporosity as the eventual size of the agglomerates is achieved.

The complexity of the decomposition sequence of alumina is due less to structural reasons than to textural ones. The typical illustration is the case of the spinel-type structure where we find four possible phases (eta, gamma tetragonal, gamma cubic, pseudogamma), which differ mainly by the nature of the superficial planes, as outlined in Table 2.6.

Macroporosity

Creating macroporosity means establishing a network of connected macropores. There are two philosophies centered around reaching this end.

The first is to add a removable material, called *porogen*, to a green body in sufficient quantity so as to create this network of macropores, to strengthen irreversibly the solid architecture around the porogens, and then to eliminate these. The void thus created leaves a corresponding volume of pores. This elimination proceeds most of the time through burning of the material. Considerable amounts of burn-out materials have been described, such as sawdust, carbon black, molasses, and petroleum coke [30, 39–42].

The alternative is to use the simple facts that a *packing of particles* always leaves a certain amount of porosity ($\geq 25\%$), with the size of the pores bearing a correlation to the size of the particles. To create macroporosity according to this scheme, it is necessary only to bind together particles that are large enough. This is the filler-binder material described in recent patents [43]. The binder is an easily peptizable, dispersible, microporous gel, which acts as a glue between the fillers. Fillers are large crystallites or agglomerates, which, by contrast, will not be dispersed under conditions of preparation.

In fact, the first method used alone leads primarily to "Swiss-cheese"-type porosity, which nevertheless is microporous, as measured, for example, by mercury porosimetry. So, the second method is to be used. But the difficulty is in avoiding dense packing of the agglomerates and aggregates. Often, it is necessary to choose a combination of the two methods to result in a looser packing of aggregates or agglomerates by adding burn-out material.

Control of Porosity

Microporosity and macroporosity are, respectively, created by the packing of crystallites and agglomerates of oxides. A schematic illustration of the distribution of pores of alumina according to this scheme is given in Figure 2.20. Table 2.7 gives the formulas corresponding to a simplified example with no mesoporosity. It could be the

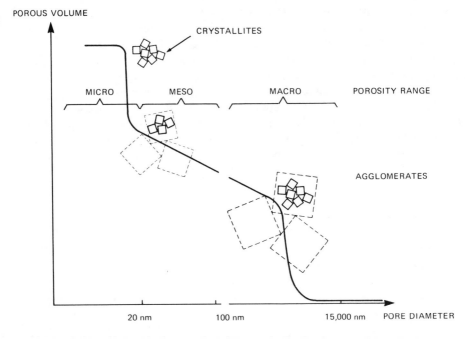

POROUS VOLUME

CRYSTALLITES

MICRO   MESO   MACRO   POROSITY RANGE

AGGLOMERATES

20 nm   100 nm   15,000 nm   PORE DIAMETER

Figure 2.20 Schematic representation of porosity distribution.

case of a pellet comprising gel agglomerates of identical size bound by a small quantity of this same gel. This description clearly shows that the art of controlling porosity is the art of controlling the crystallites, their agglomerates, and the packing of both.

In the case of trihydroxide, the large crystallites of Bayerite or Gibbsite thermally decompose into porous aggregates of small crystallites of alumina. Their sizes can be controlled during calcination, mostly by temperature, but not the interparticle volume, which remains approximately constant. The size of macropores may be controlled by the size of the starting hydrate crystals, which can be modified during the crystallization step or by grinding. This is the case of adsorbents and Claus catalysts marketed by Rhone-Poulenc, Kaiser, and Alcoa.

In the case of beohmite-derived alumina, control of microporosity, surface area, pore distribution, and pore volume can be finely tuned, each aspect almost independently, through the size, the morphology, and the packing of the oxyhydroxide crystallites. High surface area and close pore-size distribution rely on the ability to create and maintain, respectively, small and monodispersed crystallites. This may be achieved by controlling the nucleation and crystallization processes and avoiding evolution by incidental hydrothermal treatment during drying. As may be seen in Table 2.7, increase of the micropore volume (mpV) implies an increase of the volumic porosity (ϵ')— that is on expansion of the packing. This is obtained through three types of possible actions: addition of porogen [44, 45], superficial tension control during drying [46–49], or hydrothermal treatment [20, 50].

Table 2.7   Hypothetical Case of Bimodal Pellet

HYPOTHESIS

CRYSTALLITES Size $: \phi$ $= 10$ nm
      Volumic porosity$: \epsilon'$ $= 60$ %
      Absolute density $: d_A$ $= 1.2$ g/cm^3

AGGLOMERATES Size $: \phi_b$ $= 30$ μm
      Volumic porosity $: \epsilon$ $= 40$ %

The formula is established using the cylindrical pore model.

MICROPOROSITY

MICROPOROUS VOLUME $mpV \quad = \dfrac{\epsilon'}{1 - \epsilon'} \quad \dfrac{1}{d_A} = 0.5 \text{ cm}^3/\text{g}$

PORE SIZE $\phi \text{ pores} = \dfrac{2}{3} \quad \dfrac{\epsilon'}{1 - \epsilon'} \; \phi = 10 \text{ nm}$

SURFACE AREA $\text{S.A.} \quad = \dfrac{4 \times mpV}{\phi \text{ pores}} = 200 \text{ m}^2/\text{g}$

GRAIN DENSITY $dg \quad = \dfrac{1}{mpV + 1/d_A} = 1.2 \text{ g/cm}^3$

MACROPOROSITY

MACROPOROUS VOLUME $MpV \quad = \dfrac{\epsilon}{1 - \epsilon} \quad \dfrac{1}{d_g} = 0.53 \text{ cm}^3/\text{g}$

PORE SIZE $\phi' \text{pores} = \dfrac{2}{3} \quad \dfrac{\epsilon}{1 - \epsilon} \; \phi_b = 12,000 \text{ nm}$

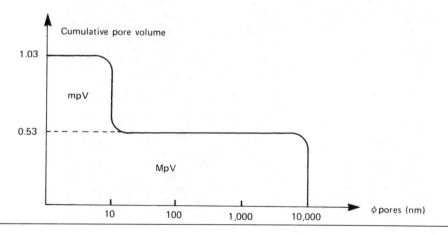

Postcombustion carriers marketed by Rhone-Poulenc [51] are obtained by pelletizing flash-calcined hydrate, which is further crystallized to boehmite. The nice bimodal design of the macroporosity is obtained in accordance with the mentioned principles. The excellent compromise of properties results from a particular type of crystallization of the boehmite, yielding chestnut-type agglomerates, as shown in Figure 2.21. The general principle attained is that of developing small pores (working pores) inherently present in dehydrated alumina hydrate into which are developed "corridor pores," the large access pores permitting easy mass transport.

PHYSICOCHEMICAL PROPERTIES OF ALUMINA

This section provides a brief overview of the various physicochemical phenomena that occur during impregnation of an alumina support with an aqueous solution containing different metallic decomposable salts.

Wettability

When the alumina comes into contact with an aqueous solution, the water quickly penetrates into the pores of the support under the influence of capillary forces [52]. A portion of the air present in the porosity will be entrapped and compressed under this influence. The hydrophilic nature of the surface of the alumina, combined with

Figure 2.21 Chestnut-type agglomerates of boehmite.

the presence of the micropores, induces very high capillary pressures inside the pellet, as indicated in the law of Young-Laplace:

$$P - P_o = \frac{2\gamma}{r} \cdot \text{Cos } \alpha. \tag{2.13}$$

Expressing pressure P, which prevails inside an air bubble, is a function of pressure P_o in the aqueous phase, of the superficial tension γ at the air-interface solid, of radius r of the pore, which is assumed to be cylindrical, and wetting angle α.

In the case of the alumina-aqueous impregnation solution system (Cos α = 1; $\gamma = 7.10^2$ N·m^{-1}), it is apparent that the capillary pressure exerted inside a pore of 5 nm in diameter will theoretically be 560 bars. The compressed air will, in fact, dissolve in the solution, diffuse, and escape the support.

The capillary forces are of obvious practical interest because they enable impregnation by spray of a solution containing exactly the quantities of metallic precursors that should be deposited (dry impregnation or capillary impregnation). They may, however, be on the verge, due to the high pressure that they exert on the walls of the solid, of breaking the alumina pellets during impregnation. This phenomenon will be very harmful in the case of supports that have only small-diameter micropores. One remedy consists of impregnating the support under vacuum, which substantially reduces the impregnation time for the alumina.

Exothermicity

The adsorption of water on the surface of the alumina generates a release of heat. The importance of this phenomenon depends on the structure, the specific surface area, and the degree of dehydration of the support [53–57]. The enthalpy of wetting is generally from 0.2 to 1 Jm^{-1}. This means that impregnation with 1 g of water will lead to adiabatic heating of the alumina between 8 and 40°C. This release of heat may have negative consequences on the quality of impregnation if the metallic precursors contained in the solution are easily decomposed. One way to remedy this disadvantage is to eliminate most of the exothermicity by a prior controlled steaming of the support.

Amphoteric Nature of Alumina

Freshly calcined alumina will rehydrate and rehydroxylate itself at ambient temperature in the presence of moist air. This phenomenon corresponds to the dissociative adsorption of water, leading to the creation of OH groups. This adsorption is pictured in Figure 2.22. These hydroxyl groups of alumina may feature amphoteric behavior in aqueous medium [58–61]. This characteristic translates into different ionizations of the OH groups according to whether the impregnation solution is acidic or basic.

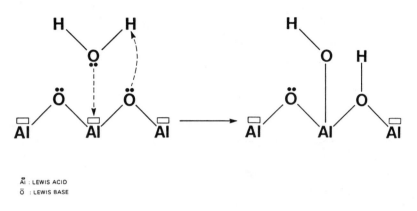

Ā̈l : LEWIS ACID
Ö : LEWIS BASE

Figure 2.22   Schematic representation of hydroxylation of alumina.

Although the phenomena occurring at the oxide-water interface are still not fully understood [62–67], the simple system of alumina and an aqueous solution containing nonchelating and nonprecipitant ions may nevertheless be represented in the following manner.

In an acid medium, the surface of alumina will become polarized positively, which will lead to adsorption of one counteranion. With S-OH symbolizing a hydroxyl group located on the surface of the alumina support, ionization may be represented by the equation

$$S\text{-}OH + H^+ = S\text{-}OH_2{}^+. \qquad (2.14)$$

The alumina thus behaves as an anion adsorber.

In a basic medium, the surface of the alumina will become polarized negatively, which may be represented by the equation

$$S\text{-}OH + OH^- = S\text{-}O^- + H_2O. \qquad (2.15)$$

In this case, the alumina behaves as a cation adsorber.

Figure 2.23 quantitatively shows the evolution of the cationic and anionic adsorption capacity of an alumina of 220 m^2/g^{-1} as a function of pH [68].
The amphoteric nature of alumina may be clearly seen: increasing adsorption of chloride anions toward the acid medium without adsorption of sodium cations and increasing adsorption of Na^+ toward the basic pH without adsorption of chloride anions. Note, additionally, the pH zone for which the alumina is, from the outset, in balance with the impregnation solution. This zone, which is between 8.5 and 9, corresponds to the *point of zero charge* of alumina (pH_{pzc}).

These ion-adsorbing properties of alumina may be profitably taken advantage of to obtain an atomic dispersion of the metallic precursor of the active phase that is to be deposited on the alumina. This results in an active-phase dispersion state close to 100% [52, 69–71] after activation of the catalyst. By adsorption competition between

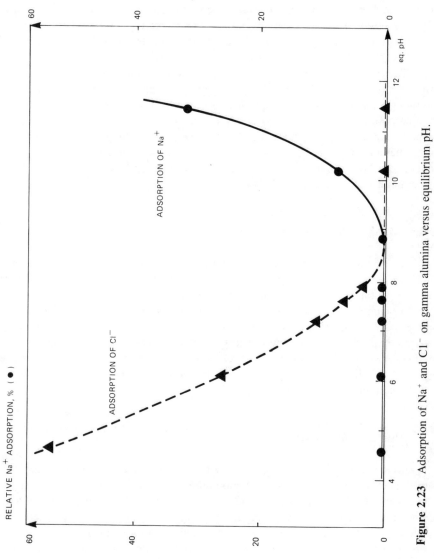

Figure 2.23 Adsorption of Na$^+$ and Cl$^-$ on gamma alumina versus equilibrium pH.

two ions of the same type and ionic exchange, it is also possible to optimize the internal distribution of the metallic precursor inside the alumina pellet.

Moreover, by using competing ions with an affinity for alumina, which is much higher than the metallic precursor (case of highly chelating acids such as oxalic acid or citric acid, which are very likely adsorbed according to the site binding model [66, 67], it is possible to block the adsorption sites located at the periphery of the pellet and require the metallic precursor to be adsorbed inside the pellet (egg white or egg yolk distributions).

These considerations indicate that the superficial characteristics of the alumina provide it with very interesting adsorption and ion-exchanging properties, which enable the preparation of catalysts of high dispersion and variable distribution of metals that may be optimized for the catalytic application. Finally, let us make clear that these properties of alumina will be in direct relationship to it textural (specific surface area) and structural characteristics, as well as its chemical purity, because the impurities contained in the support can cause modification of the surface and, notably, the value of the point of zero charge [58, 72].

USES OF ALUMINA IN CATALYSIS

The uses of alumina in the field of catalysis are many and varied. Most often, this concerns gamma alumina with a high specific surface area ($70–350 m^2/g$). Schematically, three types of uses for alumina may be distinguished: use as a support, use as an active catalyst, and use as a cocatalyst. Each of these applications is detailed, going on the basis of the criteria to be desired or avoided in the choice of alumina and the catalytic reaction used. But before taking into consideration the important role played by the surface of the alumina in its uses as an active catalyst and a cocatalyst, let us briefly recall the models proposed in the literature to describe the surface of Al_2O_3 and the configuration of active sites.

Alumina Surface Models

The surface of the alumina is made up of a combination of aluminum and oxygen ions, which may each have a coordination number lower than that existing in the bulk. These superficial ions constitute vacant sites that are always occupied at ambient temperature, either by hydroxyl groups resulting from the dissociative adsorption of water or by coordinated water molecules. This returns them to a state of normal coordination, either octahedral or tetrahedral for the aluminum ions and octahedral for the oxygen ions. Dehydration and dehydroxylation of the surface of the alumina cause the appearance of coordinatively unsaturated oxygen (Lewis base site) and aluminum (Lewis acid site). Likewise, alumina acquires catalytic properties in a certain number of reactions.

Several authors have tried to model the surface of alumina [73–77]. Peri [73] proposed the first in 1965: a model of the surface of alumina founded on the hypothesis the planes exposed preferentially are those of index (100). More recently, Knözinger and Ratnasamy [77] have proposed a model that has the merit of leading to a better understanding and visualization of the surface of the alumina. The model is based on the assumption that a mixture of low-index planes—the (111), (110), and (100) planes of the spinel lattice—are exposed on the surface of the crystallites. Relative abundance of the faces is assumed to vary for different aluminas. Five different types of OH groups are obtained and correspond to the coordination of an OH group, either to a tetrahedral aluminum, or to an octahedral aluminum, or to a combination of each, or both.

Figure 2.24 sums up the five OH group configurations able to occur, according to Knözinger, on the idealized surface of aluminas. The most important result consists

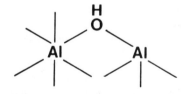

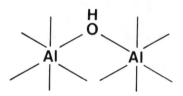

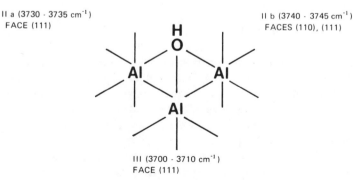

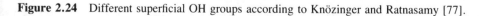

Figure 2.24   Different superficial OH groups according to Knözinger and Ratnasamy [77].

in showing that surface OH has differing net charges as a function of its environment. Thus, a Type III OH group with a net positive charge of $+0.5$ is expected to be the most acidic OH group. Since the lability is a function of their basicity, according to this model it is possible to foresee an increase in the acidity of the Al^{3+} sites and in the basicity of the O^{2-} sites with the activation temperature of the alumina.

In sum, it appears that the process of dehydroxylation leading to coordinatively insaturated oxygen (*Lewis base site*) and aluminum (*Lewis acid site*) will depend on a large number of factors: the structure of the alumina, the relative proportions of the exposed crystallized sides, atmosphere and temperature of dehydration and dehydroxylation, and others. In spite of all the elucidation offered by this attempt at visualizing the surface of aluminas, the surface of industrial supports is found to be more complex. Additionally, the reactions catalyzed by alumina do not always use the same active sites. This is why correlations between the acido-basic properties of the surface of aluminas and their catalytic properties imply gaining experimental knowledge of the nature and the force of Lewis and Brönsted acido-basic sites present at the surface of the alumina.

The principal techniques used up to the present time are

- Direct measurement in aqueous or organic medium, with a colored indicator [78, 79],
- Direct study of OH groups by infrared analysis (Figure 2.25),
- Indirect measurement by chemical adsorption of probe molecules followed by infrared analysis [80–83] or thermodesorption,
- Determination of the adsorption (heat of probe molecules) by calorimetry [84],
- Catalytic reactions on a model molecule [85],
- Nuclear magnetic resonance of the solid [86].

However, taking into consideration the limitations or disadvantages posed by each of the methods described, the experimental results obtained are not without criticism. This shows that experimental characterization of the acido-basicity of the surface of aluminas and oxides in general must also be improved.

Alumina as a Support

This is a simple case of monofunctional catalysis for which the alumina does not operate directly in the mechanism of the catalytic process. For example, automotive catalysts fall into this category. The catalytic phase is constituted of precious metals deposited either on gamma or theta alumina beads measuring 3 mm in diameter with specific surface area of 100 m^2/g, or on a gamma alumina wash coat, which itself is deposited on a cordierite monolith.

The role of the alumina is to dilute, support, and disperse the precious metals. In the case of a deposit of a quantity of an active phase that is lower than the adsorption capacity of the alumina support, it also plays a role in the macroscopic distribution of the crystallites. So it is possible to obtain a homogeneous, egg white, egg yolk, or

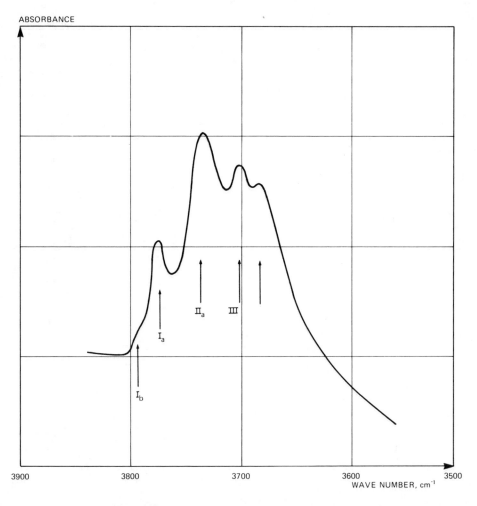

ABSORBANCE

WAVE NUMBER, cm⁻¹

SURFACE AREA = 135 m²/g. ALUMINA TABLETS OF 35 x 25 x 7 nm³

Figure 2.25   Typical infrared spectra of OH groups of gamma alumina after dehydration at 550°C.

peripheral impregnation profile (Figure 2.26) by an adequate choice of metallic precursors and impregnation conditions. The role of the support is also to stabilize the metastable dispersion of small metallic crystallites on the surface of the alumina against agglomeration and sintering.

Finally, as a result of its internal porosity, it facilitates the diffusion of reagents and products of the reactions up to the catalytic sites. This latter parameter may be essential in the case of catalytic reactions limited by the diffusion of reagents. This is

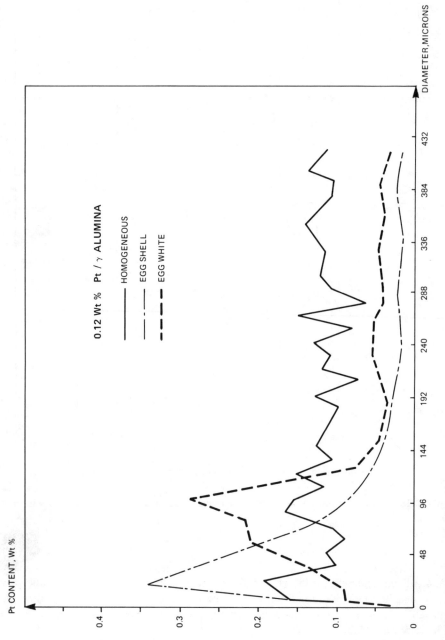

Figure 2.26 Typical platinum profiles for 0.12 Wt% Pt catalysts on 2 nm alumina beads.

the case, for example, of processes with a very high reaction rate, such as the selective reduction of nitrogen oxides by ammonia on catalysts composed of V_2O_5 deposited on alumina. The use of macroporous alumina supports clearly improves the performance of the catalyst by an increase of the effective diffusion coefficient of reagents NO_x and NH_3 [87]. This is also the case of processes in which the catalyst deactivates over time following partial plugging of external porosity of pellets by poisons (plugging by Pb, P, and Zn in automotive catalysts), or by intermediates in the reaction (plugging by V and Ni in hydrodemetallation catalysts). In this case also, the use of macroporous alumina supports with appropriate morphology and texture is advised [88].

Finally, it is necessary to mention monofunctional catalytic reactions in which the alumina support may induce undesirable secondary reactions and consequently affect the selectivity of the supported catalyzer. The selective hydrogenation of steam cracking cuts on Pd/Al_2O_3 and dehydrogenation of ethanol to acetaldehyde on Cu/Al_2O_3 fit into this category. In the first case, an alumina of structure gamma T and medium purity without surface acidity will be selected to deposit the active phase (palladium) in order to avoid parallel reactions of polymerization of acetylenics leading to the formation of green oils. In the second case, the use of an alumina support of very low specific surface area (alpha alumina), with a very low consequent dehydrating activity, is to be preferred for impregnation of copper in order to prevent parallel reactions of dehydration of ethanol into ethylene. A great number of other examples of monofunctional catalysts may be mentioned.

Alumina as an Active Catalyst

The catalytic properties of alumina have already been focused on in an important number of studies and a few articles of synthesis [89, 90]. This is due to the fact that alumina has remarkable adsorbent properties and is capable of activating a certain number of bonds such as hydrogen-hydrogen, carbon-hydrogen, and carbon-carbon bonds. Because of this fact, it features activity in the reactions of exchange [91–94], double-bond isomerization of alkenes or skeletal isomerization of alkenes [95–96], cracking of hydrocarbons, dehydration of alcohols to ethers or alkenes [89, 100–102], polymerization, hydrolysis, and others. However, industrial uses of alumina as an active catalyst are very few. The principle of these corresponds to the *Claus process*. The practical objective of this process is to transform hydrogen sulfide contained in some natural gas fields or in refinery gas into sulfur. The installed capacity of this type of catalyst may be estimated at 10,000 metric tons of alumina.

Considering the importance of this process using an alumina catalyst, a few details of this catalysis are given.

The common Claus process features two stages:

• A first stage of thermal oxidation of one-third of the initial H_2S in a high-temperature burner at nearly 1000°C

$$H_2S + \tfrac{3}{2}O_2 \to SO_2 + H_2O; \qquad (2.16)$$

- A second stage of catalytic oxidation of the two-thirds of residual H_2S by the SO_2 formed in the thermal burner according to the Claus reaction

$$2H_2S + SO_2 \rightleftharpoons \frac{3}{nSn} + 2H_2O. \tag{2.17}$$

This reaction is carried out in standard fashion on cheap, activated alumina with high specific surface area (300 m^2/g) and of medium purity (approximately 0.1% Na), such as obtained by the Bayer hydrate flash process.

The achievement of very high sulfur recovery necessary to meet antipollution standards adopted in a number of industrial countries also requires the removal of sulfur contained in very noxious sulfur compounds such as carbonyl sulfide (COS) and carbon disulfide (CS_2), which are formed in the high-temperature burner. This may be realized using the reactions of *hydrolysis of carbon sulfides:*

$$COS + H_2O \rightarrow CO_2 + H_2S; \tag{2.18}$$

$$CS_2 + 2H_2O \rightarrow CO_2 + 2H_2S. \tag{2.19}$$

Unlike the very fast Claus reaction, which is limited on alumina at 250°C by the sulfur equilibrium yield, the reactions of COS and CS_2 hydrolysis, which are slower on alumina than the Claus reaction, are limited by the activity of the alumina catalyst (Figure 2.27).

A disappointingly small amount of fundamental work has been devoted to study of the mechanism of these alumina-catalyzed reactions and to the identification of active sites. Since medium-Na-content-activated alumina leads to high initial sulfur recovery, it is known that this catalysis does not necessitate the same sites as reactions such as catalytic reforming. Moreover, it is difficult to know the exact degree of hydration and hydroxylation of alumina activated under the conditions of Claus catalysis. Taking into consideration the high partial pressure of steam (25–30%) existing in a Claus gas, this degree must be relatively high. In fact, it is generally assumed that this catalyst involves mainly basic sites (O^{2-} or OH) to absorb H_2S, SO_2, COS, and CS_2 [103–105].

The other industrial applications of alumina as active catalysts are much more modest. Nevertheless, *dehydration of alcohols*, and notably ethanol, should be mentioned. Dehydration of ethanol was one of the first ways of deriving ethylene. Over the years, this process has been completely replaced by steam cracking of hydrocarbons in countries with highly developed petrochemical industries. However, countries rich in biomass, such as Brazil, continue to use this type of catalytic process as an additional way of producing ethylene. Activated alumina may be used advantageously in such a process. Alumina is an excellent catalyst for dehydration of alcohols thanks to the simultaneous presence of acid sites and basic sites over its surface. According to the type of sites engaged in the reaction mechanism, the reaction is oriented either toward the formation of ether or toward formation of olefins. In the first case, the dissociative adsorption of alcohols leading to intermolecular dehydration uses a base-acid site (Al associated with O^{2-}). However, only the basic O^{2-} or OH sites seem to be implied in the intramolecular dehydration of alcohol [100, 102].

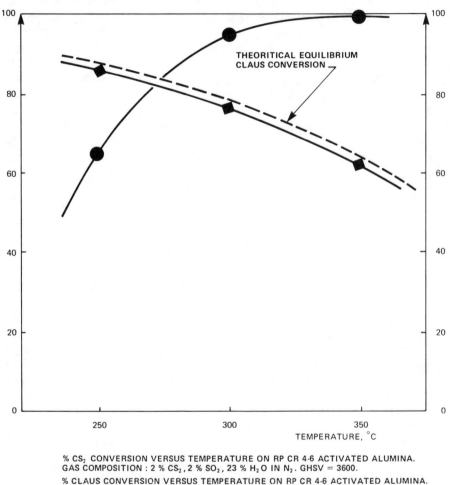

% CS₂ CONVERSION ●
% CLAUS CONVERSION ◆

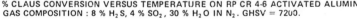

% CS₂ CONVERSION VERSUS TEMPERATURE ON RP CR 4-6 ACTIVATED ALUMINA.
GAS COMPOSITION : 2 % CS₂, 2 % SO₂, 23 % H₂O IN N₂. GHSV = 3600.

% CLAUS CONVERSION VERSUS TEMPERATURE ON RP CR 4-6 ACTIVATED ALUMINA.
GAS COMPOSITION : 8 % H₂S, 4 % SO₂, 30 % H₂O IN N₂. GHSV = 7200.

Figure 2.27   Conversion versus temperature on RP CR 4–6 activated alumina.

Alumina as a Cocatalyst

Certain catalytic reactions involve a bifunctional mechanism in which sites of the active phase and the sites of the support phase are required.

Catalytic reforming of gasoline illustrates this category. Catalysts generally are composed of 0.35% Pt associated or not with a second element (for example, Re, Ir, Sn, or Ge), deposited on very pure gamma alumina of approximately 200 m²/g of specific surface area and whose acidity is promoted by approximately 1% chloride.

The desired reactions effect the transformation, by isomerization or dehydrocyclization, of naphthenic and paraffinic hydrocarbons into hydrocarbons of a higher octane number, namely aromatics and isoparaffins. To do this, it is necessary to associate, inside a single catalyst, a metallic function (Pt) capable of dehydrogenating the saturated hydrocarbons and hydrogenating the unsaturated reaction intermediaries, together with an acid function (chlorinated alumina) capable of modifying carbonaceous skeleton of these hydrocarbons by isomerization or cyclization. It will be especially important to optimize one parameter of the alumina support: its chemical purity. In effect, certain basic impurities found in aluminas (Na, Ca, and others) have an adverse influence on the metallic phase of the catalyst.

In order to illustrate this point, in Table 2.8 we have shown the results obtained by heptane cracking [106] on various samples of alumina, which differ either by their structure and specific surface area (α, γ), by the presence of acid (Cl, F), or by the presence of basic impurities (Na). These different parameters have a large influence on the acidity of the alumina; the use of a chlorinated gamma alumina containing less than 50 ppm of sodium is to be preferred for this type of reaction.

Miscellaneous

This overview of the principal applications of alumina in the field of catalysts is obviously not complete. Other uses for alumina exist, for example, the use of tabular alumina beads with high heat capacity and thermal resistance for filling the bottoms of reactors and the use of alumina as a binder or external promoter in the production of a whole family of bulk catalysts. For all of these applications, the alumina chosen will always be the result of an optimization of textural parameters (specific surface area, pore distribution), structural and morphological parameters (form and orientation of crystallites), chemical parameters (content of impurities, strength of superficial sites), and size and mechanical parameters.

Table 2.8   n Heptane Cracking Activity of Alumina Versus Structure (α, γ), Promotors, (None, CL, F) or Impurities (None, Na)

		n C_7 CRACKING ACTIVITY
α	ALUMINA	3,5
γ	ALUMINA	38
γ	ALUMINA + 1 % Cl	54
γ	ALUMINA + 1 % F	66
γ	ALUMINA + 0,05 % Na	18

ACTIVITY EXPRESSED IN g C_4 / 100 g C_7H_{16} at 500 °C   (106)

CONCLUSION

Although this chapter has not been an exhaustive presentation of aluminas, it has discussed a number of interesting characteristics of these complex oxides:

- Availability in large quantities at moderate prices,
- Feasibility of high surface areas, usually thermally stable in common catalysis operating conditions,
- Wide range of microporosity and macroporosity of the commercially available carriers,
- Presence of both acidic and basic superficial sites, which lead to numerous interesting catalytic properties.

All of these features explain the success that alumina has enjoyed for many years and will still enjoy in the future. The numerous studies on powder synthesis and forming to design more efficient supports are finding a new impetus through the research undertaken in the field of ceramics and glasses. It is reasonable to assume that the renewed interest in this field will be the source of interesting information in the design of more optimized *alumina carriers*.

REFERENCES

1. R. S. Alwitt. 1976. *Oxides and Oxides Films*, 4; D. W. Diggle and A. K. Vigh, eds. New York: Dekker.
2. D. L. Cocke. 1984. *Catal. Rev. Sci. Eng.* 26:163.
3. H. C. Stumpf, A. S. Russel, J. W. Newsome, and C. M. Tucker. 1950. *Ind. Eng. Chem.* 42:1398.
4. R. Tertian and D. Papee. 1958. *J. Chim. Phys.* 55:341.
5. B. C. Lippens. 1961. Thesis. Delft, Netherlands.
6. B. C. Lippens and J. J. Steggerda. 1979. *Physical and Chemical Aspects of Adsorbents and Catalysts*, p. 171. B. G. Linsen, ed. New York: Academic Press.
7. Kirk Othmer. 1978. *Encyclopedia of Chemical Technology*, vol. 2, 3d ed., p. 223. New York: Wiley Interscience.
8. G. W. Van Oosterhout. 1960. *Acta Cryst.* 13:932.
9. D. Papee, R. Tertian, and R. Biais. 1958. *Bull. Soc. Chim. Fr.*, 1301.
10. B. R. Baker and R. M. Pearson. 1974. *J. Catal.* 33:265.
11. D. Grebille, T. Dupin, J. F. Berar, and P. Gregoire. 1983. *Ann. Chim. Fr.* 8:435.
12. A. J. Leonard, F. Van Cauwelaert, and J. J. Fripiat. 1967. *J. Phys. Chem.* 71:695.
13. K. Wefers and G. M. Bell. 1972. "Alcoa Technical Paper 19." Alcoa Research Lab.
14. Kirk Othmer. 1978. *Encyclopedia of Chemical Technology*, vol. 2, 3d ed., p. 221. New York: Wiley Interscience.
15. Rhone Poulenc. U.S. patent 2,915,365 (1959).
16. Rhone Poulenc. U.S. patent 3,480,389 (1969).
17. Rhone Poulenc. U.S. patent 3,628,914 (1971).
18. Rhone Poulenc. French patent 1,250,000 (1959); 1,371,808 (1963); 1,438,497 (1965); 1,460,015 (1965); 1,483,002 (1966); 1,381,282 (1963); 2,520,722 (1982).

19. R. K. Iler. 1955. *The Colloid Chemistry of Silica and Silicates*. Ithaca, N.Y.: Cornell University Press.
20. Universal Oil Products. U.S. patent 2,620,314 (1952).
21. du Pont. U.S. patent 2,915,475 (1959).
22. Rhone Poulenc. French patent 1,460,015 (1965).
23. K. Ziegler et al. 1954. *Brennstof Chem.* 35:321.
24. T. Mole and A. Jellery. 1972. *Organo Aluminum Compounds*. Amsterdam: Elsevier.
25. Petrobras. Brazil patent 8,005,302 (1980).
26. Rhone Poulenc. U.S. patent 4,292,295 (1980).
27. Mobil Oil. U.S. patent 4,447,314 (1984).
28. Chevron. U.S. patent 4,489,173 (1984).
29. R. K. Oberlander. 1985. *Proc. 17th Biennial Conference*, p. 247. Amsterdam: IBA.
30. W. Stoepler and K. K. Unger. 1983. Prep. of catalysts III, Sc. bases for the preparation of heterog. *Catalysts*, p. 643. Amsterdam: Elsevier.
31. K. Jiratova, L. Janacek, and P. Schneider. 1983. Prep. of catalysts III, Sc. bases for the preparation of heterog. *Catalysts*, p. 653. Amsterdam: Elsevier.
32. Universal Oil Products. U.S. patent 2,620,314 (1952); 2,865,866 (1958).
33. Rhone Poulenc. U.S. patent 4,273,735 (1981).
34. Snam Progetti. French patent 1,430,620 (1965).
35. Grace. French patent 2,405,900 (1979).
36. Rhone Poulenc. French patent 2,527,197 (1983); U.S. patent 4,315,839 (1982).
37. Labofina. French patent 2,261,056 (1975); 2,261,057 (1975).
38. Rhone Poulenc. French patent 1,371,808 (1963).
39. U. Hammon and M. Kotter. 1984. *Chem. Ing. Tech.* 56:455.
40. W. Veselod and T. A. de Vanyink. 1975. *Kinet. Catal.* 16:868.
41. A. B. Stiles. 1983. *Catalyst Manufacture*. New York: Dekker.
42. H. Freundlich. 1932. Leipzig: *Kapillarchemie Akademische Verlags*.
43. Rhone Poulenc. U.S. patent 4,529,718 (1984).
44. W. H. Sawyer and M. T. Duncan. U.S. patent 4,016,106 (1977).
45. C. Okkerse and J. H. de Boer. 1960. *J. Chim. Phys.* 57:534.
46. J. M. Vlesskens. 1959. Thesis. Delft, Netherlands.
47. I. E. Neimark and R. Sheinfain. 1953. *Kolloid Zh.* 15:145.
48. D. Basmaldjian, G. N. Fulford, B. I. Parsons, and D. S. Montgomery. 1962. *J. Catal.* 1:547.
49. Universal Oil Products. French patent 2,371,962 (1976).
50. Rhone Poulenc. French patent 3,494,875 (1970).
51. Rhone Poulenc. Eur. patent 55,164 (1981).
52. C. Marcilly and J. P. Franck. 1984. *Rev. de l'I.F.P.* 39:337.
53. W. H. Wade and N. Hackerman. 1960. *J. Phys. Chem.* 64:1196.
54. D. S. Maliver, H. H. Tobin, and R. T. Barth. 1963. *J. Catal.* 2:485.
55. T. Morimoto, K. Shiomi, and H. Tanaka. 1964. *Bull. Chem. Soc. Japan* 37:392.
56. T. W. Healy and D. W. Fuerstenau. 1965. *J. Colloid. Interface Sci.* 20:376.
57. D. A. Griffiths and D. W. Fuerstenau. 1981. *J. Colloid. Interface Sci.* 80:271.
58. G. A. Parks. 1965. *Chem. Rev.* 65:177.
59. C. P. Huang and W. Stumm. 1973. *J. Colloid. Interface Sci.* 43:409.
60. L. Wang and W. K. Hall. 1981. *J. Catal.* 66:251.
61. H. P. Boehm. 1971. *Discuss. Faraday Soc.* 52:264.
62. G. Y. Onoda and J. A. Casey. 1984. *Ultra-Structure Processes of Ceramics, Glasses and Composites*, p. 374. New York: Wiley Interscience.
63. D. C. Grahame. 1947. *Chem. Res.* 41:441.

64. J. Lyklema. 1968. *Electroanal. Chem.* 18:341.
65. S. Levine and A. L. Smith. 1971. *Discuss. Faraday Soc.* 52:290.
66. D. E. Yates, S. Levine, and T. W. Healy. 1974. *J. C. S. Faraday Trans. I.* 70:807.
67. J. A. Davis and J. O. Leckie. 1980. *J. Colloid Interface Sci.* 74:32.
68. J. P. Brunelle. Unpublished results.
69. H. A. Benesis, R. M. Curtis, and H. P. Studer. 1968. *J. Catal.* 10:328.
70. B. Samanos. 1971. Thesis. Paris.
71. J. P. Brunelle. 1978. *Pure Appl. Chem.* 50:1211.
72. L. Vordinis, P. G. Koistsoukos, and A. Lycourghiotis. 1984. *J. Chem. Soc., Chem. Commun.* 1311.
73. J. B. Peri. 1965. *J. Phys. Chem.* 69:220.
74. M. P. Rosynek and J. W. Hightower. 1973. *Proc. Int. Congr. Catal.* 5th. 2:851.
75. A. A. Tsyganenko and V. N. Filiminov. 1973. *J. Mol. Struct.* 19:579.
76. J. B. Butt and L. T. Starzec. 1974. *J. Catal.* 32:99.
77. H. Knözinger and P. Ratnasamy. 1978. *Catal. Rev. Sci. Eng.* 17:31.
78. K. Tanabe. 1985. *Catalysis by Acids and Bases*, p. 1. Amsterdam: Elsevier Science Publishers.
79. F. Forni. 1973. *Catal. Reviews* 8:69.
80. L. H. Little. 1966. *Infrared Spectra of Adsorbed Species*. New York: Academic Press.
81. M. L. Hair. 1967. *Infrared Spectroscopy in Surface Chemistry*. New York: Dekker.
82. J. C. Lavalley and J. Caillod. 1980. *J. Chim. Phys.* 77:373.
83. M. Benaissa. 1985. Thesis. Caen.
84. A. Auroux and J. Vedrine. 1985. *Catalysis by Acids and Bases*, p. 311. Amsterdam: Elsevier.
85. M. Guisnet. 1985. *Catalysis by Acids and Bases*, p. 283. Amsterdam: Elsevier.
86. C. Doremieux-Morin and J. Fraissard. 1985. *Catalysis by Acids and Bases*, p. 299. Amsterdam: Elsevier.
87. Rhone Poulenc. French patent 2,450,784 (1979).
88. J. C. Plumail, H. Toulhouat, G. Martino, and Y. Jacquin. 1985. 189th ACS National Meeting. Petroleum Chemistry. Miami Beach.
89. J. M. S. Scurrel. 1977. *Catalysis, Chem. Soc. London* 1:136.
90. G. H. Posner. 1978. *Angew. Chem.* 90:527.
91. H. Pines and J. Ravoire. 1961. *J. Phys. Chem.* 65:1859.
92. J. W. Hightower and W. K. Hall. 1970. *Trans. Faraday Soc.* 66:477.
93. J. M. S. Scurrel and C. Kemball. 1976. *J. C. S. Faraday Trans.* 72:818.
94. Y. Sukarai, T. Onishi, and K. Tamaru. 1972. *Bull. Chem. Soc. Japan* 45:980.
95. J. B. Peri. 1966. *J. Phys. Chem.* 70:3168.
96. J. W. Hightower and W. K. Hall. 1969. *J. Catal.* 13:161.
97. D. S. Maciver, W. H. Wilmot, and J. M. Bridges. 1964. *J. Catal.* 3:502.
98. J. E. Germain, L. Bassery, and M. Blanchard. 1958. *Bull. Chem. Soc. Fr.* 958.
99. A. Ghorbel, C. Hoang-van, and S. J. Teichner. 1974. *J. Catal.* 33:123.
100. V. R. Padmanabhan and F. J. Eastburn. 1972. *J. Catal.* 24:88.
101. G. Kallo and H. Knözinger. 1967. *Chem. Ing. Tech.* 39:676.
102. H. Pines and J. Manassen. 1966. *Adv. Catal.* 16:49.
103. H. G. Karge, I. G. Dalla Lana, S. Trevizan De Swarez, and Y. Zhang. 1984. *Proc. 8th I.C.C.*, p. 453. West Berlin.
104. M. Akimoto and I. G. Dalla Lana. 1980. *J. Catal.* 62:84.
105. R. Fiedorow, R. Leaute, and I. G. Dalla Lana. 1984. *J. Catal.* 85:339.
106. J. F. Lepage. 1978. *Catalyse de contact*, p. 588. Paris: Technip.

CHAPTER 3

Supports Other Than Alumina

Alvin B. Stiles

Alumina appears in many different crystallographic species and can be processed from many different types of raw materials. The products from the different types of raw materials are themselves different from each other. Under various preparation conditions, the types of pores, the surface area, the densities, total pore volumes, and other physical characteristics change significantly with method of preparation and raw materials. This is one reason why alumina has such broad usage. It can be tailor-made into many types of physical forms: pellets, bars, rods, fluted rods, spheres, cylinders, rings, saddles, and others.

The support can be coprecipitated with the catalytic component. Such alumina can be added from a chloride salt of aluminum, nitrate, sulfate, alcoholate, or alkali aluminate, and the precipitation can be effected with ammonium carbonate, ammonium hydroxide, sodium hydroxide or carbonate, carbon dioxide (carbonic acid), acetic or other acceptable acids.

Because alumina can be in the cationic or the anionic state, many different methods of processing can be used to derive the desired aluminum hydroxide or, ultimately, the aluminum oxide. It is obvious that the ions retained in the precipitate can be preselected or controlled by the raw materials used in the preparation. The purest alumina would result from the use of elemental aluminum, dissolving it in nitric acid or hydrochloric acid of high purity and then precipitating it with ammonium carbonate or ammonium hydroxide, also of high purity. If one wishes to have retained acidity, one can use the chloride or sulfate salt precipitated with ammonium carbonate, with the result that sulfate or chloride would be occluded in the final precipitate. In fact, this is one way of deriving the acidic alumina used in the so-called dual-functioning catalyst in which the support is strongly acidic, facilitating desired reactions such as petroleum cracking and isomerization.

SILICA

Inasmuch as silica and alumina are frequently mentioned as supports in the same breath, it is logical to consider silica next as a refractory oxide catalyst support to follow the discussion of alumina. Like alumina, silica occurs in many polymorphs, as shown in Table 3.1.

Table 3.1 Thermal Stability Range

Name	at 1 atm	Symmetry
Quartz	Below 573°C	Hexagonal-P, trigonal trapezohedral
High quartz	573–870°C	Hexagonal-P, hexagonal trapedohedral
Low tridymite	Below 117°C	Orthorhombic
Middle tridymite	117°–163°C	Hexagonal
High tridymite	163–1470°C (stable 870–1470°C)	Hexagonal, dihexagonal dipyramidal
Low cristobalite	Below 200°C	Tetragonal, tetragonal trapezohedral[a]
High cristobalite	200–1720°C	Isometric, tetaroidal[a]
Keatite	Metastable at ordinary conditions	Tetragonal, tetragonal trapezohedral
Coesite	Metastable at ordinary conditions	Monoclinic, prismatic
Stishovite	Metastable at ordinary conditions	Tetragonal, ditetragonal dipyramidal

[a]The data available are not unquestioned.

Not only do these polymorphs overlap in temperature ranges, but they are influenced by pressure (Figure 3.1). All of these factors must be taken into account as one considers catalyst stability and particularly epitaxial orientation, which is likely to change as the support itself alters. An additional factor that must be considered with regard to silica is that at temperatures of 600°C and above, pressures of 1 mP or above, and in a steam-reducing gas environment, SiO_2 will sublime and deposit downstream in a cooler or lower-pressure location. This can be disastrous to the strength of the catalyst, as well as heat exchange or pressure drop in downstream equipment.

Although silica is not used as frequently as alumina, it has characteristics that make it useful in many cases in which alumina does not fit [1]. Silica is primarily much more resistant to acid media and as a consequence is more satisfactory than is alumina in this type of an environment. Both silica and alumina, however, are adversely affected by an alkali environment, and neither is recommended for use in a basic system.

Sodium or potassium silicate is the most frequent and most convenient source of silica, either as a support or when added to a precipitate by coprecipitation. A typical way to make silica gel is to prepare a 4% solution of sodium metasilicate (Na_2SiO_3). The precipitation of a gel is effected by the addition of sufficient carbon dioxide or sulfuric or hydrochloric acids so that the pH approaches neutrality, 7. At a pH of 7, the solution will typically gel, and if it is in a container, it will become rigid much like a gelatin, and if the container is not too large in diameter, it can be turned over, and the gel will remain suspended in the container.

This gel is subsequently washed by decantation. Sodium ordinarily can be re-

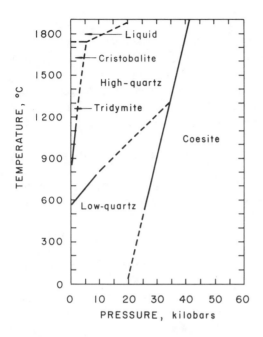

Figure 3.1 Overlap in temperature ranges of alumina polymorphs and influence of pressure on these polymorphs.

moved to a level of about 1.0% Na_2O in the finished, dried gel. Reducing the sodium below this level is almost impossible, and it is assumed that the sodium is occluded in the silica as sodium metasilicate, which cannot be extracted or removed. The lowest levels of sodium are attained by slurrying the gel in a 10% ammonium carbonate or ammonium bicarbonate solution, agitating well to break up the gel curds to small size easily accessible to the ammonium ion, which replaces the sodium ion by ion exchange. It is highly desirable to remove the sodium to as low a level as possible in order to avoid the alkalinity of the sodium, which may adversely affect any catalyst supported on the silica and also to prevent the sodium from acting as a fluxing agent for the silica (lowering the temperature at which it fuses and entraps catalytic material).

The sodium problem can be avoided if the gel is obtained by hydrolyzing silicon tetrachloride in water. A second equally effective method of avoiding alkali is to hydrolyze ethyl silicate in water.

One eventually derives a more or less pure silicon oxide hydrated to various extents. On drying, this silica shrinks dramatically, with the dried material occupying a volume not much more than 5% of the original hydrated gel. In this form, the silica can act as a support for most catalytic metals and has a surface area of approximately 400 m/g. Impregnation is effected by the many procedures known to the art. However, one of the peculiarities of silica—and in some cases alumina—is that when it is being impregnated with a liquid, the heat of adsorption is so great that the liquid, at the face of the adsorption wave, will vaporize, forming steam and causing the breakage of the granules, sometimes to a fine powder.

This decrepitation, as it is called, can be avoided by passing steam or humid air or a humidified gas over the granules in a tube to the point where the moisture content of the silica has increased to 50% or above. When the silica has reached this level of moisture adsorption, the rate of liquid entry into the pores and resultant heating of the liquid is such that no disintegration of the granules will occur. This decrepitation occurs also, but to a lesser extent, with silica aluminas and, to an even lesser extent, with aluminas, but it is a problem that must be faced and in some cases avoided by presaturation with moisture.

Silica can be derived from various sources and eventually end as granules, extrudates, pellets, or the like. However, frequently silica is used in a coprecipitated form finely and intimately dispersed through a catalytic precipitate. This can be effected in several ways. One is to have all catalytic salts in the form of a chloride and adding to that chloride solution silicon tetrachloride to the extent desired as a support and at a solution pH such that the silicon tetrachloride will remain in solution and not hydrolyze to hydrochloric acid and silica gel. Precipitation is then effected typically by raising the pH to near neutrality, where all ingredients precipitate, and the silica is finely and intimately dispersed through the catalytic precipitate.

One should bear in mind as one processes the catalyst beyond this point that the silica is in a highly reactive form and is intimately mixed with the catalytic components. In this condition, raising the temperature of the composite to a level exceeding 450–500°C will frequently cause the incipient formation of silicates. Higher temperatures will convert the catalyst almost completely to silicates if adequate silica is present. Although this precaution is being given as a warning to avoid high temperatures and silicate formation, it should not be construed to mean that a slight conversion to silicate is always harmful. It is possible and in some cases has been demonstrated that silica as a support in such conditions also reacts with the catalytic component to form silicates having excellent catalytic activity and directivity performance characteristics.

The procedure pursued in Chapter 2 to obtain the intimately and finely dispersed silica throughout the catalytic material can also be achieved by the addition of ethyl silicate to the precipitating catalytic material. This is usually accomplished by having the catalytic ingredients in an agitated vessel, to which is simultaneously added both a precipitant and the ethyl silicate, which on reaching the aqueous solution hydrolyzes to form silica in a finely divided state.

Coprecipitated silica can also be incorporated into a precipitating batch of catalyst by the following procedure. A 4% solution of one of the sodium silicates, preferably sodium metasilicate, is prepared by dissolving a sufficient quantity of the dry salt in water. This solution is rapidly agitated, and when it contains the desired quantity of silica for the preparation in question, a mineral acid such as nitric, hydrochloric, or sulfuric is added to the solution rapidly to change the pH from strongly alkaline to strongly acidic, reaching a pH below 2. In this condition, the silica will not gel but will form a stable sol. This sol is added to the solution of catalytic salts, which also must be at a low pH. A precipitant such as ammonium carbonate or ammonium bicarbonate, sodium or potassium carbonates, or bicarbonates is added until a pH of 6.8 to 7.5 is reached. Under these conditions, the catalytic components are precipitated, and the silica is occluded in such a way as to provide an effective support, which also may act as a stabilizer or even a promoter.

These methods of preparing granular silica and coprecipitated silica are effective ways of providing a silica with excellent support characteristics. Additionally, silica in high purity can be obtained as colloidal silica, which is a subject almost in itself. Colloidal silica, however, has characteristics that distinguish it substantially from the coprecipitated finely dispersed silica. Colloidal silica is ordinarily in the form of microspheres having a diameter from approximately 40 Å to 350 Å. Colloidal silica can be treated much the same as the sodium silicate described; it can be rapidly converted from the basic solution, which is normally present, to the acidic dispersion, which is also colloidal and highly stable. This can be added to solutions of catalytic materials and can be coprecipitated as was stipulated for the silica sol. Inasmuch as the silica can be added as spheres having varying diameters and these spheres can arrange themselves in open networks or comparatively closely packed clusters, the catalyst can have a complete spectrum of pore characteristics. Reference to Figure 3.2 will quickly show the open network that can be achieved with colloidal silica. (Other types of refractory oxides can be similarly obtained and similarly utilized.)

The colloidal materials can also be dried, and as they dry, they gel and become granular much the same as does the gel derived from sodium silicate. This silica will not have the extremely fine pore dimensions or the high surface area of the dried sol,

Figure 3.2 Colloidal silica: An open network and a closely packed cluster.

but it does have extremely interesting characteristics in that the pores can be essentially controlled as to diameter and total pore volume.

This colloid-derived silica is much less reactive than that derived from silica sol, and as a consequence, the formation of silicate is resisted until at a higher temperature than when the silica is derived from acidified silicate (sol). In both cases, however, at approximately 700°C, the silica does become highly reactive, coalesces, and forms silicates extensively, if not completely.

There are still some forms of silica that must be considered as possible support materials. One is fumed silica, essentially a colloidal type made in vapor phase. Another is commercial silica in various forms, either as an extracted glass or processed from sodium silicate by precipitation and washing procedures. The extracted glass is obtainable in various forms from Corning Glass, which produces it. Silica of this type has its own characteristics, described in literature from Corning Glass.

Fumed silica is derived by oxidizing silicon tetrachloride in an oxygen or air jet, with the result that a highly dispersed silica is produced. Inasmuch as it is operated at high temperature, it is the high-temperature form of silica known as alpha quartz. It is a bulky material, with a single cubic foot weighing only 2 or 3 lb, but it is readily dispersed in water and can be used as a substitute for colloidal silica. It should be pointed out, however, that the colloidal silica and the fumed silica have properties all their own, and their dispersing and stabilizing properties are entirely different, as are their tendencies to react with a catalytic material and form silicates. The fumed silica is the more inert and has the lesser tendency to form silicates. Fumed silica has a trade name of Cabosil and is sold by Cabot Corporation and through laboratory supply houses.

At times chips of fused silica are useful as a support. Fused silica is almost as inert as is fused alumina and as a consequence can be used as a support with a minimum fear that the support itself will contribute either beneficially or adversely to the reaction being studied. Because fused silica has characteristics other than fused alumina, it is the purpose of this discussion of silica to point out that it also can be a useful and relatively inert support. Fused silica in various forms can be purchased from American Thermal Quartz Company, Georgetown, Delaware.

DIATOMACEOUS EARTH

Diatomaceous earth is a naturally occurring inexpensive silicious material frequently used as a catalyst support, particularly nickel on kieselghur (another name for diatomaceous earth), a frequently used liquid-phase heterogeneous hydrogenation catalyst. Diatomaceous earth is also used as a filter aid, so as a support, it imparts improved filterability and ease of suspension in a hetrogeneous liquid-phase system. The ease of suspension usually is exploited to the extent that the liquid can be sufficiently agitated and the catalyst suspended by the hydrogen or other gas mixture bubbling up through the slurry and without supplementary mechanical agitation. This is advantageous for both capital and operating costs. On the other side of the ledger is the fact that the diatomaceous earth is porous and adsorptive, so that when the catalyst is removed and discarded, a large content of the valuable product may be included in the wet catalyst. Extraction recovery treatments usually are called for.

Diatomaceous earth occurs naturally; it is a silicified fossil of ancient diatoms in warm inland seas. Being of natural aqueous origin, the chemical composition, though mostly siliceous, falls into the range shown in Table 3.2. Figures 3.3, 3.4, 3.5, and 3.6 are microscopic views of individual diatoms. It is evident that there are important ingredients that must be taken into account when diatomaceous earth is used. The natural run-of-mine material has acid-soluble ingredients (may dissolve in a nickel or cobalt nitrate solution with pH of the typical 0.5 to 1.0). Furthermore, when the nickel is precipitated, typically using sodium carbonate, two processes occur: the reprecipitation of what was dissolved from the diatomaceous earth earlier and the dissolving of ingredients (SiO_2) in the slurry at alkaline pH. The solubilizing factors can be either harmful or beneficial. For example, at elevated pH, if the catalyst slurry is permitted to digest at 70°C at a pH of 7.5, the finished and reduced catalyst has activity of approximately $1.5X$ (X is the activity of the nondigested slurry). This activity can be duplicated by adding SiO_2 as acidified Na_2SiO_3 solution (producing a sol) to the nickel nitrate-kieselghur slurry. The implication is that the SiO_2 (as a sol) equivalent to 5% of the kieselghur is equivalent to that produced during the digestion operation. Other corroborating evidence is available of the activating factor deriving from dissolved and reprecipitated SiO_2 gel.

Other types of diatomaceous earth are available in commerce. Some have been calcined; some have been acid or base treated and then washed to remove extractable components. These forms are not reactive with alkali at a pH of 7.5 and as a consequence have a final activity of X or near $0.9X$. The activity can be increased to $1.5X$ by the treatment with 5% SiO_2 (on the basis of total diatomaceous earth) added as a sol.

Diatomaceous earth is available in reactive and nonreactive forms, as well as in different particle sizes and compositions as powder. It is also available as extrudates and spheres.

Table 3.2 Chemical Composition of Diatomaceous Earth

Grades	Ignition Loss (%)	S_iO_2	Al_2O_3	Fe_2O_3	P_2O_5	TiO_2	CaO	MgO	Na_2O + K_2O
Untreated	3.6	85.8	3.8	1.2	0.2	0.2	0.5	0.6	1.1
Calcined and alkali treated	0.2	89.6	4.0	1.3	0.2	0.2	0.5	0.6	3.3

Figure 3.3 Individual skeletons of fossil diatoms: Actinoptychus Undulatus. (Micrographs courtesy of Manville, Filtration & Minerals.)

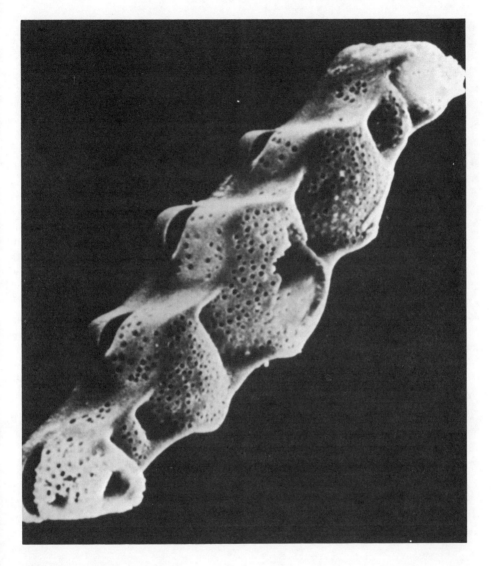

Figure 3.4   Individual skeletons of fossil diatoms: Biddulphia Tuomeyi. (Micrographs courtesy of Manville, Filtration & Minerals.)

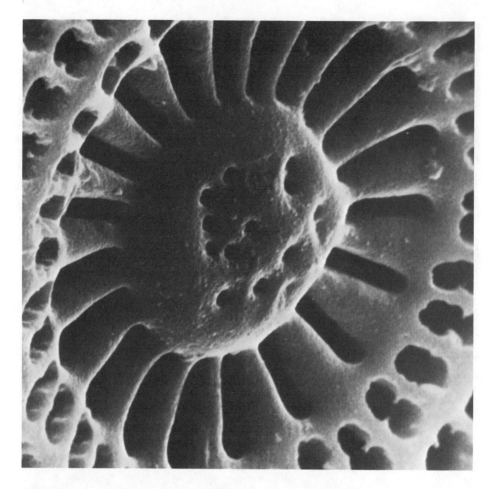

Figure 3.5   Individual skeletons of fossil diatoms: Arachnoidiscus ornatus. (Micrographs courtesy of Manville, Filtration & Minerals.)

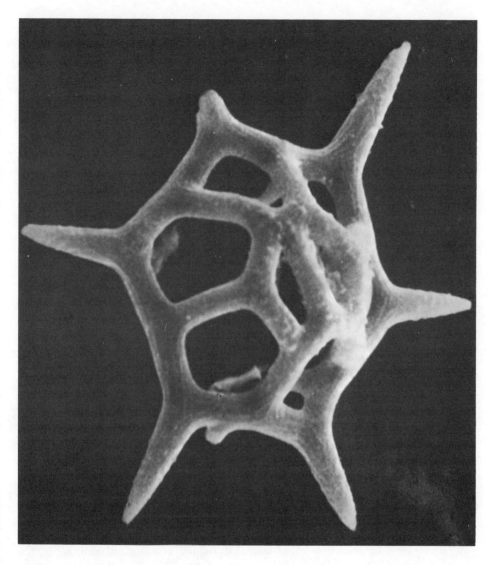

Figure 3.6 Individual skeletons of fossil diatoms: Silica flagellate. (Micrographs courtesy of Manville, Filtration & Minerals.)

TITANIA

Titania is one of the most interesting of supports [2, 3, 4, 5]. It has been and continues to be the subject of much research effort, some of which has been reported (see chapter references). One of the most interesting emanating from our own laboratories [6] is that manganese, when supported on titania and compared with manganese oxide supported on alumina, ceria, zirconia, and magnesia, behaved differently from any of the other types of composites. As an example of the extreme differences between the two is the fact that when used to oxidize methanol, manganese oxide on ceria, for example, gave total oxidation to carbon dioxide and water under very low temperature conditions. By contrast, manganese oxide on titania prepared by a method later described was very directive of methanol to formaldehyde, achieving a yield of approximately 80%. This fact reveals the effect of the support and the uniqueness of titania in contrast to other supports.

Just as alumina and silica appear as different species under different pressure and temperature conditions, titania also has three different species: brookite, anatase, and rutile. Brookite is in the rhombohedral form, anatase is tetragonal, and rutile is tetragonal close-packed. All have phase changes corresponding to temperature and pressure changes.

Titania can be purchased as a support material from Sakai Trading Company, New York, New York. The carrier is identified as CS-200. An analysis of the material is as follows: TiO_2 96% (loss on ignition 2%), SO_4 2%, Fe_2O_3 0.05%, and Na_2O 0.01%. The grain sizes can be 2 to 4 ml, 4 to 6 ml, and 6 to 8 ml. Surface area is about 35 m^2/g, apparent density is 0.93, and the mean pore diameter is 500 Å. Pore volume is 0.39 ml/g. Although there may be other vendors of relatively high-surface-area titania, they have not come to my attention.

Titania can be obtained in powder form as pigment grade. All pigment-grade titania has a coating of a foreign material on its surface, which would interfere in most applications when pure titania is to be the material of choice. The coating material is usually a proprietary formula or composition, and as a consequence it is impossible to forewarn as to the type of material actually used in all pigments. Frequently it is a silica coating, but this cannot be uniformly assumed to be the case. Pigment-grade titania is usually the anatase species.

There are a number of different sources of titania. Titanium tetrachloride is well known for its characteristic for severe fuming and difficulty in handling. However, it can be used and dissolved in either an organic solvent or a highly concentrated hydrochloric acid aqueous solution. When it is diluted with water, hydrolysis takes place, and a finely divided titania results. If one is preparing a catalyst from the chlorides and is satisfied to make a highly concentrated solution, then the titanium tetrachloride probably can be dissolved in this solution using a sufficiently concentrated hydrochloric acid solution as a cosolvent.

Another method is to make the solution of the catalytic components and have an agitated vessel so designed that a precipitant as well as a solution of titanium tetrachloride can be added simultaneously to the catalytic ingredients to be precipitated.

The precipitation and hydrolysis of the titanium tetrachloride are so scheduled that the titania forms a coprecipitate with the catalytic constituents. This procedure is not preferred.

Ordinarily titanium is considered as not readily forming the nitrate salt. However, titanium tetrachloride can readily be converted to the nitrate, and the nitrate, with a sufficiently low pH with added nitric acid if necessary, is stable. This nitrate can be formed by placing in a flask equipped with reflux condenser an aqueous solution of titanium tetrachloride. The flask is fitted with a means for adding nitric acid and for determining the temperature of the solution. The flask is heated to approximately 85°C. At this temperature, nitric acid is gradually and carefully added to evolve chloride, which will evolve from the condenser. This nitrate salt of titanium can be added to a precipitation vessel together with the catalytic ingredients and the entire mixture precipitated in a normal way, such as with sodium or ammonium carbonates or bicarbonates or other well-known precipitants.

Another highly satisfactory method of introducing titania to a precipitation is to use an organic titanium compound such as those identified as "Tyzors™" and sold by the du Pont Company. There are various grades of Tyzors™ depending on the organic acid with which they are esterified. Tyzor™ LA is the lactic acid ester. It is rather stable in aqueous solutions and as a consequence is not the preferred organic source of titania. A highly satisfactory titania source is Tyzor™ TPT, and it is tetraisopropyl titanate. It hydrolyzes quite rapidly and satisfactorily in an aqueous solution and produces a highly dispersed, finely divided titanium oxide.

Titania also can be obtained in colloidal form from Magnesium Elektron Corp. and from Nyacol. Addresses of these companies are given in *Chemical Week Buyer's Guide*. The same factors apply to colloidal titania as apply to colloidal silica; the formation of titanates (that is, the reaction with the catalytic materials) occurs less readily than with the coprecipitated titania. Also there is tendency for the generation of a more open structure to the catalyst, which translates to a larger average pore diameter.

ZIRCONIA

It is difficult to remove all of the hafnia that is present as an impurity in the zirconia. Zirconia always contains approximately 2% hafnia, so one is really dealing with a hafnia-promoted or -modified zirconia.

Zirconia ordinarily is not available in high-surface-area particles. At one time, Norton Company produced some low-surface-area zirconia, which was somewhat similar to aluminas having less than 1 m^2/g of surface area and relatively high porosity in the range of two-tenths to three-tenths of a milliliter per gram of support. Because of the inability to obtain zirconia with high surface area in granular or other forms, researchers must derive their own granular material. There are two suitable methods. The first is the precipitation of the zirconia as a gel by adding ammonium hydroxide to a zirconium nitrate solution in sufficient quantity to raise the pH to essentially neutrality. The concentration of the zirconium nitrate solution is not particularly critical, but it is advisable to hold it within a range of 10 to 15%. The gel that is formed is washed—if possible by decantation (and if not by decantation, by filtration, reslurrying, and refiltering). The gel is dried at approximately 150°C and then is heated further if desired to approximately 400°C to eliminate much of the water of hydration. The dried cake or granular material thus obtained is broken into material that passes a given screen and is retained on another screen, deriving the screen size desired.

This method produces high-surface-area granular zirconia. By this procedure one can attain a surface area of approximately 100–125 m^2/g. A colloidal sol can also be dried to produce hard granules having a surface area somewhat lower than that derived from the gel but having characteristics that may be highly desirable. A third method of producing particulate material is to derive powdered zirconium oxide either from a purchased source or by the precipitation from zirconium nitrate or the drying of the gel. The powder is then mixed with a pilling lubricant such as graphite and is pilled on a pilling machine such as that manufactured by the F. J. Stokes Co., a division of Pennwalt. Pilling of zirconium oxide is not a simple matter and must be conducted by one having full knowledge of the pilling technique.

Inasmuch as zirconium nitrate can be readily purchased commercially, a favorite way to introduce zirconia into a catalyst as a support is by coprecipitation. This procedure consists of adding the zirconium nitrate along with the other catalytic ingredients, with the zirconium being added to the extent necessary to achieve the stabilizing or support effect and then precipitating in a normal manner.

Another method is to use zirconium carbonate that can be purchased as such and is used as a slurry in the presence of the catalytic salts in solution. The carbonate can then be coprecipitated with the catalytic ingredients, or the zirconium carbonates can be dissolved in nitric acid and the total catalytic ingredient can be coprecipitated. The latter procedure produces the more uniform distribution of ingredients.

Zirconia in the colloidal form can also be obtained from Nyacol and Magnesium Elektron companies. This colloidal material can be added to a precipitation in the initial stages of preparation or to the solutions of catalytic ingredients. The colloidal material is generally stabilized with either nitric or acetic acid; both acids are usually harmless in most catalyst preparations. The colloidal materials are added to the precipitation in a quantity required for achieving the objectives, and usually the precipitation is effected essentially the same as if the zirconia were not present. When the zirconia is added as the colloid, the tendency to form zirconates and the promoting effect of the zirconia is less per unit of zirconia than is the case when the zirconia is coprecipitated and is more finely divided. On the contrary, the zirconia when thus precipitated does achieve a more porous catalyst, which may have highly desirable characteristics.

Zirconium oxide is usually the dioxide that is listed in five species, but under high temperature or reducing conditions, it also forms the suboxide or monoxide (Table 3.3). There are other suboxides that are catalytic, but these are nonstoichiometric and also, though very likely of substantial catalytic importance, are not well enough characterized to be included in Table 3.3.

Table 3.3 Five Species of Zirconium Oxide

ZrO_2, baddeleyite, monoclinic
ZrO_2, no mineral name, cubic
ZrO_2, no mineral name, orthorhombic
ZrO_2, no mineral name, tetragonal
ZrO_2, no mineral name, also tetragonal but different spacings
ZrO, zirconium monoxide, no mineral name, cubic.

RARE EARTHS AND LANTHANIDES

It is well to first explain why the heading is "Rare Earths and Lanthanides." The more technical term is *lanthanides*, and it is preferred when referring to this group of transition metal elements. They are frequently referred to as the rare earths, but for various reasons, such as the confusion with alkali earths and the designation of "rare" indicating that they might be expensive and difficult to obtain, being misleading. There are fourteen members of the regular family with atomic numbers from 58 through 71; however, yttrium and lanthanum are also usually included in this grouping.

This family of elements appears in different types of minerals in various parts of the world. Because of the different minerals and their composition, the components generally are different depending on the type of mineral being processed. In essentially all cases, the primary components of the mineral are lanthanum, cerium, praseodymium, and neodymium. These are usually present to an extent of a total of 90 to 95% of the total constituents in the mineral. The other twelve elements are in some cases indeed rare, but despite their rarity, they can be obtained as part of the so-called mixed lanthanides or mixed rare earths; a relatively inexpensive mixture of this type can be obtained as the nitrates, chlorides, carbonates, or hydroxides. There are occasions when some of the rarer elements are extracted for specific reasons, such as europium in order to obtain a highly desirable red fluorescent material for television screens. When these elements are removed the residue is sold as mixed lanthanides.

Although they are termed a family and are quite similar electronically, the *f* band has various degrees of unsaturation, and this fact imparts some chemical and physical differences in these elements. They do have many characteristics that make them excellent supports: high melting point, good thermal stability, relatively reactive in solid-state reactions, and readily available as pure salts or as less expensive mixtures. The mixtures have characteristics that are somewhat variable one from the other, but the mixture does provide a shotgun approach, which gives an interesting and challenging possibility in the exploratory catalyst preparations.

All of these elements, like alumina, have some amphoteric properties so can exist in either the cationic or anionic form. As an example, cerium will form cerium nitrate but also will form cerates with basic materials. This fact is mentioned because of the interesting characteristics that can be devised when the cerium oxide is used as a support material, particularly when the catalyst is processed or is used at high enough temperatures so that there is a solid-state reaction between the catalytic material and the cerium oxide.

Lanthanum oxide is a highly refractory material. Although it reacts in a solid-state condition with the catalytic materials, it is less reactive than is the cerium oxide and is therefore suitable as a stabilizer and support at a higher temperature without there being a reaction between it and the catalytic material. Praseodymium and neodymium also are somewhat less reactive than the cerium, but both have characteristics that make them unique in the catalytic application. Although the rare earths are a family, each behaves differently from the others, and although we paired neodymium and praseodymium together, they should each be considered as having their own physical and chemical characteristics.

A characteristic of the lanthanides that is not true of most of the other supports one considers is that they, particularly cerium oxide, will thermoluminesce. When the temperature reaches or exceeds 400°C, there is a tendency for radiation to occur. This radiation signifies that energy is being dissipated by the support, and this energy may be in a form that can be absorbed by the reacting molecules on the catalyst and thus either facilitate or adversely affect that reaction. Furthermore, one or more of the oxygens on the lanthanides can be quite readily removed (a labile oxygen) with hydrogen. This signifies that in a reaction environment, the labile oxygen and the oxygen vacancy site may play an important part in the catalytic action. In many cases, such as methanation and selective oxidation of ammonia and propylene to acrilonitrile, this is an advantageous effect. In other cases, the removal of the oxygen can introduce a disadvantageous effect, and as a consequence one must be willing to research carefully these diametrically opposite effects. Although much of what we are discussing relates especially to cerium oxide, other lanthanides are less easily reduced than cerium. As a corollary, one would say that the effect of the reduction or partial reduction of the oxide to a suboxide would be less likely to occur than would be the case with the cerium under identical operating and catalyst fabrication conditions.

The major discussion has been with reference to cerium oxide and the implication made that to a certain degree, other lanthanides can be similarly considered. It should be emphasized, however, that other oxides in this group have characteristics that make them worthy of investigation and evaluation. Cerium oxide is well known to be in both the ceric and cerous forms, signifying the ease with which these oxides can be altered one to the other. Metallic or oxide catalysts supported on these oxides influence to a major degree the temperature and conditions under which this oxidation or reduction takes place. The precious metals such as platinum, palladium, and iridium particularly facilitate the reduction of even the most difficult reducible oxides. We recognize that the oxide supports themselves can be reduced and reoxidized to varying degrees. However, it is not as commonly known that the catalytic metals or oxides placed on the support can themselves strongly influence this redox effect.

Under the conditions of operation, the catalyst support may act synergistically to produce an effect not produced by any other combination of catalyst and support. As a consequence, it becomes evident not only that the use of any of the lanthanides should be evaluated individually but also the effect of a specific catalytic entity supported thereon. But as is well known with cerium and lanthanum in the petroleum cracking processes involving the zeolites, the two components together behave entirely differently from the lanthanum and cerium individually. There is some evidence that still other mixed lanthanides are even better than the cerium and lanthanum pair. It is not my intent to belabor the lanthanides, although I consider them one of the most interesting groups of supports and deserving of attention no matter what type of catalyst is being sought.

A compilation of the crystalline species characteristic of some of the lanthanide oxides is given in Table 3.4. It is evident that there is an impressive group of possibilities as to chemical and physical makeup.

Table 3.4   Crystalline Species Characteristic of Some Lanthanide Oxides

Cerium
   CeO_2, cerignite, cubic
   Ce_2O_3, no mineral name, hexagonal
   Ce_6O_{11}, no mineral name, monoclinic
   CeO, no mineral name, cubic

Lanthanum
   La_2O_3, no mineral name, hexagonal
   La_2O_3, no mineral name, cubic
   La_2O_3, no mineral name, monoclinic
   La_2O_3, no mineral name, hexagonal
   LaO, no mineral name, cubic

Neodymium
   Nd_2O_3, no mineral name, hexagonal
   Nd_2O_3, no mineral name, cubic
   Nd_2O_3, no mineral name, hexagonal
   Nd_2O_3, no mineral name, monoclinic
   NdO, no mineral name, cubic

Yttrium
   Y_2O_3, no mineral name, 2300°C exposure, hexagonal
   Y_2O_3, no mineral name, cubic

Praseodymium
   $PrO_{1.83}$, no mineral name, cubic
   PrO_3, no mineral name, hexagonal
   Pr_2O_3, no mineral name, monoclinic
   Pr_2O_3, no mineral name, 2130°C, hexagonal
   PrO_2, no mineral name, cubic
   PrO, no mineral name, cubic
   Pr_4O_3, no mineral name, cubic

CHROMIA

Chromia is a typical component of spinels. When one forms a spinel, the oxygens are shared by both the A and B ions of the crystal. Chromia is interesting because it is one of the oxides readily forming spinels, and forming spinels can be accomplished by a number of different routes. But chromia also has support characteristics that make it uniquely suitable under certain conditions. It is a superb support for oxidation catalysts, particularly oxidation catalysts for total conversion of the combustibles to CO_2 and water vapor. Chromia also has excellent thermal stability and will permit operation of most catalysts to temperatures approaching 1000°C with little or no adverse effect on the catalyst composite.

One of the factors that must be borne in mind, however, and the pros and cons very carefully weighed, is the fact that chromia in the trivalent state will quite readily oxidize in air to hexavalent state. Thus, as a spent catalyst, if discarded in such a way that it will weather and oxidize to the hexavalent state, which is water soluble, the seepage from such a disposal site can introduce chromium 6^+ into either the aquifer or into the runoff, and both conditions are extremely objectionable. Chromium 6^+ is especially toxic to biological waste disposal systems, with parts per billion being adequate to deactivate an activated sludge completely. Chromium 6^+ entering the aquifer is also objectionable because of its migrating into domestic wells or wells supplying municipalities. For this reason, chromia is considered a special support case and its use justifiable only when suitable disposal means have been derived for the spent catalyst.

Chromium oxide is usually coprecipitated with the catalytic ingredients. The source of the chromic oxide can be chromium nitrate, chromium acetate, chromium chloride, chromium potassium sulfate, or chromium trioxide (also known as chromic acid anhydride). The chromium is in the trivalent state in all cases except the chromic acid anhydride.

Another problem—this associated with the catalyst manufacture—is the volatility of chromate or chromic acid anhydride. During preparation or handling, dust may also form. The chromates as vapor or dust entering the nose cause severe ulceration, which may result in severe nosebleeds and penetration of the septum.

Chromates are indispensable in certain catalytic operations, and, despite the problems of disposal of the spent catalyst, are a frequently used catalyst employed in relatively large volumes. Because it is used so extensively, it is important to point out the problems associated with its use. The problem of disposal has already been mentioned, but in most cases in which the catalyst is to be formed into a granule or a pellet, it must be borne in mind that both the granule and the pellet are difficult to make in sufficient hardness for most gas- or liquid-phase operations of a fixed-bed system. The problem in the pilling operation is that the catalyst powder does not coalesce without the addition of some type of a pelleting aid. A frequently used material is sodium silicate or potassium silicate, but these usually have an extremely adverse affect on the catalyst, and if the catalyst is to be used in liquid phase, it is possible that the sodium silicate will be soluble in the liquid phase, with the result that the catalyst disintegrates quickly into a powder. The addition of such material as magnesium oxide, magnesium chromate, or alkali chromates such as potassium or sodium added as a solution and mixed thoroughly into the powder and subsequently dried and mixed with the pilling lubricant in the normal way will sharply improve the pilling properties. Other pilling aids also can be used.

The fact that chromium oxides are extremely reactive in solid-state reactions is apparent in the foregoing and the fact that chromites and spinels are so readily formed. Also, the instability of the oxide is apparent from the tabulation of identified and reported stoichiometric and nonstoichiometric oxides:

CrO_3, chromic acid anhydride, no mineralogical name, orthorhombic;

Cr_2O_3, eskolaite, hexagonal;

Cr_2O_3, no mineralogical name, cubic;

Cr_3O_8, no mineralogical name, not identified as to crystal form;

CrO, no mineralogical name, not identified as to crystal form;

CrO_2, no mineralogical name, tetragonal, used in magnetic tape;

Cr_3O_4, no mineralogical name, tetragonal (distorted spinel type);

Cr_3O_{12}, no mineralogical name, orthorhombic;

Cr_3O_3, no mineralogical name, crystal form not reported.

THORIUM OXIDE

Thorium oxide has both good and bad features. The primary good feature is its extremely high melting point—above 3000°C—which is in contrast to alumina, which is approximately 2000°C. Furthermore, in cases in which one seeks to avoid any chemical interaction between the support and the catalytic material, thoria is particularly useful because it is chemically relatively (though not absolutely) inert. Thoria does enter into the reaction; one has only to consider the Fischer-Tropsch reaction to realize that this is the case. Nonetheless, it does have the two characteristics that are unusual: its chemical inertness and its extreme refractory nature. Thoria is relatively easily obtained, and in quantities less than 15 lb it is not restricted by the Nuclear Regulatory Commission.

The primary objectionable feature is its radioactivity. Although it is a relatively low emitter, it does have the reputation of being radioactive, with all of the connotations for its safe use and safe disposal. It should be noted that thoria is much less radioactive than urania, and urania has been used as a support and catalytic component in a commercially employed acrylonitrile catalyst. It is also noteworthy that the urania-modified catalyst is no longer widely used.

Thorium oxide can be obtained as a nitrate and as such offers an easily available and convenient salt for the introduction of thoria into a catalyst composition. Thorium oxide can also be obtained in the colloidal form from the typical suppliers of colloidal materials such as Nyacol. Coprecipitated thorium oxide is a much better stabilizer for a catalyst than is the colloidal material; however, the colloidal material does provide substantial stabilizing effect and a typical porosity because of the larger-than-molecular nature of the colloidal thorium oxide. It is possible that the use of both colloidal and coprecipitated thoria could produce an exceptionally interesting catalyst with high stability and unique pore structure.

If thorium oxide cannot be used, other high-melting-point oxides such as lanthanum or magnesia are available. Magnesia's melting point is only 200°C lower than that of thorium oxide and likely would be an acceptable substitute.

Thorium oxide has only two reported oxides, which gives evidence to its stability and relative inertness:

ThO_2, thorianite, cubic;

ThO, no mineral name, cubic but with different spacing.

URANIA

Uranium oxide has substantially higher radioactivity than does thorium oxide; however, uranium oxide can be obtained in the depleted form or depleted state, meaning that a processor has removed the uranium 235, the radioactive isotope, and there remains essentially a nonradioactive uranium oxide or salt. This can be converted to the uranyl nitrate and as such can be made into a solution and coprecipitated from that solution with other catalytic components. One of the characteristics of uranium, like that of thorium, is that it does not readily go through solid-state reactions and form reaction products having characteristics much different from those of uranium oxide itself. Thus the uranium oxide serves primarily and almost exclusively as a support and catalyst stabilizer.

This is not to say that the uranium oxide itself, having several states of oxidation, cannot also contribute to the catalytic effect. The point, however, is that the uranium oxide effect would not be a hybridized effect in which the uranium oxide shares oxygen with a catalyst component, thereby altering the characteristics of both simultaneously. It is noteworthy that uranium has four valency states, all of which should be expected to have different catalytic properties. These states would be expected to be reversible and would appear in a reaction environment depending on the oxidizing or reducing potential of that environment. Clearly uranium would be chosen as a support only under conditions in which it was extremely attractive and was unique because of its four valency states. Because of the alterability of these valency states and their dependence on the redox of the reaction environment, changes in operating (redox) conditions might completely alter the directivity of the catalyst containing the uranium oxide, seriously restricting the flexibility of operation.

Uranium oxide is perhaps the most heavily endowed of all oxides considered, with both states of oxidation and also crystal species and spacings. There are thirty-six different types identified of oxide or crystal states. The following are only a few of the most important oxides, but these show the wide ranges of possibilities:

U_3O_8, high temperature form, no mineral name, hexagonal;

UO_2, gamma uranium oxide, tetragonal;

$UO_{2.25}$, no mineral name, cubic;

U_2O_5, no mineral name, orthorhombic;

UO_3, alpha uranium oxide, hexagonal;

U_3O_7, low-temperature form, tetragonal;

UO_3, beta uranium oxide, monoclinic;

U_3O_8, delta uranium oxide, orthorhombic.

NIOBIA AND TANTALA

There are a number of reasons why these two oxides are infrequently used as supports or stabilizers: they are costly; their melting point is not particularly high (in the 1400–1500°C range for the niobia and the 1800–1900°C range for the tantala); and they do not form nitrates, although they do form chlorides. The chlorides, however, are extremely unstable and, like titanium tetrachloride, will react with moisture in the atmosphere to produce fumes of the hydrous oxide. The chlorides must be handled with extreme care. There is not a great deal of background of use of these oxides in catalysis. Inasmuch as they are in the family with vanadium, one could expect some similarity in the oxide characteristics. However, it should be remembered that although vanadium has four valent states, niobium has only two, and tantalum has but one. Although these characteristics make these oxides less likely to be cocatalysts with the catalyst in which they function as supports, they may be much more stable in the support role.

Many oxidation catalysts such as the iron molybdate catalyst used for the oxidation of methanol to formaldehyde are prepared from chloride salts, and as a consequence, the fact that niobium and tantalum must be used as the chlorides should not deter one from evaluating them under appropriate conditions. The catalyst, of course, must be prepared under conditions that will make possible the addition of the tantalum or niobium as the chlorides. Inasmuch as both chlorides are soluble in absolute ethyl alcohol, this could be an acceptable means of adding the tantalum or niobium to the precipitation in question.

A procedure has already been described but will be repeated here for convenience whereby one simultaneously adds two precipitants to a solution containing the catalytic ingredients. In this case, the precipitant for the catalytic ingredient could be potassium carbonate, sodium carbonate, ammonium carbonate, or hydroxides. Solutions of these precipitants could be added to the solution of catalytic ingredients while simultaneously adding the alcoholic solution of the niobium or tantalum to the aqueous solution. Because water in the aqueous solution immediately effects the hydrolysis of the chloride salt, all ingredients are simultaneously precipitated, the precipitation of the niobium or tantalum as a hydroxide thus effecting an intimate mixture of the tantalum or niobium and the catalytic ingredients. Because the tantalum and niobium are expensive ingredients, it is likely that the quantity used would be relatively small, and the hydrolysis should be made under conditions whereby even a small quantity of the tantalum or niobium is uniformly distributed during the entire precipitation of the major catalytic components. If the precipitation is effected at 80°C or above, the ethanol solvent will volatilize and be removed from the catalyst slurry. Safety precautions must be exercised to avoid the ethanol, which is heavier than air, from collecting in an area where fire or explosion could result.

Uranium oxide is very generously endowed with various states of oxidation and crystal species states; thirty-six have been identified. Runners-up in this respect are niobium oxide with twenty-eight and tantalum oxide with fourteen. As in the case with uranium oxides, only the following species are most likely to be encountered:

NbO_2, no mineral name, tetragonal;

NbO, no mineral name, cubic;

Nb_2O_5, no mineral name, monoclinic.

There are ten other niobium oxides having the formula Nb_2O_5. None has a mineral name; all have different spacings and of these ten, seven are monoclinic, one is orthorhombic, one is pseudo-hexagonal, and one is tetragonal.

TIN OXIDE

This oxide is one of the lowest melting oxides of any that we will consider as supports and stabilizers. Like niobium, it has only two valent states, but it has excellent hybrid stabilizer-cocatalyst characteristics. It also, like niobium and tantalum, does not form a nitrate salt and consequently must be used in the chloride form. There are both the stannous and stannic chloride salts, with the preferred one being stannous because it is soluble in a larger group of solvents. It is soluble in absolute ethyl alcohol, acetic acid, and diethyl ether. Diethyl ether, however, is not recommended for many reasons, including its tendency to form an explosive peroxide and its extreme volatility and flammability.

The method of addition of this stabilizer is the same as has been described for other chlorides or salts that hydrolize in water: first to form a solution of the catalyst ingredients and then set up the equipment so that the precipitant and the tin chloride solution can be simultaneously added to the solution of catalytic ingredients so that simultaneous precipitation of the catalytic ingredients and the occlusion or inclusion of the tin hydroxide will simultaneously occur. If the precipitation is effected at a temperature above that at which the solvent boils, the solvents can simultaneously be removed with the precipitation operation. This is essentially the same operating procedure as that described for niobium and tantalum. Tin has extremely interesting catalytic properties as a stabilizer, a support, and also as a catalytic ingredient because it has, in addition to the two states of valency, amphoteric properties so that the tin ion can appear either in the cation or the anion of the catalytic complex.

Tin oxide has a melting point just above the arbitrarily chosen 1000°C for the inorganic catalyst supports. The oxide can appear as both the stannous ($+2$) and the stannic ($+4$) valencies. The stannic form also has at least three distinct crystalline species:

SnO_2, no mineralogical name, cubic;

SnO_2, cassiterite, tetragonal;

SnO_2, no mineralogical name, hexagonal;

SnO_2, no mineralogical name, rhombohedral.

ZINC OXIDE

Although zinc oxide is rarely thought of as a catalyst support or stabilizer, it does have a melting point of nearly 1900°C and is divalent only, signifying a restricted catalytic capability. However, let us consider methanol synthesis catalyst, which comprises zinc oxide and copper oxide predominantly, and, optionally, stabilizers such as aluminum oxide, chromium oxide, and the like. It has been reported in the literature that the zinc oxide is itself only a support for the elemental copper or reduced copper oxide. The facts are, however, that one can increase the amount of copper in the copper-zinc catalyst to a point where there is only about 15% zinc oxide remaining and still have an effective catalyst. If, however, one proceeds to remove the zinc oxide entirely, the copper alone becomes a totally unsatisfactory catalytic material. It is strongly inferred that the zinc oxide and the copper oxide form a species sharing oxygens, probably as a copper zincate or a copper oxide, zinc oxide solid-state reaction product not identifiable as zincate. This is an additional example of the interplay of what would be considered ordinarily an inert material. Zinc oxide, which by itself produces little or no methanol, particularly at low temperatures, taken with the copper, which by itself is also an unsatisfactory catalyst, will when the two are combined as the oxides and subsequently reduced produce an exceptionally active commercial methanol synthesis catalyst. Recent work by Schraeder and Edwards [7] indicates that the zinc is an important part of the catalyst, activating the carbon monoxide of the synthesis gas.

Because zinc is available in essentially all types of salts, such as nitrate, chloride, sulfate, and acetate, there is no problem in making a solution that will comprise the desired ratio of copper and zinc salts. These are usually precipitated using a carbonate or bicarbonate precipitant such as sodium, potassium, or ammonium.

Zinc oxide is also amphoteric and can form the zincate or zinc chloride, for example. This property gives the zinc multiple opportunities for solid-state reactions with other oxides in the catalyst composition. Zinc has ionic dimensions that permit it to fit nicely into the spinel lattice; that is, it can be substituted for the magnesium oxide in the model spinel. This gives further credence to the possibility or likelihood that in the methanol synthesis catalyst, the oxygens of the copper and the zinc are shared to form a zincate or other species. It should be noted that although the copper oxide, zinc oxide catalyst has been discussed primarily from the standpoint of methanol synthesis, it is also the catalyst of choice for the conversion of carbon monoxide plus steam to carbon dioxide and hydrogen (the water gas reaction). The copper oxide, zinc oxide catalysts have been used extensively for decades in both methanol synthesis and the water gas shift services and have served well in both.

Zinc oxide enjoys at least two characteristics that make it an attractive ingredient in many catalysts. First is its high melting point and thermal stability; second is its unique catalytic attractiveness (for example, in the CuO-ZnO-Al_2O_3 methanol synthesis catalyst in which it imparts substantial cocatalytic effect in conjunction with the copper oxide). The indexed zinc oxides are ZnO, zincite, hexagonal, and ZnO_2, zinc peroxide, not identified in nature; consequently no mineral name, cubic. It is not generally recognized that zinc forms a peroxide that is unstable under even mild temperature and reduced pressure of O_2.

ALKALINE EARTHS: BERYLLIUM, MAGNESIUM, CALCIUM, STRONTIUM, AND BARIUM OXIDES

All of these oxides have very high melting points, with magnesium oxide having a melting point in excess of 2800°C and even barium, the lowest-melting-point oxide, having a melting point in excess of 1900°C. Consequently, as stabilizers, they are among the best that one could select. Beryllium, however, has carcinogenic properties, particularly if ingested or through misadventure injected below the skin.

As the family name implies, the alkaline earths are all basic and as a result enhance reactions that are benefited by an alkaline environment. They also are of an ion size such that they can be accommodated into perovskite-type crystal lattices. Further, calcium, barium, and strontium form insoluble sulfates and carbonates, which also have excellent support and stabilizing characteristics.

Another characteristic that should not be lost sight of, particularly with the magnesium hydroxide and also, but to a lesser extent, with the other hydroxides, is their tendency to form a hydrous gel. Although this hydrous gel has excellent stabilizing and support characteristics, on drying it coalesces as any typical gel and tends to form a denser, more compact structure with comparatively small pore size but high surface area.

These all form soluble nitrates, and as a consequence they are easily added to a solution so that they as stabilizers or supports can be coprecipitated simultaneously with the catalytic material, thus providing the desired intimate, finely divided mixture of the catalyst and the support or stabilizer. All of these materials form insoluble carbonates so that if the catalytic material is precipitated as a carbonate, as is so frequently the case, these alkaline earth carbonates will simultaneously precipitate as is desired. Furthermore, most of them precipitate in essentially the same range of pH as most of the catalytic materials—that is, between approximately 3.2 and 4.5. All except beryllium in this group are relatively inexpensive, and even beryllium is not prohibitively expensive. Except for beryllium, there are no health problems in the utilization of these materials in catalysts.

Because of the coalescing properties of these oxides, particularly as the hydroxide, the catalysts lend themselves to extrusion as well as to rather easy pilling. After extrusion, the catalysts are relatively hard, and because of the high moisture content, which is lost during the drying operation following extrusion, the surface area and total pore volume are high. The number of pores in the small size range is unusually large.

A final factor that must not be overlooked is the chemical reactivity of these as oxides. They, particularly barium, form peroxides, and in the environment of containing CO_2, they will tend to form carbonates corresponding to the equilibrium and controlled by temperature and CO_2 partial pressure.

ALKALINE EARTHS: CARBONATES, OXIDES, SULFATES, PHOSPHATES, ALUMINATES, SILICATES, TITANATES, AND ZIRCONATES

This is a polyglot group used as coprecipitated or granular supports. The carbonates are used occasionally because of their basic nature, and the sulfates are used also occasionally because of a surface acidic character. Neither the carbonates nor sulfates can be used in a strongly acidic environment, but they usually will tolerate a pH as low as 5.5 to 5.0. The basic pH can be quite high except in the case of $MgCO_3$, which may solubilize in an aqueous ammoniacol solution, particularly at temperatures in excess of 50°C.

Another factor to be aware of is that when these alkaline earth carbonates are used in processes requiring temperatures in excess of 600°C, a substantial partial pressure of CO_2^- is developed, and the catalyst structure may weaken or even disintegrate. This is particularly true if the catalyst is used in a gas flow that is itself fluctuating in CO_2^- content. Calcium carbonate is especially prone to disintegration caused by CO_2 evolution and readsorption.

All of the sulfates (even barium) are soluble in water to varying extents. Under mild conditions of 100°C and in the absence of mineralizers such as acids and bases, they are soluble to the extent of 200–300 ppm but at elevated temperature and pressures, above 200°C and above 500 psi, solubility sharply increases. This is the typical hydrothermal condition that occurs in nature to produce these magnificent calcite, magnesites, strontianite, and witherite crystals. This hydrothermal solubilizing effect in a liquid-phase catalytic reaction could cause the loss of the carbonate support or its reorientation as a crust on the catalyst or on the reactor walls, heat exchangers, or interconnecting piping.

Each alkaline earth carbonate has a number of crystal species and spacings into which it will metamorphose as temperature or other environmental factors change. These forms are as follows for the various carbonates. These data are from the ASTM X-ray standards.

$CaCO_3$

Aragonite, low-temperature form, orthorhombic;

Calcite, high-temperature form, hexagonal;

Calcite, high-pressure form, orthorhombic.

In addition to these three observed forms, there are two hexagonal forms whose forms and dimensions have been calculated to be possible. One is identified as Vaterite.

Calcite II is monoclinic (Merrill and Bassett), Acta Crystallogr, Section B, 31,343 (1975). Each of the foregoing differs not only in crystal form but also in lattice spacing. It is apparent that as operating conditions change, profound changes are likely also to take place in the support.

$MgCO_3$ magnesite is hexagonal; its structure is calcite type. Magnesium carbonate probably has as many crystal forms as does calcium carbonate, but they have not been studied or reported to the extent that calcium carbonate has.

$SrCO_3$ strontianite is low-temperature rhombohedral form, which converts to hexagonal at 926°C, the high-temperature form. Other forms probably also form under elevated pressures and other environmental conditions in parallel with calcium carbonate.

$BaCO_3$ witherite is gamma barium carbonate, rhombohedral, which converts to beta barium carbonate at 811°C.

Beta witherite is high-temperature barium carbonate, which transforms to alpha barium carbonate at 982°C.

Alpha witherite is the highest-temperature-form of barium carbonate and is hexagonal.

It is likely that there are additional crystal and spacing differences in barium carbonate similar to the larger number identified for calcium carbonate.

Alkaline Earth Oxides

These oxides are too reactive ordinarily to be found in nature and hence do not have mineral names. The facts that they are basic and have a strong tendency for the chemisorption of water make it likely that any alkali earth oxide will transform in a natural environment to the carbonate or hydroxide. Consequently the specific crystalline species and changes in species with environmental change are less significant than the effect of acidic or moisture partial pressure or components of the surrounding liquid or gas. A warning signal should rise when one matches catalyst composition—alkaline earth component with a processing fluid that has moisture or acidic content. It is surprising how frequently this is overlooked. As an example, a catalyst utilizing a support consisting of calcium oxide was employed in a process having variable CO_2 and moisture content as well as functioning at varying temperatures. The result was a catalyst that adsorbed and desorbed one or more ingredients; cycling weakened the catalyst, causing it to disintegrate.

Alkaline Earth Sulfates

These are used when an acidic support is required and the sulfate ion can be tolerated. Magnesium sulfate (Epsom salt) is water soluble and has little value as a support. Calcium sulfate is fairly soluble (0.2%) in water so also has limited use. Both strontium and barium sulfates are quite water insoluble; neither goes through a phase change under usual operating conditions, but both convert from rhombohedral to monoclinic at about 1100°C.

At temperatures above 500°C and especially in a reducing atmosphere, the sulfate may be reduced to sulfite, and eventually the sulfur may be evolved as SO_2 or H_2S depending on operating conditions.

Alkaline Earth Phosphates

These, like the sulfates, have both temperature and environmental limitations. The phosphate ion may become fugitive as P_2O_5 or as PH_3. Calcium phosphate as "bone char" was once a popular support, as well as a commercially used decolorant for crude sugar solutions.

Alkaline Earth Aluminates

Calcium aluminate is used as a cement binder in some catalysts but is not considered a useful support and as a binder usually has a severe adverse effect on catalyst activity.

Alkaline Earth Silicates

The alkaline earth silicates are usually thought of as components of enamel frits and consequently as having low melting points and as sintering easily. This image should be corrected because they all have high melting points above 1500°C (metasilicates, $MSiO_3$) whereas the orthosilicates (M_2SiO_4) have melting points above 1900°C. Furthermore, the metasilicates are more prone to hydrolysis in a humid or moisture containing atmosphere. The orthosilicates are much more thermally and chemically stable, as is shown in the following tabulation:

$MgSiO_3$, metasilicate, chlinoerstatite, monoclinic, melting point 1551°C;

Mg_2SiO_4, orthasilicate, forsterite, orthorhombic, melting point 1910°C;

$CaSiO_3$, metasilicate, pseudowollastonite, monoclinic, melting point 1540°C;

Ca_3SiO_5, trisilicate, natural alite, monoclinic, melting point 1900°C;

$SrSiO_3$, metasilicate, not known in nature, monoclinic, melting point 1580°C;

Sr_2SiO_4, orthosilicate, not known in nature, monoclinic, melting point 1750°C;

$BaSiO_3$, metasilicate, not known in nature, rhombohedral, melting point 1605°C.

Alkaline Earth Titanates

Rare earth titanates resemble somewhat the silicates, but it would be a mistake to describe them as closely resembling the silicates. The titanates, too, like the rare earth silicates, are frequently used in enamel frits, giving inference also that they are low melting and sinter easily. This thought should be dispelled because the melting point of calcinum titanate is 1975°C. Calcium titanate is the mineral perovskite that has received much research attention as a model crystal form, with other ions being substituted for the Ca^{2+} and particularly in a nonstiochiometric imperfect crystal form:

$CaTiO_3$, perovskite, cubic altering to rhombohedral, at elevated temperatures.

The Mg, Sr, and Ba titanates are less well characterized as to crystal species and melting point, but because of the tendency for the titanates to develop a labile oxygen ion in a reducing or a high-temperature environment, they should be subjected to close scrutiny in exploratory catalysis.

Alkaline Earth Zirconates

The zirconates are also poorly characterized, with the exception of calcium zirconate, which surprisingly has a melting point of 2550°C; even more surprising is that this melting point is almost 400°C higher than the melting point of alumina. It is realistic to assume that the other alkali earth zirconates are similarly high melting and consequently good thermal stabilizers. The zirconates do not have oxygen ions, which are as labile as those in the titanates. This characteristic makes the zirconates more stable in reducing atmospheres. They are less likely to form peroxides that would make them more likely to be inert in a selective oxidation reaction environment:

$CaZrO_3$, metazirconate, monoclinic, melting point 2550°C.

REFERENCES

1. Haller, G. L., et al. 1983. The effort of silica support texture and anion of impregnating solution on ruthenium dispersion and on ruthenium-copper interaction. *J. Catal.* 84:477–79.
2. Spencer, M. S. 1983. Models of strong metal-support interaction (SMSI) in platinum on titanium dioxide catalysts. *J. Catal.* 93:261–23.
3. Brumberger, H., et al. 1985. Investigation of the SMSI catalyst platinum/titanium dioxide by small angle x-ray scattering. *J. Catal.* 92:199–210.
4. Kozlowski, R., et al. 1983. X-ray absorption fine structure investigation of vanadium (V) oxide, titanium oxide (IV) oxide catalysts. *J. Phys. Chem.* 87:5172.6.
5. Liu, Y. C.; Griffin, G. L.; Chan, S. S.; and Wachs, I. E. 1985. Photo-oxidation of methanol using MoO_3/TiO_2: catalyst structure and reaction selectivity. *J. Catal.* 94:108–19.

6. Baltanas, M. A., et al. 1982. An infrared spectroscoptic study of the adsorption and surface reactions of oxygen on supported manganese oxides. *J. Catal.* 88:362–73.

7. Schraeder, G. L., and Edwards, J. 1985. In situ Fourier transform infrared study of methanol synthesis—mixed metal oxides catalysis. *J. Catal.* 94:175–86.

CHAPTER 4

Physical Variations in Support and Their Control

Alvin B. Stiles

There are at least seven physical characteristics in a support or in a catalyst that must be controlled for proper performance of the catalyst or support. They are all interrelated, and because of this interrelationship, there may be a need during the design of a catalyst to compromise one to achieve the optimum in another. In the catalyst preparation, there is usually a need to compromise one physical or chemical characteristic in order to achieve a level of performance that is optimum for the operation in which the catalyst is being used. The physical characteristics that must be controlled are hardness, density, total pore volume, pore distribution, pore sizes, particle size, and particle shape. Crystalline species may not be controllable.

Hardness is generally the first consideration to take into account when adapting a catalyst to an operation. If the catalyst is to be used in a fixed-bed operation, the hardness must be such that the catalyst will withstand gas or liquid flow and any vibration or dancing that occurs due to the liquid or gas movement. If the catalyst is to be used in a slurry system, other characteristics must be taken into account, such as the abrasion of one particle against another or the abrasion of the catalyst particle against the reactor walls, the transport tubing, and the valves and cylinders of a pump or compressor.

It is essential that the catalyst density be controlled to the optimum for the process requirement. If the catalyst is to be used in a slurry system, the catalyst must not be so dense that it settles out and is difficult to maintain in suspension by mechanical or gas agitation. This usually means that the density must, in a dry state, be in the order of unity down to 0.2 or 0.3 g/ml. A further consideration is the catalyst cost. Many catalysts are sold on a weight basis, so it becomes essential that the density be as low as possible in order for the minimum weight to be required for the filling of a reactor. An additional consideration is that in a fluidized bed, the density must be compatible with the gas flows that will be experienced. The catalyst must, first, be fluidizable. Second, it must not be so low density that it will move out of the reaction region as a dust that must be separated from the effluent stream. Hardness is again a consideration in the fluidized system in that the moving of the particles along the reactor walls or through the regeneration system must be possible without excessive abrasion of the walls of the equipment.

Another essential characteristic of the catalyst and the support is surface area. In a gas-phase operation, the maximum possible surface area is sought. Generalized statements in catalysis are sometimes misleading and sometimes dangerous, and it should be pointed out that in vapor phase operations in which large or complex molecules are being processed, high surface area may be deleterious because of the difficulty and slowness of mass transport of the large molecules through the inherently smaller pores concomitant with the high surface area. By contrast, in liquid-phase operations, in which a denser medium is being processed, it is essential that the pore size be relatively large, which means that the surface area must be relatively low. In speaking of high and low surface areas in general terms, a definition of low surface area would be in the range from 1 to approximately $125m^2/g$, whereas high surface area would be in the range of 125 to 2000. Some activated carbons have this very high surface area of 2000 m^2/g. Surface area also is of major consideration when the support is impregnated with a cocatalyst or a catalytic material. If the surface area is large corresponding to small pore diameters, it is relatively obvious that the pores for the most part will be filled and blocked with the catalytic material added to them. When this consideration is made, it is obvious again that lower surface area with large pore diameters is a requirement.

The fourth of the primary requirements for a catalyst or a catalyst support is the total pore volume. Total pore volume is of great concern because it indicates the reactive area available in the catalytic material—whether a compound comprising the support plus the catalyst or the support itself. It is probably the characteristic that is the last to be considered in the compromise, resulting in the development of the catalyst, but it has such a sharp effect on the previously mentioned characteristics that it eventually comes into play in an important way later.

Pore distribution is also a factor usually tailor-made for specific catalysts. Ordinarily, if a catalyst is to be used in rather large granular or spheroidal form, the pore distribution must be such that there are large access pores that permit the easy mass transport of gases or liquids to the smaller auxiliary pores where a major fraction of the reaction generally is performed. On the other hand, when the particles are small, as in a fluidized gas bed, then the pores can be uniformly quite small because the need for the large access pores is obviated by the fact that one is dealing with a system in which the reactants have easy access to the total required depth for the reaction to be achieved.

All of these catalyst or support characteristics are interrelated. The ultimate catalyst must represent a consideration and blend these factors into the final product to achieve the optimum for any given operation. Many of these characteristics cannot be adjusted to their optimum until after a plant test has been made—and usually after a relatively long period of time when the abrasion characteristics and catalyst life become better established.

Figure 4.1 shows the interrelation on an equilateral triangle. On one apex is hardness, on another pore size, and on the third pore volume. The purpose of this diagram is to show that as the hardness increases, the pore volume and pore size will decrease. As the pore volume increases to the maximum, the pore size and hardness also decrease. This may seem a bit anomalous because pore volume generally is thought

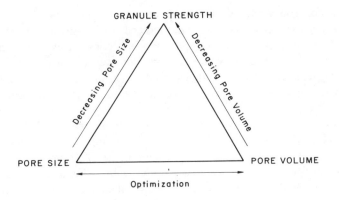

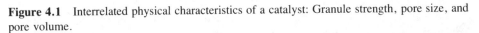

Figure 4.1   Interrelated physical characteristics of a catalyst: Granule strength, pore size, and pore volume.

of as being directly related to the pore size, but if one considers the fact that grains of sand can be coalesced to form very high pore volume with an equally very small pore size, the contention becomes obvious. It is also true that as total pore volume increases, granule strength will decrease. (It is probably a good idea to make a concession to someone who might be argumentative about this equilateral triangle and say that it should be more appropriately an isosceles triangle, with the surface area and pore volume more closely related than the density and hardness. I would make that concession, but it would be difficult to quantify it, so I have simplified the consideration by making a simple equilateral triangle.)

Figure 4.2 also illustrates an equilateral triangle with the first apex occupied by granule strength and the second by pore volume, but the third apex, instead of being occupied by pore size, is occupied by density. Study of this diagram will show the validity of the relationship following an explanation similar to the one used for Figure 4.1.

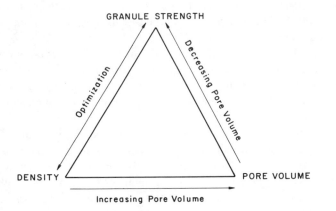

Figure 4.2   Interrelated physical characteristics of a catalyst: Granule strength, density, and pore volume.

These diagrams represent a pair of models by which one can point to a rough relationship to what catalyst physical characteristics are needed for a given description of a new reaction or new process. As an example, if one is considering a fluidized vapor system, the point of compromise would be very close to the apex of surface area. If one is working with a vigorously agitated slurry system, the point of compromise for these characteristics would be toward the hardness apex, though not neglecting pore size.

Pore size distribution is critical. In some cases, it is highly desirable that the pores be large; in other cases, they should be quite small. In still other cases—and probably the majority—the preference is for a distribution between large pores and small pores, with a major fraction of surface area and pore volume being in the small pores. By small pores is generally meant 60 Å in diameter and smaller. By large pores is usually meant 60 to 400 Å in diameter.

A variety of facilities are used for the determination of these characteristics. Density is usually determined by a simple weight measurement of a given volume. A 250 ml graduate is the frequent volume measured, but when very large catalyst particles such as 1/2 in. by 1/2 in. cylinders are being measured, it is likely that a box made to a cubic foot size would be used for the density measurement.

There are many methods for the determination of hardness. In a simple compression test, a pressure is applied to a piston, which is forced down against the flat surface of a pellet and the force measured to cause destruction of the pellet. In some cases, the pressure is applied against the rounded surface. In still other cases, a given quantity of the catalyst or support is placed on a wire mesh screen of chosen size, put into a device similar to a Rotap, and agitated for a given period of time, usually 30 minutes. Abrasion resulting during that period of time is taken as the abrasion resistance of that catalyst structure.

Ball mills are used in some cases. In other cases, the catalyst is allowed to drop repeatedly through some given distance onto a hard surface where measurement of disintegration is made.

Total pore volume, pore distribution, surface area, and surface area attributable to the catalytic material placed on a support are all measured by equipment supplied by Micromoratics. (See Figures 4.3 and 4.4.)

Last to be considered in the physical characteristics of the catalyst or the support are particle size and particle shape. Since we are dealing with heterogeneous systems, the particle size is greater than molecular, which would be the ultimate size in the homogeneous system. The smallest size used is generally microspheres, which are in the order of 20 to 40 microns.

As one considers the larger sizes, one then refers to the extrudates, which can be as small as 1/32 in. in diameter, usually with the length substantially longer than the diameter; larger extrudates, also usually in the form of cylinders and containing a hole similar to macaroni, can be as large as 1 in. in diameter by 1 in. long with a hole in the center of approximately 1/4 to 1/2 in. Instead of the single hole, there can be a number of holes, with the structure then resembling somewhat a honeycomb. The support structures can also be in the form of saddles or stars or almost any other

Figure 4.3 Chemisorphic analyzer, metals area determination. (Photograph courtesy of Micromeritics, Norcross, Ga.)

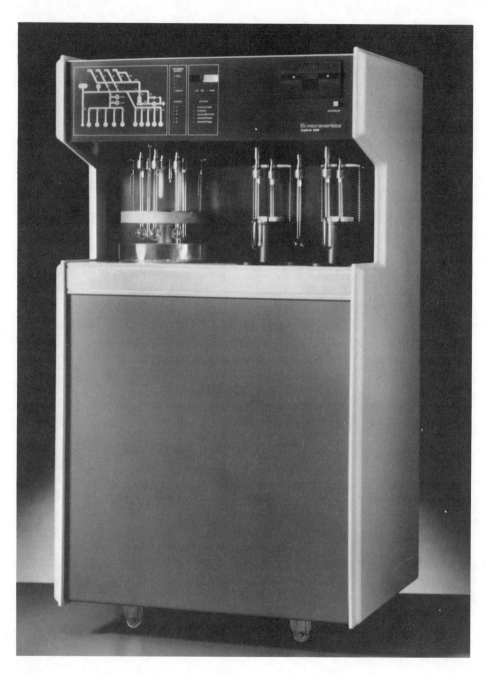

Figure 4.4 Analyzer for pore volume, surface area, and pore size. (Photograph courtesy of Micromeritics, Norcross, Ga.)

conceivable shape, usually with the objective of increasing gas-solid or gas-liquid contact or decreasing pressure drop in the process system.

A frequently used type and size is cylinders formed in a compression machine manufactured by F. J. Stokes, a subsidiary of Pennwalt. These are usually in the form of cylinders with the diameter equal to length and the diameter varying from 0.125 to 1 in. in diameter. Cylinders, too, can be designed so that they are in the form of stars, peripheral corrugations, or flutings and one or more holes going parallel to the curved surface from end to end.

At times support or catalyst compositions are such that it is difficult to extrude them or pellet them to form sufficiently hard and durable structures. In this case, the catalyst is made into a cake—either by compression while wet or further strengthened by the inclusion of a coalescing agent. Coalescing agents may be colloidal silica or other colloidal materials or binders such as sodium silicate. Any of the coalescing or binding agents has a generally deleterious effect on the catalyst, so they are used only when all other granulating or forming processes fail.

One support material that has come into substantial prominence, particularly since the introduction of the catalyst used in automotive exhaust systems, is the honeycomb, manufactured by many different procedures and by several different companies. It usually has a composition comprising largely refractory materials, permitting the operation at temperatures in excess of 1000°C, which may occasionally be encountered in automotive exhaust handling. The honeycomb can be obtained in blocks 12 or more inches square and are 1 to 4 in. thick. The form can also be obtained as cylinders, which range from 1/2 in. in diameter to as large as 6 to 8 in. The cell size is usually measured by the number of openings per square inch of surface. This can be on the order of 50 openings per square inch to as many as 400 openings per square inch. Because these honeycomb structures must be catalytically coated, the size of the opening is restricted to a size that can be impregnated and not be blocked by the residual catalytic material. The upper size is generally stipulated by the need for low pressure drop, but here again there is a need for compromise to obtain the adequate catalytic surface while not exceeding the permissible pressure drop and not introducing problems related to the impregnation and coating of the honeycomb [1].

The honeycomb structure is most frequently fabricated from ceramics (alumina, mullite, or cordierite). It also can be fabricated from sheet metal. In this case, the method of impregnation and activating is substantially different from that employed with the ceramic. Usually in the case of ceramic, a priming coat of high-surface-area support such as alumina, alumina magnesia, or the like is first coated onto the honeycomb. This coat is then dried and calcined to form a thin, highly adsorptive high-surface-area layer on the honeycomb surfaces. The catalytic material is added onto this anchor coat in the next step. In the case of metal supports, however, not only can this procedure be used, but the metal surface can be etched or oxidized to produce either a catalytic coating or an anchor for the catalytic coating. (The priming coat is not particularly suitable because of the spalling caused by the difference in thermal expansion of the oxide coating on the metal surfaces. If, however, the oxide coating on the metal is formed by the oxidation of the metal itself, then this oxide is an integral part of the metallic surface and as a consequence is strongly adhering.) This metallic oxide surface can be impregnated further by the typical catalytic metals, which will also be strongly adhering because they are coated onto the strongly adhering etched or oxidized metallic surface of the metal.

In addition to the metal being formed into the honeycomb-type form, it can also be simply matted wires, which are similarly treated to form an oxide surface that can be further treated with catalytic elements or oxides to derive an enhanced catalytic surface. Wires thus treated can be formed into pillows or blocks for charging to a catalytic converter. The advantages of the wires on metal are the resilience to shock and also the ability to mold into a shape that conforms more to the shape of the catalytic bed.

As a further refinement of the activation of metallic surfaces is another procedure (described in Chapter 6). In this system, the surface(s) of a sheet, tube, bar, rod, heat exchanger, or anything else of these general types can be diffusion coated with an extractable metal such as aluminum. This surface then can be activated by the removal of the aluminum by the typical sodium hydroxide extraction procedure. It becomes evident that if the surface, which was diffusion coated with the aluminum, was nickel, brass, or stainless steel, the constituents of these metals remained behind in a highly dispersed, high-surface-area, extremely active form. It is evident that a catalyst derived from a nickel tube could be effective for hydrogenations and methanation as examples. If the surface was brass, the catalyst that would be derived should be an active zinc copper structure, which could be used for synthesis of methanol and other products from CO and hydrogen. The stainless steel could be used for total oxidations or, under proper preparative conditions, for Fischer-Tropsch synthesis.

FORMATION OF MICROSPHERES

Catalysts in the form of microspheres have many advantages, one of which is that the diameter of the microsphere is so small that mass transport is usually not a problem for the reactants. Microspheres are usually used in a fluidized bed reactor, which means the regeneration and return to the reaction can be effected on a continuous basis. This fact is a saving grace for catalysts with short life between regenerations.

Microspheres can be produced from almost any catalyst composition to which is added a colloidal material such as silica, alumina, or ceria. The equipment for producing the microsphere is produced by a number of manufacturers listed in the *Chemical Engineering Buyer's Guide*.

CONTROL OF PHYSICAL CHARACTERISTICS

There are many reasons to control the physical characteristics of catalysts: (1) to obtain adequate activity; (2) to attain adequate physical strength; (3) to permit adequate flow rate through the reactor system; (4) to obtain suitable resistance to thermal and chemical deactivation; and (5) to obtain the maximum efficiency or directivity of the catalyst. As an example, one may control pore diameter to the larger pore size because catalyst deactivation by carbonaceous deposition has been shown to be initiated quite frequently in the smaller pores, and once it is initiated in the smaller pores, it self-propagates to the larger pores. Eventually the catalyst is deactivated by the physical blockage by the organic or other deposits in the pores of the catalyst. Quite often when the smaller pores are collapsed by thermal treatment, an auxiliary benefit can be derived by the removal by annealing of some of the unwanted catalytic sites. It is almost axiomatic that a catalyst that is overactive—that is, produces excessive by-products—can be corrected by a suitable thermal treatment that may cause annealing (lattice defect relaxing), or it may cause solid-state reactions between the catalyst and the support material or between different constituents in the catalyst itself.

Control of Surface Area

The primary method of controlling surface area is by means of the method of preparation of the catalyst. The most effective method of obtaining high surface area is to precipitate the catalyst as the hydroxide or, even better, as the carbonate using such precipitants as ammonium or an alkali metal carbonate. The precipitation as a hydroxide or the carbonate generally results in the production of a gel-like precipitate that on drying and calcining liberates either water or water and carbon dioxide, thus developing high porosity and surface area.

Usually precipitation at low temperatures and with dilute solutions also facilitates the development of high surface area. The coprecipitation of a gel, which ultimately will become the support material as well, also can develop extremely high surface area for the composite catalyst support. An additional factor that affects the surface area is the rate of precipitation and the direction of precipitation—whether adding the base to an acidic solution or adding acidic solution to a basic precipitant. The factor to be considered in addition to the surface area attained by these precipitations, whether acid-base or base-acid, is that in the case of the acidic catalytic components solution being added to the base, a large amount of base is occluded in the precipitate. This may be harmful to the final catalyst. In other words, while attempting to attain optimum surface area and porosity, one may occlude unwanted ions such as the alkali or sulfate ions, which can be extremely difficult to remove and may be extremely deleterious to the final catalyst.

Other ways of controlling pore size and surface area include the replacement of the aqueous phase with a part-aqueous, part-alcoholic phase or totally with an alcohol. When the precipitate is dried from an alcoholic environment, it has reduced tendency toward syneresis or coalescing of the structure, with the result that a finely divided particulate precipitate is formed. This precipitate has high surface area and unusually high porosity, as can be inferred from Figures 4.1 and 4.2. As one increases these characteristics, the strength and density simultaneously decrease.

Another method of controlling the porosity and surface area is by drying in a vacuum system at low temperatures or, still better, freeze drying in a vacuum system. Here again the strength and density are low, and these factors must be taken into consideration as one designs and fabricates the catalyst.

Control of Pore Volume

There is a similarity in the methods of controlling pores to the methods described for the control of surface area. Because of changes in petroleum crudes, the control of pore volume has recently become even more important than in the past. Usually one seeks high pore volume in order to increase the average pore size, which in turn gives more facile access of the reactants to the reaction site. More recently, however, particularly in the petroleum processing industry, pore volume is considered a requirement for those catalysts that are to have the greatest life and durability when processing crudes containing large quantities of porphyrins such as nickel, vanadium, and alkalis. As a consequence, research into methods for controlling porosity to attain the highest porosity possible without sacrificing other desirable catalytic properties has become a major objective in many laboratories. The catalyst may, in fact, have only sufficient catalytic properties to cause the breakdown of the porphyrins, with the consequent deposit of the metallic ions in the catalyst. The low-cost catalyst then becomes a sacrificial trap, which upon complete filling of the pores is discarded and replaced.

Porosity control is most frequently performed by an adaptation of the procedures described for surface area control. There are, however, several additional procedures.

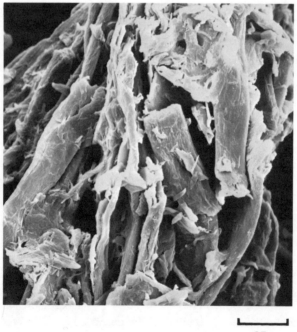

25 μm

Figure 4.5 Avicel microcrystalline cellulose. (Photograph courtesy of FMC Corporation, Philadelphia.)

The most prominent and frequently used one is incorporation of certain fusible or combustible components into the slurry prior to filtration—during precipitation or in a separate mixing operation after the filter cake has been obtained.

One of the more sophisticated procedures consists of incorporating into the slurry either during or subsequent to precipitation of catalyst a so-called crystalline—finely divided cellulose produced and sold by the Westvaco Corporation. This cellulose has a very narrow size and crystalline dimension (Figures 4.5 through 4.8), and as a consequence, when it has been removed by combustion, the shape of the void remaining has dimensions corresponding to the celulose occupying the void prior to combustion. It is an obvious follow-up of this consideration that certain molecules can also be incorporated into the slurry or into the filter cake upon completion of precipitation. Such molecules as organic amines, alcohols, organic acids, and mixtures such as tall oil are acceptable pore volume control agents.

There are also other much less sophisticated procedures, such as the incorporation of sawdust, cotton linters, linters from various types of synthetic fibers such as the polyimids, polyamids, polyesters, and polyacrilonitriles. Polyvinyl alcohol and poly-ethylene or polypropylene fluff may also be used.

If one has developed a porosity in a material that is being extruded or formed into pellets, one can incorporate into the composition before extrusion such decom-

100 μm

Figure 4.6 Avicel microcrystalline cellulose. (Photograph courtesy of FMC Corporation, Philadelphia.)

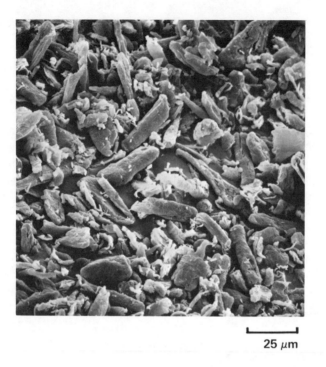

25 µm

Figure 4.7 Avicel microcrystalline cellulose. (Photograph courtesy of FMC Corporation, Philadelphia.)

posable or extractable components as ammonium carbonate and ammonium nitrate for the decomposables and calcium carbonate or other acid-soluble materials, which can be removed after the catalyst and support have been developed into a final usable extruded or pelleted shape. The decomposable material is removed by heating to a temperature of decomposition, which in the case of the ammonium nitrate or carbonate would not exceed 200°C.

The acid-extractable material such as the alkaline carbonates are removed from the final extrudate or pilled article by exposing these particles to acetic, nitric, hydrochloric, or other suitable acid.

Control of Pore Distribution

Ordinarily the pores of the catalyst are random distribution, and in many cases this is preferable. There are other situations in which one would prefer to have mostly larger or mostly smaller pores. Then the question becomes how one achieves these characteristics. In order to address this question, one must consider the pores because they very likely are in a catalyst composite structure. Many people are accustomed to thinking of the pores as little cylinders resembling a test tube sticking down into the

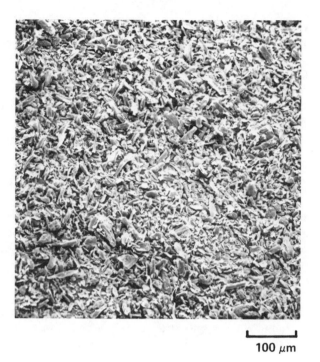

100 μm

Figure 4.8   Avicel microcrystalline cellulose. (Photograph courtesy of FMC Corporation, Philadelphia.)

solid pores in a nicely arranged sequence of test tubes parallel to each other except when the catalyst is spheroidal, in which case they all point toward the center of the sphere in a neatly arranged sunburst. This, of course, is not true. The best way to look at the porosity factor is to consider first the unit crystal of a given catalytic material. Because I am fond of spinels and many catalysts are spinels, let us consider the unit spinel structure. Let us think of dozens of these randomly arranged in an as-yet disoriented crystallite, which for this reason should be considered amorphous (nonoriented). This "crystal" has now grown to a catalyst granule, which, let us say, is approximately 100 nm across. Before we leave this structure, let us realize that in that structure are already two types of pores. The larger pore is that spacing between the unit crystals as they are randomly placed in the agglomerated particle. The second pore is on an atomic scale and can, for example, be developed by the reduction of the spinel to remove an oxygen; a site, or a minute pore, results.

Dozens of the 100 nm size particles are now agglomerated, and as a result of this agglomeration, a still larger-size pore is developed between these fairly large composites. The next size pore is that which would be developed as this larger-size composite is allowed to form into even larger clumps or clusters.

To put the description into a more easily visualized form, one could say that the tiniest particle could be represented by a very tiny sphere—say, 10 Å in diameter, or about the size of a unit crystal. These then are agglomerated and become the next-size sphere, which is porous and, say, 100 Å in diameter. The next-size sphere is approximately 1000 Å in diameter. We now have spheres that are 1000 Å in diameter, which are composed of spheres 100 Å in diameter, which are composed of very small spheres 10 Å in diameter. There are various size pores developed by the size of the spheres that comprise the various composites developed in normal processing of a catalyst or a finely divided powder.

It also becomes apparent that one must attain specific pore sizes by the control of real world spherulites. The easiest way to control spherulite size is to have as an ingredient or ingredients a colloid such as silica, titania, zirconia, or other commercially available sols or colloids. The spherulites comprising those colloids may be coated with a monolayer of many catalytic materials, and when they are coated with the monolayer (or a greater layer if one chooses), these spheres of the colloid, which come in sizes from 4.0 nm to as high as 30.0 nm, can be agglomerated with the coatings and thus attain specific dimensions dependent on the size of the colloid from which they are derived. The derivation of controlled pores by this means is contingent on the acceptability of the colloid component in the catalytic environment. In the absence of the compatibility, one must resort to the previously described methods of control of the pore and particle size. It is obvious that one can combine the colloid and the control method of precipitation to attain a still different type of pore distribution and predictable size.

Miscellaneous Pore Control Methods

A controlled pore size can be developed by the coalescing of granular ceramic materials such as fused alumina, fused silica or mullite, and similar silica alumina materials. These are available with specific densities, specific pore size, and pore volume from such companies as Carborundum Company, and Norton Company. These can be impregnated by various procedures that produce different types of coatings or porosities as desired.

Still another type of support is identified as diatomaceous earth, which means that they are derived as siliceous skeletons from diatoms from prehistoric seas. These diatoms take on very specific skeletal shapes as shown in Figures 3.3, 3.4, 3.5, and 3.6. These inherently porous materials can be coated by precipitation thereon, by various methods—usually slurry-type precipitation of oxides such as nickel, cobalt, copper, and zinc.

A support that goes back into almost ancient catalytic history is pumice, the product of the ash from volcanic action. This has a glassy structure with a rather coke-like form with a large number of bubble-like openings and cavities into and onto which catalyst can be dispersed. Adherence of the catalyst to the pumice generally is quite poor so the use of pumice is not ordinarily recommended—not only for this reason but also because it is of unpredictable composition and fusion point.

MISCELLANEOUS SUBJECTS

Hydrothermal Treatment and Its Effects

In discussing the effect of intentional and unintentional hydrothermal treatments, some basic, almost elementary, statements should be made. First is to recall an ancient statement to the effect that water is the universal solvent. Second is that crystallization occurs because of the dissolving, redeposition, and reorientation of ions or molecules into an ordered form. The third is that a growing crystal will follow a crystalline species, orientation, and spacing that previously existed in a solid even though that solid is not of the same composition as that being deposited. Furthermore, this orientation may be in a spacing and crystal form other than the typical crystal form of the growing crystal. This may produce bond strains or lattice defects in the crystal as it grows, which from the catalytic standpoint may be highly desirable.

Such lattice defects would be influenced by the characteristics of the substrate on which the crystal is growing. It may be expedient to select the substrate characteristics (spacing and species) to achieve the lattice defects desired. Surface growth and epitaxial orientation will also be affected by the temperature and pressure of operation and the solvent and foreign ions in the nutrient solution. During precipitation of a catalytic material on a support, such as particulate alumina or silica, for example, the precipitate may not form in the crystalline species typical of the precipitate but follow the spacing and crystallinity of the substrate that is already present in a particulate and oriented form. This orientation to a substrate of differing space is termed *epitaxial relationship*. It becomes evident also that the degree to which this occurs can be influenced by the severity of conditions of precipitation, such as temperature and pressure and concentration of solution and foreign ions, as well as the time of exposure of the precipitate to the supernatant liquid following precipitation and before washing, filtering, and drying.

The hydrothermal effect extends also to the particulate material previously described as the substrate. If, for example, the substrate itself is attacked by one or more of the ions in the supernatant liquid or the liquid used as a solution of the catalytic ingredients, then the surface of the support may be so altered that it becomes hydrated, reduced, peroxidized, or in some other way reoriented or disoriented. In so doing, the altered substrate can interact in a much different way toward the precipitating catalytic material. Not only would the spacings be changed but the degree of reactivity of the support with the catalytic material could substantially change.

As an example, when silica is used as a support and a highly alkaline condition exists in the solutions of the catalytic material or the slurry following precipitation, an entirely different effect is obtained, and an alkaline silicate is formed, which itself goes into solution and reorients in and throughout the precipitate. This phenomenon has been observed in the precipitation of nickel carbonate on kieselguhr, which is essentially totally silica. When a catalyst prepared in a way in which the final pH was between 7.5 and 8, the silica of the kieselguhr was in part converted to a siliceous gel, which during digestion of the slurry following precipitation diffused rather completely through the nickel carbonate, resulting in a gel-like nickel carbonate silica-gel mixture. This catalyst, when completed, was significantly different in texture and catalytic activity from a catalyst that was not given the hydrothermal (digestion) treatment.

In essence, the hydrothermal treatment of the catalyst can produce two effects. We have previously discussed the reorientation brought about due to the epitaxial orientation of a catalytic material on a previously oriented particulate support. This was meant to show that the particulate matter serving as support can materially alter the precipitate structurally and, hence, catalytically. A simple and practical consideration is that if one is preparing a catalyst and is not meticulous in adhering to preselected precipitation, washing, digestion, and filtering conditions as to time and temperature in all respects, one is likely to find in two separate preparations that the catalysts vary significantly one from the other. The type of support used may be selected as alumina, silica, or titania, but unless the species is identified (alpha, gamma, eta, and so on for alumina), one has not given sufficient description for visualization or reproduction of the catalyst. As an example, a description of a catalyst as supported on alumina is not useful to someone who wants to duplicate that catalyst because if in case one has used alpha alumina, he or she is quite likely to derive a catalyst in which the alumina has been little altered chemically but because alpha alumina is well oriented and consequently, so may be the catalyst supported thereon. Quite by contrast, gamma or chi aluminas each has its own orientation characteristics for the precipitate but also is extremely reactive, particularly in a basic solution for the formation of hydroxide, hydrate, or aluminate.

Perhaps the most effective ion in reorientation is the ammonium ion, particularly when the catalytic material is of a metal that will form an ammine. The ammines are soluble in solutions containing the ammonium ion and consequently reorient quite rapidly. However, one should not confine the consideration to ammonia but should consider the other ions such as carbonate, chloride, sulfate, alkalis, such as sodium and potassium, alkaline earths, such as magnesium, calcium, and barium, and halides such as fluorine and bromine. More rarely one must factor in the effect of borate, molybdate, and nitrate.

One need only look to the mineral kingdom to see how these ions enter into crystal structures that vary from zeolite to precious gems. These ions or molecules that aid in crystallization and orientation are termed *mineralizers*. The zeolites will be examined in Chapter 10, so they will not be considered again here. But the more exotic and unexpected types of effects of hydrothermal treatment are the ones just mentioned and the ones that are customarily neglected in the consideration of catalyst preparation and catalytic effect.

Control of Depth of Impregnation

There are two basic ways of controlling the depth of penetration of the catalyst into the support material. It is customarily the intent to locate the catalytic material, which generally is more expensive than the support material, as close to the surface as possible but not so close to the surface that it will be less than the depth of penetration of the reactants during mass transfer.

A typical method of impregnation to a given depth is first to determine the amount of liquid that will be picked up by the support materials themselves. For example, 100 g of the support material are weighed, immersed in water, and then weighed again after removing excessive moisture on the surface. This operation gives the weight of water picked up (pore volume). This information is used in preparing the volume of solution of the precipitant, which is next applied to the support (exactly sufficient to wet with no excess liquid). A quantity of precipitant stoichiometrically equivalent or more than equivalent to the amount necessary to precipitate the catalytic material is dissolved in a quantity of water slightly less than that previously determined to be the adsorptive capacity of the support. The support is next treated with this total quantity of precipitant and is dried to deposit the precipitant near and on the surface of the support.

A quantity of water that is again essentially equivalent to the amount that will be adsorbed by the support is measured, and a quantity of catalytic salt or salts is dissolved in this liquid, which usually is water.

The support material with the precipitant is now immersed in the solution of catalytic materials, which are in just enough solution to wet the catalytic support without having excessive liquid on the surface or in the vessel being used. This treatment gives a catalytic coating, which is essentially on the surface of the support.

There may still be in the support soluble salts such as alkali or other precipitants that must be removed by washing. Washing is effected by immersing the support with catalysts fixed on the surface in sufficient wash water to cover the support plus catalyst to a depth at least five times as great as the depth of catalyst. The catalyst and liquid are stirred to effect solution of the salts, which are then removed by decanting the supernatant liquid. This washing operation is repeated until the alkali has been adequately removed. It may be desirable to use a solution of an ion exchange salt (ammonium carbonate or bicarbonate) to ion exchange volatile for nonvolatile ions.

This procedure produces a catalyst located essentially as a skin-like surface on the support. If it is desired to have the depth of penetration of the catalyst somewhat greater, then the support after impregnation with the precipitant solution is dried slowly in a stream of gas (usually air) humidified at a controlled temperature and relative humidity condition so that the precipitant, which is diffused completely through the support, will dry to different distances from the surface of the support. The location of the precipitant is controlled by both the temperature and the humidity of the gas stream. The humidity of the gas stream is controlled by the temperature of a reservoir of water through which the gas stream bubbles to be saturated (Figure 4.9). After the precipitant location has been fixed, the support plus precipitant is heated to a sufficiently high temperature to dehydrate it to the level normally used for the precipitant-impregnated support. Following this specific location of the precipitant, the support plus precipitant is impregnated with the solution of catalytic ingredients. Washing or ion exchanging, or both, can also be performed.

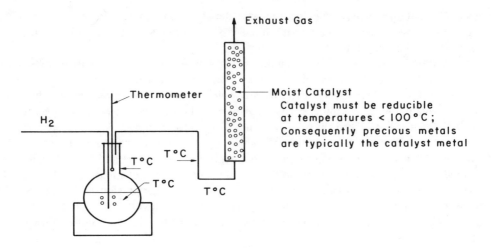

Figure 4.9   Apparatus for control of catalyst location on support by control of efflorescence.

The catalytic material can be dispersed almost uniformly through the entire support by impregnating the support first with the catalytic material, which is in contrast to the instructions just given for the procedure when the catalyst is supported close to the surface. It is necessary in this case for the catalytic material to be precipitated by ammonia, effected by placing the support into which the catalytic material has been totally impregnated and while still in a moist condition into a closed tube into which gas can be introduced at one end and exhausted in the other (Figure 4.10). This tube

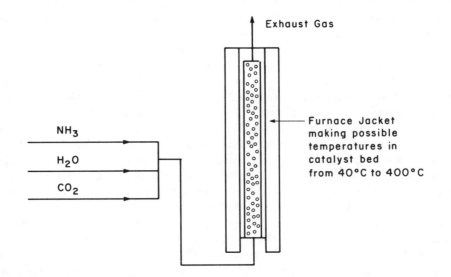

Figure 4.10   Apparatus for uniform impregnation of catalytic material throughout catalyst support.

is usually placed in a split furnace or in a jacketed tube so that the temperature of the moist catalyst can be maintained at a level between 35° and 110°C.

With the catalyst in this tube and the tube at a temperature previously determined to be the optimum, anhydrous ammonia is passed through the tube. The anhydrous ammonia is adsorbed throughout the support and catalytic material, and the catalyst is precipitated and fixed in a location usually completely dispersed through the support material. The control of the location of the catalyst to the desired position is generally a case of cut and try until such time as the desired location has been established.

In addition to anhydrous ammonia, there can be passed as a portion of the gas stream carbon dioxide, which will give a carbonate or basic carbonate instead of the hydroxide of the catalytic material. In the case of either type of precipitant, as soon as the catalytic material has been fixed by precipitation, the temperature of the catalytic material is raised to the point where the hydroxide or the ammonia complex or the carbonate is decomposed to form the oxide of the catalytic material, presuming this is the desired eventual form.

These two procedures are a bit more time-consuming than the typical immersion, drying, and calcining, but the results are usually vastly superior to the less sophisticated preparation methods.

Liquid Catalysts in a Foraminous Support

One usually does not think of catalytic material as being molten, at least not an industrial catalytic material; however, in the case of the sulfur dioxide to sulfur trioxide oxidation catalyst, which comprises a eutectic mixture of vanadium pentoxide and potassium pyrosulfate, it is used at a temperature above its melting point in at least the upstream portion of the multitray converter. The support in this case is usually a foraminous material such as kieselguhr, which is the silicified skeletons of fossilized diatoms. The fossilized diatom skeletons are themselves very porous, and when the skeletons are massed together, there are large interstices.

The catalytic mixture or composite is prepared by mixing in a kneader-type machine about 50% kieselguhr, about 35% potassium sulfate, which becomes pyrosulfate during the operation of the catalyst, and 15% ammonium metavanadate, which becomes vanadium pentoxide during the course of operation. The kieselguhr or diatomaceous earth forms the matrix in which the molten potassium vanadate persulfate is dispersed.

Kieselguhr has a surface area of only about 4 m^2/g, and there is some evidence that by replacing some of the kieselguhr with colloidal silica, a much higher surface area is provided, enhancing the foraminous structure; additionally, the activity of the catalyst is improved substantially. The colloidal silica not only provides a much higher surface area but additional foraminous structure as well.

A similar catalyst is used for the oxidation of benzene to maleic anhydride and also for various raw materials to phthalic anhydride. These three are the only examples of this type of catalyst entity in commercial operation.

If one were to generalize on this type of catalyst preparation, it would be to say that probably kieselguhr in its various grades produces the best type of relatively inert and acceptable support material. The characteristics of the kieselguhr itself are enhanced by the incorporation of a higher-surface-area foraminous material such as colloidal silica, which also is available in various spherulite sizes. Consequently, the colloidal silica can have different surface areas and also different interparticle interstices.

REFERENCES

1. Lachman, I., et al. 1985. Monolithic honeycomb supports for catalysis. *Chem. Eng. Prog.* (January).
2. *Chemical Engineering Buyer's Guide*. 1987. New York: McGraw-Hill.

CHAPTER 5

Activated Carbon Supports

Alfred J. Bird

Carbon is a ubiquitous element that forms the basis of all known and unknown life processes in the biosphere. It forms many millions of compounds ranging in complexity from simple compounds such as carbon monoxide to the highly complex molecules found in living organisms, some of which mediate the life processes and are known as enzyme catalysts.

Simpler organic compounds—for example, organic peroxides and tertiary amines—are used as catalysts in important industrial reactions such as polymerization of hydrocarbons to produce elastomers, plastics, and rubbers.

In its elemental form, carbon is found in nature in two allotropic forms: diamond and graphite. Although no catalytic properties can be ascribed to diamond, graphite is known to be an active catalyst in some oxidation reactions, particularly when in the form of activated charcoal, and is used industrially in effluent gas treatment to remove sulfur compounds from gas streams. Graphitic carbon is also used as a support material on which other catalytic entities such as metals, oxides, sulfides, and chlorides of the elements may be dispersed in order to increase the surface area they expose to the chemical reactants.

Besides elemental carbon allotropes, organic polymers of the polystyrene and nylon types have been used as catalyst supports. The former require functionalization with chemically active groups such as phosphines and sulfides in order to form a bond with a catalytically active transition metal center. Nonhydrocarbon polymers, typified by nylon, frequently contain groups that can form bonds with transition metal compounds that are sufficiently strong to prevent loss of active centers during reaction but not so strong that the catalytic properties of the active metal centers are impaired.

Thus, in its strictest sense, carbon-based catalysis should include elemental and organic compounds as both catalyst and support. However, this would present far too large a subject for this review, and carbon-based catalysis is restricted to the narrower subject of catalysis over elemental carbon and elemental carbon-supported catalysts.

TYPES OF GRAPHITE CARBON

Graphite is found in nature as roughly hexagonal crystals in metamorphic rocks. The hexagonal crystals have four axes of symmetry, three of which are horizontal and are of equal lengths, meeting in the center at 60° angles. At right angles to these three axes is a fourth, vertical axis, shorter than the horizontal axes. This structure arises from the bonding adopted by the carbon atoms. Each carbon atom is trigonally hybridized, and the atoms of each hexagon are linked by sigma bonds. The remaining, fourth, electron is part of a generalized orbital system above and below the plane of the hexagon. It is the electrons of the generalized orbital that are responsible for the electrical conductivity. In the plane of the hexagons, the electrical conductivity is 10^{-4} ohm cm and 2–3 ohms at right angles to it. Each layer of carbon hexagons is separated from those above and below by 3.35 Å, which is too large for chemical bonding. The layers are held together by van der Waals forces, and it is this weak interlayer bonding that allows them to cleave so easily. Figure 5.1 illustrates the structure of graphite.

The electron concentration above and below the carbon layers makes it possible for "foreign" atoms or molecules to slip between the layers, donating to or accepting electrons from the generalized orbital to form a chemical bond. These compounds are known as interstitial compounds. They have unusual properties, and many of them have proved to possess catalytic activity.

Graphite crystallites can be found in virtually all of the carbon materials used as catalysts or catalyst supports. Where the graphitic structure is well ordered and long

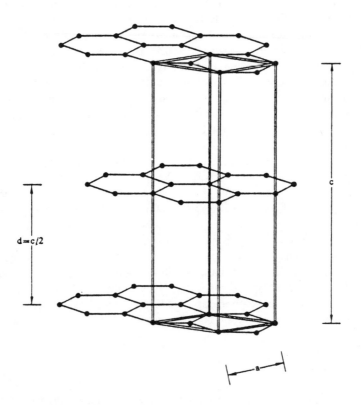

Figure 5.1 Hexagonal lattice structure of graphite.

range, the material is usually described as graphite. Where the order is of shorter range, a spectrum of products arises which can be called graphitic carbons.

Well-ordered graphitic carbons and graphite of small particle size are sometimes used as supports for catalysts that will have to endure severe oxidizing conditions, such as at the oxygen electrode of a fuel cell. Graphitized carbon blacks, in which the graphitization process reorders the small graphite crystallites present in ordinary carbon blacks, give carbon particles in which the graphite layers are either stacked radially to the surface or parallel to the surface, as in Figure 5.2, are particularly useful under severe oxidizing conditions.

Carbon blacks and charcoals also contain graphitic crystallites, but here the crystallites are not stacked with their layers parallel to one another. Rather they are distributed randomly. This type of graphitic carbon is termed *turbostratic carbon*. Because the crystallites are small and have only short-term structure, they are more easily oxidized than graphitized carbons or graphite and in consequence are used only in applications involving reducing, neutral, or very mildly oxidizing conditions.

Some commercial carbons, although they may contain graphitic nuclei, are so highly cross-linked that only soaking them for very long times at high graphitizing temperatures can they be made to show graphitic structure by X-ray diffraction. For all practical purposes, therefore, they may be thought of, and indeed are described as, nongraphitizing carbons. Such materials are manufactured from synthetic polymers and form the basis of some of the carbon cloths and felts that recently have made an entry to commercial catalysis as catalysts for gas phase reactions.

The Form of Carbon Materials

Carbon is used industrially in many different forms, which include powder, granules, spheres, extrudates, cloths, and felts, most of which have had a use in carbon-based catalysis (Table 5.1).

Powders are usually defined as particles passing a 20 mesh sieve (0.84 mm). Particles larger than 20 mesh with an irregular shape are usually termed granules and may have a diameter of up to 3/8 in. Carbon spheres are used industrially with diameters ranging from 1/10–1/2 in., but it is unusual for them to be used as catalyst supports above about 1/8 in. diameter. Extrudates are cylinders in which the length axis is

Before   After

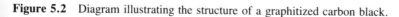

Figure 5.2   Diagram illustrating the structure of a graphitized carbon black.

Table 5.1 Classification of Graphite Carbons by Their Industrially Useful Form

	Graphite	Activitated Charcoal	Carbon Blacks	Carbon Fibers
Powder	X	X	X	
Granules		X		
Spheres		X		
Extrudates		X		
Pellets		X		
Tablets		X		
Cloths				X
Felts				X

greater than the diameter, while compressed powder cylinders in which the length axis is roughly equal to the diameter are known as pellets. Where the length axis is shorter than the diameter, the particles are known as tablets. Extrudates and pellets are frequently used as catalyst supports, most often 1/8 in. in diameter, but more infrequently as 1/16 or 3/16 in. diameter. Tablets are only rarely used as catalyst supports. Carbon cloths and felts are manufactured from synthetic fiber cloths and felts by carbonization and activation, the carbon form being a pseudomorph of the original material.

Cloths are usually woven from continuous fibers, while felts are compacted mats of short fibers. At present at least nine-tenths of the carbon used industrially for supported catalysts is in the form of powders, granules, or extrudates.

Manufacture of Carbons

Only rarely is a carbon manufactured as a catalyst support. For the most part, the catalyst manufacturer has to utilize commercially available carbons. This imposes many limitations on the catalyst manufacturing process and not infrequently involves the pretreatment of the carbon to make it suitable as a catalyst support. This may vary from the removal of magnetic iron-containing particles electromagnetically to the air classification of powder carbons to obtain a specific particle-size cut suitable as a catalyst support. Researchers may even resort to chemical treatment of the carbon with acid or alkali. Pretreatments in general do not alter the basic structure of the carbon.

Chemical pretreatment is able to modify the surface chemistry of the support, but it is essentially ineffective at modifying the pore structure or the crystallite structure of the carbon support. Because the basic carbon structure, the support surface properties, and the pore structure have such a profound effect on both catalyst manufacture and catalyst properties, it is incumbent on the catalyst manufacturer to understand how these features arise during carbon production.

Essentially all carbons arise by the pyrolysis of a carbonaceous material such as natural gas, wood, peat, or coal or an organic polymer like PVC or PVDC, and it is the nature of the starting material and the pyrolysis conditions that determine the proportion, size, and orientation of graphitic to nongraphitic carbon and hence the incipient pore structure. An activation process will have to be used to open up the incipient pore structure by burning away the nongraphitic carbon, and it is the activation agent, the length of time over which it is used, and the type of activation catalyst used, if any, that will determine the surface area, pore size, and surface chemistry that the final carbon will have.

Graphite and Graphitized Carbon Black

Natural graphite is found in Austria, Canada, Ceylon, Czechoslovakia, Germany, Italy, Korea, Madagascar, Mexico and the USSR in commercially mineable amounts. In some areas, such as Ceylon, it is found in rich vein-like concentrations, whereas in others, such as Madagascar, it forms irregular masses scattered throughout the mother rock. In all cases, it appears to have been formed by high temperatures and intense pressure during the metamorphism of sedimentary rocks containing carbonaceous materials, such as coal. Natural graphite is very highly structured and on occasion can be pure. Normally, however, commercially available natural graphite contains silica and other mainly metal impurities, which require treatment with hydrofluoric and other acids to make it suitable as a support material.

Artificial or synthetic graphite is made by subjecting a carbon material to temperatures in the region of 2000–3000°C at ambient pressure. Not all carbon materials are suitable for conversion to graphite. Graphitizable carbons appear to be mainly those formed by the carbonization of an organic material that passes through a molten state at between 400–500°C, before solidifying to form a coke at higher temperatures. Cokes used for commercial production of graphite are petroleum coke, coal pitch coke, gas retort carbon, and carbon blacks.

The manufacturing process requires that the raw carbon is ground to give two fractions, one of 20–40 mesh, the remainder of 50 mesh and below. Portions of the two coke fractions are then mixed with about 25% (W/W) of pitch at about 165°C. The mixture is then extruded into blocks, fired at 750°C, and allowed to cool to ambient temperature. The blocks are impregnated with pitch, packed in coke dust, and fired in an electric graphitizing furnace at temperatures of about 2800°C. If high-purity graphite is required, halogenated hydrocarbons are injected into the furnace during graphitization. The time and temperature of graphitization are important parameters in determining the perfection of the graphite structure. The higher is the temperature and the longer is the time of graphitization, the more perfect is the structure. However, temperatures much over 3000°C are to be avoided as sublimation of the carbon atoms destroys the structure as fast as it is formed.

Graphitized carbon blacks are manufactured by heating carbon blacks to temperatures of 2000°C plus. During graphitization, the spherical carbon black particles recrystallize to form angular solids, usually twelve-faced. Each face is then a separate crystallite of graphite, limited in extent to about one-third to one-half of the original particular diameter.

Carbon Blacks

Originally carbon blacks were manufactured from methane, acetylene, and other easily vaporized hydrocarbon materials. Today acetylene has virtually ceased to be used as a carbon black source, while methane and residual oil fractions have become important sources.

The chemistry of the process is still the subject of speculation, but the following stages are reasonably well established. The hydrocarbon precursor is injected into a very highly turbulent natural gas flame. The temperature of the flame is about 1400°C, and the residence time of the hydrocarbon in the reaction zone is about 0.05 sec. Within the reaction zone, hydrocarbon molecules are cracked to ethylene and acetylene, which in turn polymerize to give polycyclic compounds such as pyrenes, anthracenes, and coronenes. The polymerized materials condense to give (oil) droplets, which are the true precursors of the carbon black, for they then dehydrogenate to give small graphite nuclei. Within an oil droplet, graphitic nuclei, because they are in a liquid medium, arrange themselves in a random fashion to form turbostratic carbon particles of a characteristic spherical shape. Where (oil) droplets collide during dehydrogenation, they tend to fuse together into a chain structure.

The degree of structure can be controlled by regulating the concentration of oil droplets in the reaction zone, while oil droplet size can be controlled by varying the residence time within the reaction zone, short residence times giving rise to small-particle diameters. Droplet concentration can be controlled by diluting the flame gases with an inert gas; residence time can be controlled by the length of flame. Immediately after the reaction zone, the furnace gases are quenched with a water spray to lower their temperature to 200–250°C, at which temperature further reaction of the graphitic particles with oxidizing components of the gas stream (carbon dioxide and steam) is prevented. Some reaction with oxidizing gases, however, is inevitable, and from this arises the oxygen surface groupings. Because the residence time within the reaction zone is so small, insufficient time is provided for the formation of a pore structure.

Charcoals

Charcoals are manufactured in two principal ways:

1. Carbonization of the raw material, followed by activation with steam or carbon dioxide, or both;
2. Incorporation of the activating agent with the raw material and carbonizing and activating in one operation.

The raw material for charcoal manufacture can vary from coal, through lignite and peat to wood, nutshells, fruit pits, and still others. Recently petroleum residues have been carbonized, and the resulting needle cokes activated with steam give microporous charcoals of very high surface area.

During activation, some of the carbon is burned away to give a pore structure. The degree of porous structure is, for any particular raw material, a function of the time of activation. With short times of activation, only small amounts of carbon are gasified; the yield of carbon is high, but the degree of pore structure formed is low. As activation time increases, so does the degree of pore structure formed, while the yield of carbon decreases. All carbon manufacturers operate their process to give the highest yield of carbon consistent with the application.

An essential difference between the two methods of activation is that gaseous activating agents operate from the outside inward, giving rise to a particle that is more activated on the outside than in the center. This feature is particularly noticeable with the larger particle size materials. Chemically activated charcoals, however, because of the way in which the activating agents are incorporated into the raw material prior to activation, give a more homogeneous structure.

Steam and Carbon Dioxide Activation.   The organic raw material is impregnated with a small amount of a substance, such as sodium carbonate, which acts catalytically during the activation process to increase the rate of gasification. The impregnated material passes through an inclined rotary furnace where it is activated.

The activating gas is introduced at the bottom of the furnace, close to the point at which the activated charcoal is discharged to a cooling apparatus. As the raw material proceeds through the furnace, it sees first spent activation gas at a temperature of 400–600°C, at which carbonization takes place. The precise manner in which carbonization occurs is dependent on the chemical constitution of the raw material but can be broadly divided into two classes: (1) carbon formed from cellulosic structures and (2) that formed from lignin structures. Cellulose on carbonization does not melt and produces a poorly graphitizing carbon, while lignin, which does melt to form a liquid mesophase, gives graphitic carbon. The exact amounts of each are a function of the proportions of cellulose and lignin in the original raw materials and the time and temperature of carbonization. Nutshells, which contain more lignin than wood, give a more graphitic carbon on activation.

Fossil raw materials, such as peat, lignite, and coal, can be looked upon as materials in which the carbonization process has been partially carried out naturally, and the completion of the process is artificial. Peat, which contains most of the original cellulosic and lignin material of the original plants, gives a less graphitic carbon than coal, which to a large extent has been aromatized during its formation.

The graphitic nuclei formed in all of these materials, being formed at low temperature, are able to develop their structure only in two dimensions to form plates, which are randomly orientated to one another. The degree of orientation is a function of the carbonization temperature and is greater the higher the temperature.

When the proportion of cellulose is high—more than 40%—the carbonized material forms a pseudomorph of the original material and is frequently so perfect that scanning electron microscopy can reveal the plant species from which the material was formed. Figure 5.3 shows the plant origin of a commercial charcoal to perfection.

Activation of the carbonized material gasifies mainly the tarry and nongraphitic carbon material, attack on the graphitic material being minimal. The gasification opens up the internal structure of the carbon particles, giving rise to a pore structure that is initially microporous but that progressively widens to give a more meso/macroporous structure as the degree of activation increases. Within the furnace, activation occurs

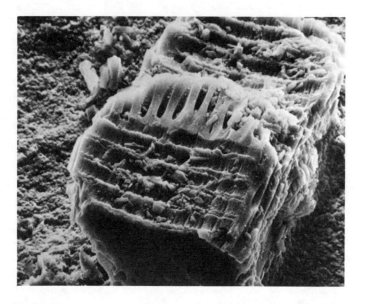

Figure 5.3   Scanning electron micrograph of a wood charcoal.

to a progressively greater extent as the carbonized material falls toward the furnace bottom, the oxidizing power and temperature of the bases increasing. The highest temperature seen by a charcoal during activation is about 900°C.

In a few cases—coconut charcoals and some wood charcoals—carbonization and activation are separated both temporally and spatially. The carbonization is accomplished in the country in which the plant material originates (the Far East or Australia, for example), while the activation process is carried out in Europe or North America after transportation of the carbonized material.

After activation, the charcoal is often washed with water to remove sodium salts and sulfur compounds. The resulting charcoal still retains some of the sodium salts and is alkaline in reaction. If a neutral carbon is required, it is acid washed after an initial water wash.

Chemical Activation.   Chemically activated charcoals are made by impregnating the raw material with the activating agent and heating it in an inert atmosphere at 600–800°C. The activating agents are commonly zinc chloride or phosphoric acid, although other agents, including sulfuric acid, have been used. Zinc chloride is the favored activating agent in Eastern Europe, while phosphoric acid is used in Western Europe and the United States. The graphitic nuclei formed are similar in size to those formed during normal carbonization, the carbonization conditions being essentially the same in both cases. Activation occurs simultaneously with carbonization, and some of the activating agent becomes irreversibly incorporated into the carbon structure.

As with steam-activated charcoals, the material burned away during activation is the nongraphitic carbon and tarry residues formed by carbonization.

Chemical and Physical Properties of Carbons

It is thought that most of the chemical properties of catalytic importance to carbon arise from the incorporation of oxygen into its surface during manufacture. It is probably these oxygen groups that are the active centers when carbon itself acts as a catalyst. They also appear to act as nucleation centers during the impregnation stage of catalyst preparation. It is therefore surprising that despite their importance, very little is known about these surface groups and their constitution, distribution within the pore structure, and behavior at certain critical stages of catalyst manufacture and during use in catalytic reactions.

The major part of our ignorance of the surface chemistry of carbons can be attributed to the nature of the graphitic nuclei, which make them, for instance, opaque to radiations in the visible and infrared region of the spectrum from which we would expect to derive most information concerning their chemical constitution. Only by employing multiple surface analysis techniques has any progress been made, and even then a lot of our knowledge is guesswork. Titration of the surfaces of carbon with alkalies of varying strengths suggests that some of the groups are acidic in nature, and phenolic, carboxylic acid, and lactone groups have been proposed. Reacting the surface with Grignard reagents shows that both hydroxyl and ketonic groups may be present. However, only about one-quarter of the oxygenated groups could be accounted for by this reagent. Reflectance infrared spectra also show absorptions that can be attributed to phenols and ketones, while potentiodynamic analysis lends support to this by proposing that the surface contains a quinone-hydroquinone redox system.

Each type of carbon has a different proportion of its oxygen content that can be ascribed to any particular grouping, and although broadly the surface area and method of surface activation determine both the amount of oxygen present and the type of groupings present, no unvarying rules can be given to predict either factor. For example, batch-to-batch variations on activated charcoal for any one of the groupings can vary by several hundred percent, and repeat determinations on the same batch of charcoal separated by several months always differ. Catalyst chemists long ago learned that the only measurements that they can rely on for catalyst preparation are those just completed.

With the measurement of the physical properties of carbons, we are on much safer ground. The surface area and pore size distribution can be obtained by just two techniques: nitrogen Brunauer, Emmett, and Teller (BET) and mercury porisimetry. From the adsorbtion-desorption isotherm of the former technique can be obtained the total surface area and the pore size distribution up to about 300 Å, while with the mercury porisimeter, the pore size distribution may be completed out to the largest pores. From the point of view of liquid-phase catalysis, the larger transport pores are less important than the mesopores and micropores, within which many catalytic reaction take place, so that mercury porisimetry is less frequently used than nitrogen physisorption.

The surface area of each type of carbon is characteristic of that type of carbon, and although some overlap does occur, it is possible to recognize the type of support material from its surface area. Table 5.2 contains a list of carbon supports with their surface area limits.

Table 5.2   Surface Areas of Various Carbon Materials

Carbon	Surface Area (m^2/g^{-1})
Graphite (natural)	0.1–20
Graphite (synthetic)	0.3–25
Graphitized carbon blacks	20–100
Carbon blacks	70–250
Activated carbons	
Wood charcoal	300–900
Peat charcoal	350–1000
Coal carbon	300–1000
Nutshell charcoals	700–1500
Petroleum needle coke carbon	1500–3000

The pore size distribution, however, enables a much more accurate description of the support to be made. Graphites and carbon blacks have only small pore volumes, which can be interpreted as essentially microporous (<20 Å), while nutshell carbons and activated carbons made from petroleum cokes have very much larger pore volumes, again predominantly microporous. Although wood and peat charcoals contain a high proportion of micropores, they differ from other charcoals by having a substantial mesoporous pore volume. This is especially true of many wood charcoals. Figure 5.4 illustrates the type of pore structure frequently seen with peat and wood charcoals.

Examination of the absorption-desorption isotherms of catalysts sometimes reveals a loss of pore volume. This only happens at the upper metal loadings for that particular support. Thus, with low-surface-area charcoals (300–500 m^2/g^{-1}), loss of

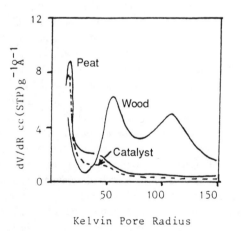

Figure 5.4   Pore size distributions for typical peat and wood charcoals, and a 10% palladium on peat charcoal catalyst illustrating loss of pore volume due to pore blocking.

pore volume can frequently be detected in the microporous region at low metal loadings (5% metal). With higher-surface-area charcoals (800–900 m^2/g^{-1}), the loss of pore volume becomes apparent only at loadings of 10–15% metal. The region of the pore structure in which the loss takes place is dependent on the method of preparation. Where the metal is impregnated as an outer mantle, pore volume loss is not generally seen, but with preparations in which the metal penetrates the pore system, loss in either or both the micropore and mesopore volume can occur. This is illustrated in Figure 5.4 where loss in both of these regions occurred when a peat charcoal was loaded with 10% palladium using a total penetration method of preparation.

CARBON AS A CATALYST

Carbon is much more frequently used as a catalyst support than as a catalyst in its own right, but at least one carbon-catalyzed reaction has been industrially important and is still used today: the formation of phosgene (carbonyl chloride).

Some of the catalytic effects seen with charcoal can be ascribed to ash components—in particular, the transition metal components such as iron. Of those reactions not catalyzed by the ash, the majority would appear to be mediated by the surface oxygen groups present. However, no direct evidence has ever been given to support this. Removal or generation of various surface oxygen groupings is known to modify the catalytic activity of carbons, but whether it is the oxygen group that participates in the catalytic reaction or the modified electronic properties of the graphitic nuclei is not clear. A list of carbon-catalyzed reactions is given in Table 5.3.

Two reactions in which hydroxyl surface groupings are thought to play an important part are the decomposition of hydrogen peroxide,

$$(C+)OH' + H^+OOH' \rightarrow (C^+)OOH' + H_2O$$

$$(C+)OOH' + H_2O_2 \ 1 \rightarrow (C^+)OH' + H_2O + O_2,$$

and the decomposition of formic acid,

$$C(OH) + HCOOH \rightarrow (C)H + H_2O + CO_2,$$

although the latter is not catalytic unless oxygen is present.

Industrially the formation of phosgene by the combination of carbon monoxide and chlorine over carbon is of importance, although little appears to be known about the mechanism. The reaction is conducted over activated charcoal at temperatures of 200–250°C. In 1972 production of phosgene amounted to 0.84×10^9 lbs and in 1983 to 1.42×10^9 lbs. About 85% of phosgene produced in the United States is used in tolylene diisocyanate manufacture. Sulfuryl chloride (SO_2Cl_2) is also manufactured on an industrial scale by the combination of sulfur dioxide and chlorine in the presence of activated charcoal.

Table 5.3   Reactions Catalyzed by Carbons

General Type	Examples
Reactions involving hydrogen	H_2-D_2 exchange
	o-p H_2 exchange
	$H_2 + Br_2 \rightarrow 2HBr$
	$RX + H_2 \rightarrow RH + HX$ (X = Cl,Br)
	$HCOOH \rightarrow CO_2 + H_2$
	$CH_3CHOHCH_3 \rightarrow CH_3COCH_3 + H_2$
	$H_2O + C \rightarrow CO + H_2$
	$H_2 + D_2O \rightarrow HDO + HD$
	$H_2 + N_2O \rightarrow N_2 + H_2O$
Reactions involving oxygen	$2H_2O_2 \rightarrow 2H_2O + O_2$
	$SO_2 + \frac{1}{2}O_2 \rightarrow SO_3$
	$NO + \frac{1}{2}O_2 \rightarrow NO_2$
	$2H_2S + O_2 \rightarrow S_2 + 2H_2O$
	Catalytic oxidation of inorganic anions
Reactions involving halogen	$H_2 + Br_2 \rightarrow 2HBr$
	$CO + Cl_2 \rightarrow COCl_2$
	$C_2H_4 + 5Cl_2 \rightarrow C_2Cl_6 + 4HCl$
	$SO_2 Cl_2 \rightarrow SO_2Cl_2$
	$C_6H_5CH_3 + Cl_2 \rightarrow C_6H_5CH_2Cl + HCl$
Polymerization/isomerization	$3C_2H_2 \rightarrow C_6H_6$
	α-olefins $\rightarrow$ polyolefins
	double bond isomerization

Source: D. Trimm, "Catalysis," *Specialist Periodical Reports*, Vol. 4, RCS, 1980.

CARBON AS A SUPPORT

Very little of the graphite, carbon black, and activated charcoal manufactured annually is used as catalyst support. For example, in 1978, some 561,000 metric tons of activated charcoal and 4,241,000 metric tons of carbon blacks were manufactured worldwide, but worldwide sales of charcoal-supported catalysts amounted to only 9 million lbs in that year, or 0.78% of charcoal production. If only the industrialized countries, the major producers of carbon-supported catalysts, are considered, then the ratio of charcoal used as support compared to that used for other purposes increases, but it is still only a small proportion. Production in the United States of charcoal-supported catalysts reached 4 million lbs in 1978, or 2% of U.S. manufactured charcoal.

The amount of graphite and carbon blacks used as support is even smaller than that for activated charcoals. However, when the value of carbon-supported catalysts is considered, it can be seen as an extremely valuable business, grossing about $25 million in the United States in 1979 and expected to grow to more than $30 million by 1988.

The major catalytic use of charcoal and carbon blacks is the support of metals, although charcoals are used to support compounds, such as sulfides and halides. Some graphite is used to support metals, but the most important feature of graphite is its ability to form intercalates, graphite compounds in which the metal or compound inserts between and bonds to the graphite layers. Table 5.4 lists the metals and compounds supported on charcoal, carbon black, and graphite. One surprising feature of Table 5.4 is that iron, nickel, and cobalt, although used as catalysts for large numbers of industrial reactions, are never supported on carbon. The reason is the ease with which these elements form inactive carbides during the manufacturing process. Nickel can be supported in an elemental form on charcoal by precipitating the dimethylglyoxine complex within the pore structure and then decomposing it thermally, under carefully controlled conditions. The cost of preparing nickel catalysts this way is prohibitive for industrial application despite having some interesting catalytic properties.

Initially the support was conceived as an inert material, which merely served as a surface on which the catalyst could be spread out to present a greater surface area to the reactants. This picture is undoubtedly true of some catalysts, and indeed of some carbon-supported catalysts. The bulk of metal and metal compounds supported on carbon are, today, thought to owe at least some of their catalytic properties to catalyst-support interactions. These can range from relatively weak interactions with metal compounds supported on charcoal, through metals supported on charcoal and carbon blacks where the interaction is somewhat more noticeable to metals and com-

Table 5.4   Carbon-Supported Metal and Metal Compound Catalysts

Carbon Support	Element	Compound
Charcoal	Platinum group Metals (PGMs) Silver Rhenium	PGM sulfides PGM halides Rhenium sulphides Mercuric chloride Zinc acetate Mercuric acetate
Carbon black	Platinum Palladium	
Graphite	Alkali metals Alkaline earth metals Platinum metals	PGM halides Ferric chloride Cupric chloride Aluminum chloride Palladium oxide Palladium sulfide

pounds forming intercalates with graphite in which the interaction is so strong that the catalyst has properties different from either of the entities forming it. The following sections describe the preparation and catalytic properties of each of these groups of catalyst.

Preparation and Catalytic Properties of Graphite Intercalates

Graphite intercalation compounds of the alkali metals, alkaline earth metals, platinum metal halides, base metal halides, and palladium sulfide are usually made by heating graphite and the metal or metal compound in either an inert atmosphere or a vacuum. Platinum metal-graphite intercalates can be made only by reducing a platinum halide-graphite intercalate with alkali metal vapor, sodium borohydride, lithium aluminum hydride, sodium in liquid ammonia, lithium biphenyl, or sodium naphthalide. The use of hydrogen for such reductions is invariably disastrous; the platinum metal migrates from between the graphite layers to form crystallites of metal on the graphite particle surface. Liquid-phase reductions with sodium borohydride, lithium aluminum hydride, lithium biphenyl, and sodium maphthalide are conducted at temperatures close to ambient, although lithium biphenyl can be used at temperatures as low as $-50°C$, while sodium potassium in the vapor form operates best at temperatures of 300–350°C.

Graphite intercalation compounds have a surprisingly large catalytic range, including ortho-para hydrogen conversion, deuterium exchange reactions, hydrogenation, dehydrogenation, isomerization, alkylation, hydrodealkylation, dimerization, and polymerization of olefins, ammonia synthesis, Fischer-Tropsch synthesis, oxychlorination, carbonylation of methanol, and small-scale organic syntheses.

Deuterium Exchange and Ortho-Parahydrogen Conversions

Both reactions have been conducted over alkali metal-graphite intercalates. Although not of industrial importance, these reaction are unusual for the alkali metals.

Hydrogenation

The alkali metal-graphite compounds will hydrogenate acetylenes first to olefins, then to paraffins, and aromatics to the corresponding cycloparaffins. However, nickel, palladium, and platinum metal intercalates show even higher selectivities than alkali metal intercalates in that they form exclusively the olefin when hydrogenating acetylenes.

Dehydrogenation

The dehydrogenation of cyclohexanol to cyclohexanone and isopropanol to acetone has been observed over nickel metal intercalates at temperatures of 370°C.

Isomerization

The double bond isomerization of olefins can be conducted over alkali metal intercalates at temperatures of 125–250°C and atmospheric pressure. In the liquid phase, long reaction times and elevated pressures are required.

Alkylation

Alkali metal intercalates are active for the alkylation of benzene with both ethylene and propylene. With propylene, a small amount of cyclization of the side chain occurs to give 2-methylindane, as well as isobutylbenzene.

Hydrodealkylation

The hydrodealkylation of alkylaromatics occurs over alkali metal intercalates and alkali metal–promoted transition metal chloride intercalates, without cracking of the aromatic nucleus and coke formation, and at high selectivity.

Polymerization

Alkali metal intercalates will polymerize olefins (ethylene), dienes (butadiene and isoprene), vinyl monomers (acrylonitrile and styrene), vinylidene monomers (methyl methacrylate methacrylaldehyde and methacrylonitrile), crotonaldehyde, and acetaldehyde. Polymerization of dienes gives polymers with 1,2- and trans-1,4- addition structures.

Ammonia Formation

Alkali metal intercalates possess a weak ability to combine hydrogen and nitrogen to form ammonia, but the yield can be significantly increased by using alkali metal–promoted transition metal intercalates. These latter compounds are said to be insensitive to the presence of sulfur or oxygen in the synthesis feed. Thus ammonia was formed when air was used as the nitrogen source.

Fischer-Tropsch

The intercalates that are catalytically active for this reaction are similar to those for ammonia formation. Alkali metal intercalates possess some activity, but by far the best catalysts are the alkali metal–treated transition metal halide intercalates. They are selective for the formation of lower alkanes and alkenes, giving selectivities of 90% for an ethane-ethylene mixture. The selectivity remains constant when carbon dioxide is substituted for carbon monoxide, but the yield drops.

In some cases oxygenated compounds are formed. Thus with alkali-promoted palladium chloride intercalate, dimethyl ether was formed.

Charcoal-Supported Oxides, Sulfides, and Halides

Mixed oxide species known as hopcalites, supported on high-area charcoals, are used as absorbers in some gas masks. Hopcalite charcoals have markedly higher performance in this field than ordinary charcoals. Part of this performance arises from the ability of hopcalites to act as stoichiometric oxidizing agents, but over and above this, part of the hopcalite composition appears to act catalytically on some of the toxic components, oxidizing them to less toxic materials. The function of the charcoal remains that of acting as a reservoir for toxic materials, allowing the bulk of the oxygen through for respiration, but the high surface area also allows the hopcalite to be spread, exposing a greater surface to the toxic gaseous components.

Hopcalite charcoals are prepared by wetting high-surface-area granular coconut charcoals with a solution of the metal salts and alkali metal chromate. Sufficient solution is added to fill the pore volume and wet the outside of the granules. The material is then drained and dried at 100–110°C. All hopcalite charcoals are subject to heat treatment, details of which are proprietary. Broadly, the heat treatment consists of heating the dried, impregnated charcoal to 150–250°C in air for a period of time. During the heat treatment, the basic metal chromates decompose to give a mixture of oxides. The main metals present in hopcalites are copper, manganese, and chromium, with smaller additions of silver, iron, and sometimes vanadium, to act as promoters.

Metal sulfides supported on charcoal are primarily used in hydrogenation reactions in which the substrate, product, or an impurity would poison a metal catalyst. The only metal sulfides commercially supported for this purpose on carbon are rhenium and the platinum group metals. Rarely supported on carbon are nickel sulfide and the sulfided nickel, cobalt, and tungsten molybdates where the active components are thought to be nonstoichiometric mixed metal sulfide species. The normal support for sulfide metal molybdates is alumina.

The preparation of metal sulfides on charcoal has been the subject of much patent literature. In general four methods for preparing the precious group metals (PGM) sulfides exist:

1. In situ preparation during the hydrogenation of organic sulfides.
2. In situ preparation during hydrogenation by the deliberate addition of an organic sulfur compound.
3. Sulfiding a previously prepared PGM catalyst with hydrogen sulfide or an organic sulfur compound and a reducing agent.
4. Precipitating the metal sulfide onto charcoal by decomposition of a metal hexathiocyanato-acid.

The first method of preparation is the historical method by which PGM sulfides were found to be catalytically active. This method is only applicable to organic sulfides that will desulfurize on PGM surfaces, and the depth of sulfiding is probably only one or two lattice layers. The second method is a variation on the first and is used where superficially sulfided catalysts are required. It requires skill in application, if the catalyst is not to be poisoned completely, but if used carefully can give excellent results.

Preprepared charcoal catalysts can be sulfided by suspending the catalyst in water, saturating the catalyst with hydrogen and then with hydrogen sulfide. After removing hydrogen sulfide with an inert gas, the catalyst is filtered off and kept for use. An essentially similar process is the use of a reducing agent such as hydrazine or hydroxylamine in place of hydrogen and a sulfur compound such as sulfur dioxide, alkali metal sulfites, organic sulfoxide, and so on in place of hydrogen sulfide. The use of sulfur compounds allows a more accurate adsorption of sulfur to the metal surface.

Finally, sulfided catalysts can be made by adding a metal salt to a carbon-water slurry, allowing time for the salt to absorb onto the charcoal and then gassing the solution with hydrogen sulfide.

Sulfided catalysts are used mainly for the selective hydrogenation of nitro compounds.

Reductive Alkylation

Here an aromatic nitro compound is reduced to the corresponding amine,

$$R–NO_2 + 3H_2 \rightarrow RNH_2 + 2H_2O,$$

and then coupled with a ketone to form a Schiffs base

$$R–NH_2 + R_1R_2CO = R–N = CR_1R_2 + H_2O,$$

which is hydrogenated to a secondary amine useful as an antioxidant,

$$R–N = CR_1R_2 + H_2 \rightarrow RNHCHR_1R_2.$$

If the catalyst used is too active, a large proportion of the relatively expensive ketone can be hydrogenated to the alcohol. The use of sulfided catalysts prevents this.

Reduction of Nitrohaloaromatics to Haloamines

When platinum group metal catalysts are used to hydrogenate nitrohaloaromatics, a considerable amount of dehalogenation can take place, reducing the yield of haloamine. Yields of haloamine can be improved by using sulfided catalysts to such an extent that the product may not require further purification.

Reduction of Unsaturated Nitrocompounds

Platinum sulfide on charcoal can be used to reduce selectively unsaturated nitrocompounds to the corresponding unsaturated amines.

p-Aminophenol Production

The hydrogenation of nitrobenzene in dilute sulfuric acid can lead to a variety of products, among which is the important material p-aminophenol. The first step in the production of this chemical is the hydrogenation of nitrobenzene to phenylhydroxylamine:

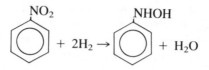

This then rearranges in the acidic medium to p-aminophenol,

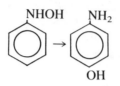

Sulfided catalysts are much more selective than metal catalysts for this reaction.

Production of Hydroxylamine

Sulfided catalysts are used to reduce selectively nitric oxide in sulfuric/phosphoric acids to hydroxylamine,

$$2NO + 3H_2 \rightarrow 2NH_2OH,$$

without the formation of nitrous oxide,

$$2NO + H_2 \nrightarrow N_2O + H_2O.$$

Reduction of Sulfur Compounds

Sulfided catalysts are used to reduce sulfur compounds that contain carbon-carbon unsaturation, nitro groups and so on, without cleaving the carbon-sulfur bonds, to form saturated and amino sulfur compounds.

Charcoal and Carbon Black–Supported Metals

Platinum, palladium, ruthenium, rhodium, rhenium, osmium, and iridium metals both singly and in combination have been supported on charcoals and carbon blacks. By far the largest volume of charcoal catalysts support platinum or palladium, while carbon blacks are used exclusively for platinum fuel cell catalysts. Much smaller volumes of rhodium and ruthenium catalysts are manufactured for small but industrially important reactions. Rhenium on charcoal and iridium on charcoal have very little industrial application, being used mainly in laboratory organic reactions. Osmium on charcoal is an exclusively laboratory catalyst, which has problems of storage; oxygen in the air can oxidize the very small osmium metal crystallites at room temperature to osmium tetroxide, which is lost from the catalyst.

The main industrial uses of charcoal-supported metal catalysts are (1) in the hydrogenation and small-volume organic synthesis of fine chemicals such as pesticides and herbicides, pharmaceuticals, and fragrances and perfumes; (2) the manufacture of high-volume intermediates for the plastic and fiber industries such as polyurethane, polyesters, and nylon; and (3) the dehydrogenation of alicyclic compounds to form aromatic intermediates.

Manufacture of Carbon-Supported Metal Catalysts

The manufacture of supported metal catalysts takes place industrially on a scale varying from grams to metric tons per day. On the largest scale, steam-heated glass-lined pans, steam-heated blenders, centrifuges, rotary filters, and continuous dryers are employed, while on the smallest scale, beakers, Buchner funnels, and vacuum drying ovens are the common apparatus. Recent innovations include the use of rotary vacuum equipment for the manufacture of catalysts by chemical vapor deposition.

The methods of manufacture can be divided into three broad groups:

1.   Wet impregnation (Pt, Pd, Ru, Rh, Ir, Os, Re, and alloys);
2.   Hydrolysis impregnation (Pt, Pd, Rh, Ru, and alloys);
3.   Chemical vapor deposition (Pt, Pd).

The specific details of industrial catalyst manufacture are proprietary secrets. A great deal more is known of the interactions between the metal salt, carbon, and hydrolyzing and reducing agents than is ever published in the journal and patent literature. The methods given here have been published and are part of the general body of information available in the literature dealing with catalyst manufacture.

Wet impregnation is the name given to that form of catalyst manufacture in which the charcoal pore volume is filled with a solution of a metal salt. The solvent is then evaporated from the pore structure, leaving the metal salt as small crystals within the pores. Reduction of the metal salt may then take place thermally in an inert atmosphere, thermally in a hydrogen atmosphere, or by filling the pore structure with a solution of a reducing agent and evaporating the solvent from the charcoal at elevated temperatures (100–150°C), during which process the metal salt is reduced.

Hydrolysis impregnation covers a very wide group of phenomena that take place in aqueous media varying from ion exchange to precipitation. Once bonded to the carbon, the metal ions are reduced to the metal by the addition of an aqueous reducing agent and heating the aqueous catalyst suspension to the boil.

Chemical vapor deposition employs a volatile salt of platinum or palladium, which may be easily decomposed thermally. The volatile salt is vaporized and allowed to come into contact with a tumbling bed of charcoal heated to the decomposition temperature of the volatile metal compound. At the surface of the carbon, decomposition takes place, depositing the metal on the surface of the support.

A list of the salts used in the preparation of metal catalysts by all three methods is given in Table 5.5, and a list of common reducing agents is given in Table 5.6. A more detailed discussion of salts and reducing agents is given in the following sections.

Table 5.5   Salts Used in the Commercial Manufacture of Catalysts

	Wet Impregnation—Impregnant	Hydrolysis Deposition—Impregnant	Chemical Vapor Deposition
Platinum	H_2PtCl_6, platinum ammines	H_2PtCl_6, K_2PtCl_4, platinum ammines	Pt acetylacetonate
Palladium	$PdCl_2$, Pd ammines, alkali metal chloropalladites, $Pd(NO_3)_2$, Pd ammines	$PdCl_2$, alkali metal chloropalladites, Pd ammines	Pdacetylacetonate
Ruthenium	$RuCl_3$, alkali metal chlororuthenates, Ru nitroso nitrate, Ru ammines	$RuCl_3$, alkali metal chlororuthenates, Ru ammines	
Rhodium	$RhCl_3$, alkali metal chlororhodites, Rh ammines	$RhCl_3$, alkali metal chlororhodites, Rh ammines	
Iridium	$IrCl_4$, alkali metal chloroiridates, Ir ammines	$IrCl_4$, alkali metal chloroiridates, Ir ammines	
Osmium	Potassium osmate, Alkali metal chlorosmates	Potassium osmate, Alkali metal chlorosmates	
Rhenium	Ammonium perrhenate		

Metal loadings for charcoal and carbon black–supported catalysts used industrially vary from 0.01 to 15% metal. The upper metal loadings can be justified economically only for processes with a large increase in added value during processing and a low catalyst loss. Normally PGM catalysts are manufactured in loadings of between 1% and 5% for liquid-phase hydrogenations.

Impregnation.   The impregnation step is probably the most important step in catalyst manufacture. It is the primary determinant for both metal location and crystallite size and as such demands attention from industrial catalyst chemists. If a charcoal or carbon black surface were merely a set of random orientated graphite crystallites, free of oxygenated groupings, then the depth within the pore system to which metal reached would be determined by the viscosity and surface tension of the salt solution used for impregnation. Crystallite size would be determined by salt stability and solubility and solvent boiling point, viscosity, and surface tension. However, no carbon surface is free of oxygenated groups, and they play a major role during impregnation.

First let us look at a simple wet impregnation. The choice of carbon will be determined primarily by its particle size and pore structure, for it is these parameters that broadly determine the behavior of the catalyst in the process. However, not all charcoals with a suitable particle size and pore structure will possess the same surface chemistry. The activation process will leave the charcoals with different balances of reducing and oxidizing oxygen groups.

Table 5.6   Reducing Agents Commonly Used in the Preparation of Carbon-Based Catalysts

Metal	Wet Impregnation	Hydrolysis Impregnation
Palladium	Hydrogen (Formaldehyde) (Hydrazine)	Hydrogen Formaldehyde Hydrazine
Platinum	Hydrogen (Formaldehyde) (Hydrazine)	Sodium formate Sodium hypophosphite Sodium borohydride
Rhodium	Hydrogen (Formaldehyde) (Hydrazine)	Glucose (Hydroxylamine) (Acetaldehyde)
Ruthenium	Hydrogen (Hydrazine)	Hydrogen Hydrazine
Iridium	Hydrogen	Hydrogen
Osmium	Hydrogen	Hydrogen Formaldehyde
Rhenium	Hydrogen	Hydrogen

Note: The list is not exhaustive.

Some charcoals have so many reducing groups on their surface that by using an easily reduced PGM salt, it is possible to "plate" out the metal onto the carbon surface so that it has a shiny metallic appearance. With yet other carbon surfaces, the metal salt can be oxidized to a higher oxidation state, modifying its solubility and stability and altering the way in which it deposits on the carbon. Within this broad spectrum of surface chemistry, order can be wrought by chemically pretreating the surface to modify this balance, providing it is economically viable to do so. Sometimes a more economical way is to change the metal salt, but even here economic penalties may ensue at the reduction stage. Choice of solvent will also affect the oxidation-reduction properties for the charcoal-salt combination. Once the metal salt solution has filled the pore structure, it will react with the surface groupings, depositing part of the metal by ion exchange, part by reduction, giving nuclei on which further deposition can take place during the drying stage.

Although a simple technique, drying can have a profound effect on catalyst properties. As the solvent evaporates, the liquid meniscus retreats from the pore system, and the concentration of metal salt in solution increases. As the concentration rises, the salt precipitates out of solution at the metal nuclei previously formed. This process can be helped by choosing a metal salt that hydrolyzes in solution, giving rise to a species with a much lower solubility. If the researcher chooses the salt stability properties correctly and sets the evaporation-hydrolysis parameters of time and temperature, the metal salt may be made to deposit on the carbon surface to give any combination of deposition from many small crystals to fewer larger clusters of crystals. The degree of latitude available to catalyst chemists in the deposition stage is also determined by the metal loading. High loadings (10% or greater) are more difficult to control than low loadings (1–3%), but some ingenious methods of wet impregnation have been devised, such as multiple impregnations, which to a large extent overcome the inherent problems of depositing large concentrations of metal within a charcoal pore system.

As with "wet impregnation" the term *hydrolysis impregnation* covers a number of phenomena that can be acting individually or in concert during the impregnation stage. However, all impregnations covered by this term take place with the carbon slurried in a large excess of water (ten to fifty times charcoal weight of water). The simplest case of hydrolysis impregnation is that in which a charcoal rich in reducing groups is chosen as support. It is slurried with water, and a solution of an easily reduced metal salt is slowly added. Control of the rate of addition and temperature will enable the crystallite size to be controlled.

A somewhat more complex impregnation is that of ion exchange deposition. Some oxygenated groups on carbon surfaces will exchange a hydrogen ion for a metal ion. Because the surface concentration of such species is low, only low concentrations of catalytic metal may be built up in this way. Modification of the exchange properties may be obtained by preexchanging the hydrogen ions for alkali metal or alkaline earth metals. Where the catalytic metal salt is an ammine, preexchange with ammonium ions can be advantageous.

Very early in the history of charcoal-supported catalysts, Willstater, Frampton, and others devised a range of preparations in which the catalytic metal salt was hydrolyzed onto the support. One method consisted of slurrying the chosen charcoal with a large excess of water, adding an alkali, and then adding the catalytic metal salt. The slurry was then raised to the boil in order to hydrolyze the salt onto the carbon surface. Nearly all published preparations of catalysts of the platinum group metals by the hydrolysis technique consist of variations of the original Willstater method. Choice of alkali is important. Sodium salts appear to be less effective than potassium, and carbonates can be used to give hydrolysis at lower pH than with hydroxides. Rate of temperature rise and maximum hydrolysis temperature also affect the way the catalytic metal oxide (hydroxide) is deposited on the carbon. Low rates of temperature rise, giving larger metal areas than rapid rates. High maximum hydrolysis temperatures usually ensure complete hydrolysis of the catalytic metal to the oxide rather than an intermediate insoluble hydrolysis product that is difficult to reduce.

In another variation, the catalytic metal salt is added to the charcoal slurry before the addition of alkali. This allows the formation of nuclei by ion exchange and reduction that can be grown to the desired crystallite size (metal area) by the careful use of alkali and temperature. Sometimes in this variation, hydrolysis and reduction are carried out simultaneously, but this requires careful attention to a number of parameters—temperature, pH, and reductant concentration—error on any one of which can give less than the best catalyst.

A general but by no means unvarying rule for carbon-supported catalyst preparation is to use the wet impregnation methods with granular catalysts and the hydrolysis technique with powders. Above all, to ensure success with the impregnation stage of catalyst manufacture, "know thy carbon."

Reduction.   Once the carbon has been impregnated with the catalytic metal salt, it may be reduced to the metal in the dry with gaseous hydrogen or wet with dissolved hydrogen or a liquid-reducing agent such as formaldehyde or hydrazine. Which way is chosen will depend in part on whether the carbon has been impregnated by the wet impregnation method or hydrolysis. With the wet impregnation method, it is best not to risk relocating the metal by refilling the pores with liquid, so the dry reduction technique is usually used. With hydrolysis-impregnated catalysts, drying of the catalyst, so that the dry reduction technique may be used, causes the hydrated oxide to lose water and become more intractable to reduction; here the wet reduction technique is normally applied.

The gaseous hydrogen reduction of carbon-based PGM catalysts is a common practice, but to maintain high metal dispersion is not as easy as some authorities claim. Metal migration on charcoal can occur easily if the main factors affecting reduction are not controlled. Hydrogen partial pressure, temperature, and rate of heating are important, and it is in deciding the magnitude of each of these parameters that the new technique of temperature programmed reduction (TPR) has become a key tool.

By examining the effect of each of the above factors on a small sample of catalyst, a reduction routine can be decided that will give accurately reproducible reduction. (The technique can also be used with advantage to check reproducibility of the impregnation stage of catalyst preparation, by holding TPR conditions constant, and by examining samples of catalyst from the preparation for changes in temperature of reduction and size of reduction peak.)

With PGM catalysts, the degree of sintering experienced is a function of metal loading, as well as temperature profile and hydrogen concentration. High metal loadings always lose a disproportionate amount of metal area (dispersion) unless reduction is carefully investigated on a small scale by TPR before committing the bulk of the preparation to reduction. High hydrogen concentrations narrow the width of the windows within which nonsintering reduction can be achieved. The risk of local hot spot temperatures as the metal oxide reduces is a constant danger and is best controlled by a low hydrogen partial pressure. One to 10% hydrogen in nitrogen is usually sufficient to ensure controlled reduction.

Reduction within the liquid phase is not as fraught with sintering problems as gas-phase reduction, but disastrous losses of metal area can occur due to the formation of polymerized products that cover the metal surface. The most common reducing agents are formaldehyde and hydrazine, but hydrogen, hydroxylamine, sodium hypophosphite, sodium formate, glucose, acetaldehyde, and others have been recommended in the literature. Of these, all but sodium hypophosphite operate best under alkaline conditions, with the pH held at between 8 and 12. Higher pH than 12 with aldehydes causes the formation of tarry reduction products, and this situation pertains at pH 9 with glucose and other reducing monosaccharides. Reductions with alkaline reducing agents are best conducted at the boil to ensure the minimum formation of tars.

Sodium hypophosphite is a powerful reducing agent that is used at or close to ambient temperature in neutral or slightly acidic conditions. Similar to sodium hypophosphite is sodium borohydride, which is also used at ambient temperature but with a wider range of pH conditions. Reductions of PGMs with sodium borohydride always leave a residue of boron in the reduced metal, which is thought to point to the presence of PGM borides.

Control of Crystallite Size and Metal Distribution. Although the oxygenated surface groupings control nucleation of catalytic centers, the growth of these centers is a function of the stability of the metal salt at the pH conditions obtaining in aqueous medium. Although a large number of nuclei may be present, by the judicious control of the rate at which hydrolysis products are formed, the preferential growth of some nuclei rather than others can be induced. Naturally, when the hydrolysis products are formed in the bulk solution, diffusion to the carbon surface will favor the growth of particles located on the surface of the carbon particle. These conditions will give rise to a mantle-impregnated catalyst. The size of the deposited centers will be a function of the number of nuclei present on the outer surface and the amount of material being loaded on the surface. By adjusting the rate of hydrolysis, nuclei deeper in the pore structure can be made to grow, until in the final stage of rapid hydrolysis, virtually all nuclei can be made to grow at about an equal rate.

The resulting catalyst contains crystallites of approximately equal size, spread throughout the pore structure. Figures 5.5, 5.6, and 5.7 are electron micrographs of palladium catalysts showing mantle impregnation, impregnation throughout the pore structure, and an intermediate situation of partial internal growth. The carbon used is a commercially available powdered carbon (average particle size 10–15 microns).

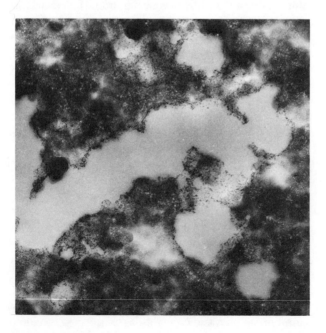

Figure 5.5 Mantle preparation.

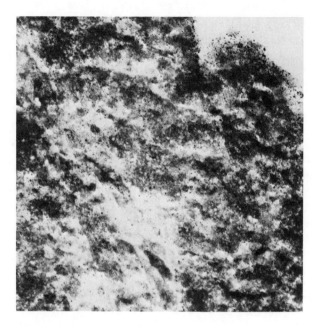

Figure 5.6   Partial mantle impregnation.

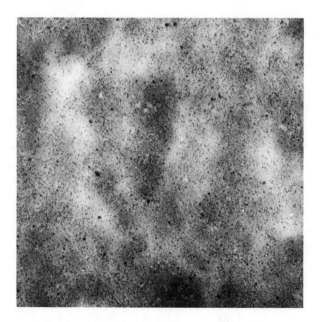

Figure 5.7   Total impregnation.

Obviously it is easier to control the deposition of metal and hence its location when the metal loading is low (0.1–0.5%), but such now is the industrial understanding of the impregnation process that the control of metal location can be accomplished with metal loadings of 5% metal and with some PGMs up to 10%. Details of the procedures used are proprietary secrets.

Reactions

Carbon-supported metallic catalysts are used almost exclusively for reactions in which hydrogen is transferred to or from a substrate molecule. The reaction can take place in the gas phase where two phases are present (gas-solid) or in the liquid phase when there are two or three phases present (liquid-solid or gas-liquid-solid). The majority of the reactions for which carbon-supported catalysts are employed are liquid-phase reactions with three phases.

Hydrogenation

$$R - C \equiv CH + H_2 \rightarrow R - CH = CH_2.$$

$$R - CH = CH_2 + H_2 \rightarrow RCH_2 - CH_3.$$

$$CH_3CH = CHCHO + 2H_2 \rightarrow CH_3CH_2CH_2CH_2OH.$$

$$RCN + H_2 \rightarrow RCNH_2.$$

This is the simple addition of hydrogen to a compound, a reaction for which carbon-supported catalysts are ideal. All of the reactions take place in the liquid phase with or without solvent.

The reduction of acetylenic compounds to the olefinic compound is usually accomplished over palladium. By carefully controlling conditions, almost complete reduction of the acetylenic to the olefinic compound can be achieved before saturation of the latter occurs. By the continuation of the reaction beyond formation of the olefinic compound, complete saturation may be obtained. Rhodium is excellent in acetylenic carbinol to olefinic carbinols hydrogenations.

For the hydrogenation of aliphatic aldehydes and ketones, ruthenium is undoubtedly best, particularly when water is present to act as a cocatalyst. With aromatic aldehydes and ketones, however, palladium is the metal of choice. Careful control of conditions is required to prevent hydrogenolysis to the aromatic hydrocarbon.

A more difficult type of reaction is the hydrogenation of unsaturated aldehydes to unsaturated alcohols, such as crotonaldehyde to crotyl alcohol, cinnameldehyde to cinnamyl alcohol, and citronellal to citronellol. Many metals have been claimed as catalysts for this reaction, but the best are rhenium and osmium, although both platinum and ruthenium may be used if they are modified with, for example, alkali.

Reduction of the aromatic nucleus can be accomplished with a variety of metals but is critically dependent on the other functions present on the ring and the conditions of reaction. In general, platinum, palladium, rhodium, or ruthenium may be used. For example, the reduction of anilines to cyclohexylamines is best attempted over ruthenium or rhodium. However, if dicyclohexylamines are required, then reduction is best achieved with platinum or palladium. With the hydrogenation of phenols to cyclohexanols, ruthenium and rhodium are the metals of choice, while for the conversion of phenols to cyclohexanones, palladium is best, although it is only infrequently supported on carbon.

The hydrogenation of nitriles is a complex business—primary, secondary, and tertiary amines resulting. Acidic conditions and the use of palladium, platinum, or rhodium usually give high yields of the primary amine, providing the solvent reacts with the amine to prevent further reaction. Secondary and tertiary amines are formed in nonreactive solvents. Secondary aliphatic amines are formed over rhodium and secondary aromatic amines over palladium in the presence of traces of an aliphatic secondary amine. Aliphatic tertiary amines can be formed over palladium and platinum catalysts.

Hydrogenolysis.   The following are examples of hydrogenolysis of the substituent group on a benzenoil nucleus and a carboxyl group on an alkyl chain:

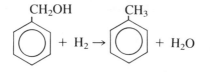

$$RCOOH + 2H_2 \rightarrow RCH_2OH + H_2O$$

The hydrogenolysis of carboxylic acids to alcohols is a difficult reaction that normally requires high pressures (200–300 atm) and high temperature (>200°C). The use of rhenium or ruthenium can lower the pressure of operation to 70 to 160 atm, but recently it has been found that even lower pressures may be used with alloy catalysts of rhenium and ruthenium.

The hydrogenolysis of aromatic nitro functions can take place in several steps. If palladium is the catalyst, then complete hydrogenolysis to the aniline occurs, but if platinum is used in dimethyl-sulfoxide containing solvents, then the aromatic hydroxylamine can be formed. The hydrogenation of nitrobenzene in aqueous dilute sulfuric acid over a platinum catalyst can give high yields of p-aminophenol by the acid-catalyzed rearrangement of the intermediate phenylhydroxylamine.

The reduction of nitro haloaromatics to the corresponding halomine is best accomplished over platinum.

The hydrogenolysis of aromatic alcohols to aromatic hydrocarbons can be easily achieved over palladium catalysts.

Dehalogenation.   The following is an example of a selective dehalogenation of a dihalide to a monohalide and the removal of the halogen as hydrogen chloride:

$$CL$$
$$CHCOOH + H_2 \rightarrow CHClCOOH + HCl$$
$$Cl$$

The removal of a halogen from an organic halo compound is very much a function of the halogen present. Fluorine is hardest to remove and iodine easiest. The best catalytic metal for their removal is palladium, particularly in the vapor phase.

Dehydrogenation.   Alicyclic hydrocarbons can be dehydrogenated to fully or partially aromatic hydrocarbons over palladium catalysts at temperatures of 280°C and above. If the hydrocarbon is functionalized with other groups, they may be hydrogenated. Thus orthocyclohexylcylohexanone is dehydrogenated to orthophenylphenol over palladium catalysts.

Coupling Reactions.   The following represent coupling reactions that can occur to partially hydrogenated substituent groups and can be either a desired, selective reaction or a yield loss in nitrobenzene.

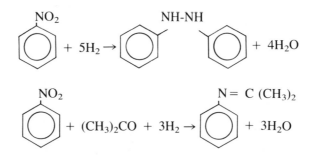

The best catalyst for coupling reactions of this type is platinum. Reaction conditions are important, and the charcoal should be acidic in nature. Frequently an acid charcoal is added as a cocatalyst to promote the coupling reaction. When Schiffs bases are formed as a result of a coupling reaction, they are always further hydrogenated to the secondary amine.

Industrially Important Reactions
over Charcoal-Supported Catalysts

Charcoal-based catalysts, especially those of the platinum group metals, are used industrially in many hundreds of reactions. Most of these reactions consume only small amounts of catalyst, although the added value that they confer on the product is frequently great. The added value is greatest in some of the pharmaceuticals, and it diminishes through perfume and fragrances, pesticides, and antioxidants, to plastics and fibers. The quantity of catalyst consumed is in the reverse direction. Six of the largest consumers of charcoal-supported platinum group metals are reviewed.

Crude Terephthalic Acid Purification.   During the oxidation of p-xylene to terephthalic acid, a partial oxidation product is formed, 4-carboxybenzaldehyde. If this impurity remains in the product, it causes difficulties during the polymerization stage, so its removal is imperative. To remove the impurity, terephthalic acid is brought into solution in water at a temperature of 285°C or more. Below this temperature, the solubility of the acid is too low to be of practical use. The acid solution is then run through a fixed bed of 0.5% Pd on charcoal granules countercurrent to a flow of hydrogen at about 1000 psig. The impurity product is hydrogenated to toluic acid,

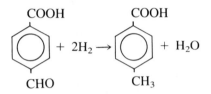

which stays in the solution from which terephthalic acid has been recrystallized. A single charge of catalyst lasts about a year. Only charcoal may be used as a catalyst support; other materials dissolve under the rigorous reaction conditions.

Dinitrotoluene Hydrogenation.   Dinitrotoluene is hydrogenated to toluenediamine, a polyurethane intermediate, over a 1–3% Pd on charcoal powder catalyst. The reaction is conducted in the liquid phase, with either the dinitrotoluene dissolved in a solvent, methanol, ethanol, isopropanol-water, or a molten state. Precise conditions vary with solvent but broadly are 70–120°C and 3–10 atm H_2 pressure. The reaction is usually a batch process employing dead-end reactors. However, Olin Mattheson has patented a continuous-flow reactor with a powdered catalyst.

The reduction of dinitrotoluene is not as facile as nitrobenzene, and to obtain complete conversion, the reaction must be run for a period of time after apparent completion to ensure total conversion. Another problem with the reaction is the leaching of palladium from the catalyst by the substrate and reduction products. This, however, can be overcome by catalyst design and process operating conditions.

Monochloroacetic Acid Cleanup.   Production of monochloroacetic acid by the chlorination of acetic acid also gives rise to some dichloroacetic acid. The simplest way of removing the dichloroacid from the monochloro compound is to dehalogenate it partially over a 0.5–1.0% Pd on charcoal granule catalyst. The reaction is conducted in the vapor phase in the presence of hydrogen.

p-Aminophenol.   p-Aminophenol is produced by the hydrogenation of p nitrophenol in dilute sulfuric acid at temperatures close to the boiling point using a 1% platinum on charcoal catalyst. To prevent complete hydrogenation to aniline, the partial pressure of hydrogen is kept low—usually 0.1–0.5 atm. The yield is also improved by the addition of a surface-active agent such as a tetraalkylammonium chloride. The purpose of the surface-active agent is twofold; it serves to disperse the nitrophenol better in the aqueous phase and to modify (selectively poison) the platinum surface. Higher rates of conversion and selectivity are also obtained if the nitrophenol is added slowly to the boiling reaction mixture. Yields of 80–85% p-aminophenol are common, the remainder of the product being aniline.

Selective Hydrogenation of Methylbutynol to Methylbutenol.   One route to isoprene (2 methyl-1, 3-butadiene) involves condensing acetone with acetylene to form 2-methyl-3-butyne-2-ol. This is then hydrogenated to 2-methyl-3-butene-2-ol and subsequently dehydrated to isoprene. The hydrogenation step employs a 3% palladium on charcoal catalyst poisoned with copper ions.

FUTURE DEVELOPMENTS

The chemical industry today stands at a crossroad. Its traditional source of hydrocarbons, petroleum, has a doubtful future. Worries about the supply and the politics of petroleum production prevalent in the 1970s have given way to problems associated with the possible flooding of chemical commodity markets in Europe, Japan, and the United States with cheap petrochemicals from the oil- and gas-rich countries, such as Saudi Arabia, Mexico, Canada, and those in Southeast Asia. The necessity for the "old" petrochemical producers to stay competitive has never been so strong. To stay competitive, they have revamped plant to make it more energy and feed stock efficient, and this process will continue. However, sooner or later, new feedstocks will have to be sought for processing to chemicals.

 This trend has started. Synthetic fatty alcohols at one time dominated certain parts of the detergent industry; natural fatty alcohols, made by the hydrogenation of fatty carboxylic acids, were on the decline. Recently this decline has been halted and reversed, brought about by the rise in ethylene prices since the mid-1970s. Coal is now being converted into methanol, acetic acid, and acetic anhydride in the United States by synthesis gas. In all likelihood, the remainder of this century will see a growth in this process, requiring new catalyst and new supports. The new biomass and coal feedstocks are composed of macromolecules, and although it might suffice at present to convert them to the simplest of molecules, carbon monoxide, so that we may rebuild them into usable products, we will in the future process these macromolecules directly into wanted products. Coal is a giant aromatic molecule; what could be more logical than to convert it directly into benzene, toluene, and xylene (BTX) rather than indirectly into synthesis gas, methanol, and so forth, and then BTX? So it is with many of these new feedstock molecules.

 To process the new macromolecules will require supports with much larger, less tortuous pores than present supports. In the area of carbon supports, one approach has been that of Walker, who has "glued" carbon black particles together to give a mesoporous carbon, but some tortuosity in the pores still remains. A different patch to a mesoporous low-tortuosity carbon has been taken by Jacques who has agglomerated spherical PVDC latexes into regularly stacked lattices, which on carbonization give

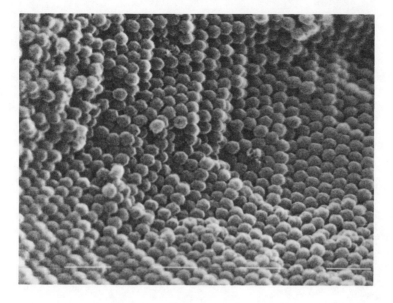

Figure 5.8   A highly mesoporous carbon produced by carbonization of agglomerized spherical PVDC latexes.

rise to a highly mesoporous carbon (Figure 5.8). Comparison of the activity of a palladium catalyst supported on the Jacques carbon with that for a normal liquid phase absorption charcoal, PCB, of equal particle size, in the hydrogenation of dinitrotoluene shows that the mesoporous catalyst is about an order of magnitude more active, although its metal area was only 80% that of PCB.

CHAPTER 6

Activated Metal Supports

Alfonso L. Baldi

It is the purpose of this chapter to fill a major void in the catalyst literature relating to self-supported metal catalysts and high-surface-area metal supports. Although the activated metal can be used an an excellent support for cocatalysts, for many applications it can be effectively used as the unmodified catalyst. Therefore, one should keep in mind that the disclosed technology can have this twofold application. Other than noble metal gauzes such as platinum and its alloys used as a wire screen catalyst in the synthesis of hydrogen cyanide and nitric acid, few low-surface-area metal catalysts are in commercial use. In the past, these catalysts, in the form of screens, plates, sheets, foils, and single crystals, were of significance only in laboratory catalysis studies. But the technology of high-temperature metal transport, diffusion, and lattice depletion has led to an advancement in the art of the Raney nickel-type approach to synthesize catalysts. Very active metal and alloy catalysts and supports in the form of screens, tubes, sheets, foils, honeycombs, sponges, and, in fact, any other configuration can now be made employing this novel technology. The flexibility in design, together with the excellent thermal conductivity, permits an active metal support with both good heat transfer and low-pressure-drop characteristics. A good thermal-conducting metal support would be of major importance for use in exothermic and endothermic catalytic reactions to maintain the optimum temperature for efficient direction of the reaction to the desired product. Activated metal tubes, for example, can be heated in the case of the endothermic reactions or cooled in the case of exothermic reactions to increase efficiency and product yield.

In addition to the catalytic application of activated metal, another major application lies in the field of self-igniting pyrotechnics. In the case of catalytic applications, the processing parameters are tailored to avoid this property, but when pyrophoricity is especially sought, the activation of the metal in question can be controlled to attain the maximum degree of pyrophoricity from the metal substrate.

RANEY METAL

In 1925 Murray Raney was granted a U.S. patent [1] to form an intermetallic compound disclosing a finely divided (foraminous) nickel catalyst. It was prepared by reacting nickel and aluminum in the molten state to form a 50% by weight Ni and 50% by weight Al alloy. The solid material was ground into small particles and reacted in sodium hydroxide to dissolve the aluminum and leave behind catalytic nickel. Other related patents [2] were granted to Raney in 1927 and 1933. A number of other metals have been prepared in small-particle skeletal form, including cobalt, iron, copper, silver, and rhenium. These catalysts can be used as fixed-bed catalysts or as fine particles distributed in a slurry operation. The very nature of these catalysts, however, precludes their use as convenient thermal conducting catalysts or ones with low-pressure-drop characteristics.

BALDI-DAMIANO (BD) TECHNOLOGY

The discovery of the activated catalytic properties of the alloys the BD technology was deriving was accidental. In July 1976, laboratory stripping experiments were being conducted in an attempt to remove a particular diffusion coating from a nickel-base super alloy gas turbine airfoil component. While examining one of the airfoils after the stripping operation, one of the researchers received a severe finger burn due to an apparent surface reaction. The stripping experiment was repeated but this time the specimen was removed from the stripping solution [3], rinsed in water, and placed on a paper towel to dry. Within seconds after the specimen appeared to be dry, it became very hot and ignited the paper towel. It was apparent then that a very active surface had been produced to cause this exothermic reaction resulting from the metal surface's reacting with oxygen in the air. This was the advent of the BD process [4] named after the inventors A. L. Baldi and V. V. Damiano. After many experiments, the process emerged as a unique technique to prepare self-supporting metal catalysts and metal supports in any configuration into which the metal can be fabricated. In general the process entails the steps of high-temperature metal transport, high-temperature metal diffusion, and selective metal removal to produce a foraminous but stable structure with inherent high surface area and catalytic sites. Impregnation with cocatalysts results in further improvement in the catalytic activity. The following group reactions depict in more detail the mechanism of the BD technology:

- Formation of the diffusion metal gas $(M_D X_2)$,
- Deposition of the diffusion metal on base metal (M_B) substrate,
- Diffusion to form a specific metal compound,
- Depletion of M_D to form M_B catalyst.

Formation of Diffusion Metal Gas $(M_D X_2)$

$$M_D(s) + X_2(g) \rightarrow M_D X_2(g); \tag{6.1}$$

$$M_D(s) + 2HX(g) \rightarrow M_D X_2(g) + H_2(g); \tag{6.2}$$

$$M_D(s) + 2NH_4X(s) \rightarrow M_D X_2(g) + 4H_2(g) + N_2(g). \tag{6.3}$$

X represents one of the halogens—namely, fluorine, chlorine, bromine, or iodine. In the form of elemental halogen, halogen acid, or halide salt, they react with the diffusion metal at elevated temperatures to form a vapor of the metal halide.

Deposition of Diffusion Metal on Base Metal Substrate

$$M_DX_2 \rightarrow M_D(s) + X_2(g); \qquad (6.4)$$

$$M_DX_2(g) + H_2(g) \rightarrow M_D(s) + 2HX(g); \qquad (6.5)$$

$$M_DX_2(g) + M_B(s) \rightarrow M_D(s) + M_BX_2(g); \qquad (6.6)$$

$$3M_DX_2 (g) \rightarrow M_D(s) + 2M_DX_3(g). \qquad (6.7)$$

Depending on the thermodynamics, one or more of these reactions can take place at elevated temperatures. Reaction 6.4 is a decomposition reaction. Reaction 6.5 is a reduction reaction. Reaction 6.6 is an interchange reaction and causes loss of some of the base metal surface. Reaction 6.7 is a rearrangement reaction.

Diffusion to Form Intermetallic or Metalloid Compound on Base Metal Surface

Upon deposition of the diffusion metal M_D, both inward diffusion of M_D and outward diffusion of M_B occur to form the new compound $(M_D)_X (M_B)_Y$. The exact proportion of the elements will depend on the feasibility of formation of the particular compound as depicted by the established equilibrium phase diagrams [5] and thermodynamics of phase formation. Diffusion temperature, gaseous environment diffusion metal potential, and diffusion time must all be considered to prepare the specific compound. Constitution diagrams for many multi-element alloys are nonexistent. Only by conducting diffusion coating experiments followed by surface analysis, including energy and dispersive X-ray analysis and X-ray diffraction studies, can one determine the phase formation. A more complete discussion of diffusion coatings, including application techniques, chemistry, structures, and properties, can be found in a paper presented at the Inter-American Conference on Material Technology [6].

Depletion of the $(M_D)_X (M_B)_Y$ Compound to Form the M_B Catalyst

$$(M_D)_X(M_B)_Y + XR^*_M \rightarrow YM_B + XM_DR_M.$$

Selective removal of the diffusion metal M_D is now accomplished by subjecting the compound to a liquid or vapor selectively to dissolve or leach out the diffusion metal and thereby leave behind a depleted metal lattice M_B with high surface area and active sites.

BASE METAL SELECTION AND ITS TREATMENT

The composition of the support, whether it is an elemental metal or a bimetallic or multimetal alloy, should be one that has shown some catalytic behavior as a dispersed metal or oxide on a nonmetallic support such as silica, titania, zirconia, clays, zeolites, carbon, and others as discussed in Anderson's book, *Structure of Metallic Catalysts*, or as a bulk metal catalyst in laboratory tests [7]. Some typical reactions catalyzed by metals are shown in Table 6.1.

Since over 75% of the elements in the periodic table are metals and since hundreds of alloys can be made by their combination, the list in Table 6.1 is infinitesimal compared to those for exploration. Furthermore the catalytic action of alloys has been investigated to a relatively small extent. Once a particular base metal is selected for BD treatment, we must consider the appropriate diffusion metal to form an intermetallic compound through the reaction mechanisms. The diffusion metal must meet some basic requirements; it must be diffusable to form a predicted intermetallic compound with the base metal and be extractable by chemical leaching or gaseous depletion techniques. Preliminary studies of equilibrium phase diagrams, thermodynamics of phase formation, and preferential reactions of the diffusion metal are prerequisite to the formation of the active metal support.

Let us now consider a typical approach in forming a BD metal support for the methanation reaction. Finely divided nickel on an alumina support as described in A.B. Stiles, *Catalyst Manufacture*, is a conventional methanation catalyst [8]. This catalyst suffers from its poor inherent thermal conductivity and high pressure drop. A self-supporting metal catalyst would overcome these disadvantages. The sequence of steps in devising self-supporting nickel catalyst for methane synthesis follows.

Table 6.1   Catalyst Composition and Application

Metal Catalyst	Reaction
Nickel	Methanation
Iron	Ammonia synthesis
Platinum-rhodium	Nitric acid synthesis (HCN synthesis)
Silver	Ethylene oxide formation
Brass	Methyl alcohol synthesis
Stainless steel	NO_x reduction
Manganese	Hydrocarbon oxidation
Osmium	Hydrogenolysis of C-C bonds
Tungsten	Deuterium-alkane exchange
Platinum	Propane and CO oxidation
Palladium	Hydrogenolysis of C-O bonds
Ruthenium	Hydrogenation of alkenes
Iron-cobalt-ruthenium	Hydrogenation of CO (Fischer-Tropsch)

Step 1. Examination of Ni-Al Equilibrium Phase Diagram and Thermodynamics of Phase Formation. The binary Ni-Al equilibrium phase diagram and enthalpy of each phase is shown in Figure 6.1 [9]. The intermetallic phases that can form include the following:

Ni_3Al phase: Face-centered cubic lattice;

NiAl phase: Body-centered cubic lattice;

Ni_2Al_3 phase: Hexagonal lattice;

$NiAl_3$ phase: Orthorhombic lattice.

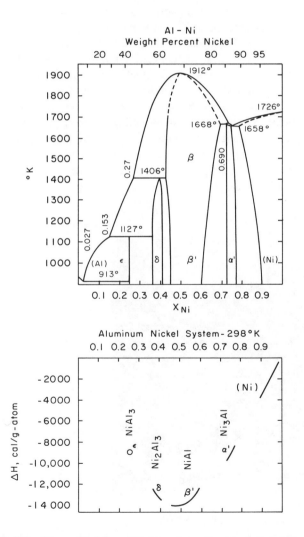

Figure 6.1   Binary Ni-Al equilibrium phase diagram and enthalpy of each phase.

The integral heats of formation for the solid alloys at 298°K are quite negative and are indicative of the feasibility of their formation. Oelson Middel [10] as early as 1937 determined that Ni-Al alloys of the approximate atomic proportion 1:1 are formed with such violent reaction after mixing that some silica from the calorimeter lining was reduced.

Step 2. Selection of Optimum Al-Ni Intermetallic Compounds. Considerations as to selective aluminum removal and resulting structure stability are the most important requirements in determining which intermetallic compound should be formed. Experience has shown that the formations at $NiAl_3$ and Ni_2Al_3 phases are the most desirable compounds for the aluminum dissolution step.

Step 3. Aluminum Diffusion into the Nickel Substrate. Aluminum is best diffused into the nickel-base metal by gaseous or pack cementation processes. Aluminum activity in the source material, as well as temperature and time of diffusion, must be controlled to form the selected and intermetallic compounds.

Step 4. Selective Removal of Aluminum from Nickel-Aluminum Intermetallic Compounds. Controlled concentrations of aqueous alkali solutions such as sodium or potassium hydroxide have been found effective in selectively removing aluminum from the intermetallics. The chemistry of the sodium or potassium aluminate hydrolysis is such that some hydrolysis occurs, leaving behind an Al_2O_3 that stabilizes the finely divided metal (Ni, for example). Subsequent washing and proprietary posttreatments thus provide a stable and promoted metal-aluminum oxide intimate mixture that will act as a good catalyst for $CO + 2H_2 \rightarrow CH_4$ reaction. The catalytic activity can, however, be enhanced by impregnating the porous metal support with cocatalyst salts, such as those of cerium, ruthenium, and chromium.

Figure 6.2 17 Cr-Fe stainless steel: BD-activated 5000X.

SURFACE MORPHOLOGY

Examination of the active metal surfaces with the scanning electron microscope (SEM) has revealed a microfissured surface with pore sizes ranging from smaller than 0.1 micron to several microns. The SEM photomicrographs in Figures 6.2 through 6.10 show the surface morphology of BD-activated and unactivated 17 Cr-Fe stainless steel,

Figure 6.3   17 Cr-Fe stainless steel: Untreated 5000X.

Figure 6.4   80 Cu-20 Zn brass: BD-activated 2000X.

Figure 6.5 80 Cu-20 Zn brass: Untreated 2000X.

80 Cu-20 Zn brass, nickel wire screen cloth, and platinum gauze. Very small pores can be observed under 10,000X magnification of the activated platinum gauze. Pore geometry and size will depend on many factors, including base metal composition, composition and phase of the diffusion coating, and leaching and posttreatment conditions. An extensive study has been made by Freel, Pieters, and Anderson [11] on

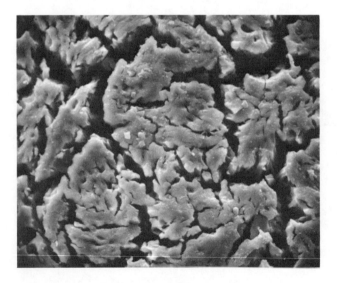

Figure 6.6 Nickel: BD-activated 2000X.

Figure 6.7   Nickel: Untreated 2000X.

pore structure of Raney nickel. They found, for example, that significant differences
in pore structure were observed between samples leached with sodium hydroxide at
50°C and those subjected to the same solution at boiling. Preparations at 50°C had a
surface area of 110 $\pm$ 10 m^2/g and a pore volume of 0.07 $\pm$ 0.02 cc/g compared with
80 $\pm$ 10 m^2/g and 0.12 $\pm$ 0.02 cc/g for extractions at 107°C. Examination of the various

Figure 6.8   Platinum: BD-treated 5000X.

Figure 6.9   Platinum: Untreated 5000X.

activated metal surfaces in the micrographs shows a collection of crystallites in the form of platelets for the stainless steel, rod-like configuration for brass, and a sponge texture for nickel and platinum. The most important requirement in preparing the active metal surface is that the microfissured surface be stable and firmly anchored to the base metal substrate since this will dictate their performance as a good, stable metal

Figure 6.10   Platinum: BD-treated 10000.

support. The processing parameters necessary to ascertain this quality can be determined only after conducting a series of studies of all the processing steps in preparing the surface. Voorhoeve and Trimble [12] of Bell Laboratories have determined a surface area of 6.0 m^2/g on BD 90 Pt-10 Rh for ammonium cyanate synthesis by reduction of NO with CO and H_2. Wiley [13] at the University of Massachusetts has determined a surface area of 30 m^2/g for BD-430 stainless steel used for NO_x reduction with ammonia.

APPLICATIONS

This new technology provides a means to synthesize a metal support and in some cases a unique self-supporting metal catalyst, in any size, shape, or form. It should find application in the troublesome exothermic and endothermic reactions and in processes in which a catalyst pressure drop is a hindrance. The fact that these supports are thermally conductive and can be made to almost any configuration provides a solution to these prevailing problems.

The high surface area developed on nickel screen permitted our first commercial use of the BD-activated surface as cathodes in electrolyzing cells for hydrogen and oxygen generation. The activated metal screens lower the overvoltage and show about a 15 to 20% improvement in practice in efficiency over untreated nickel screen. They have been tested in production cells for more than three years with little or no change in their activity. Figure 6.11 shows the current versus voltage relationship of untreated

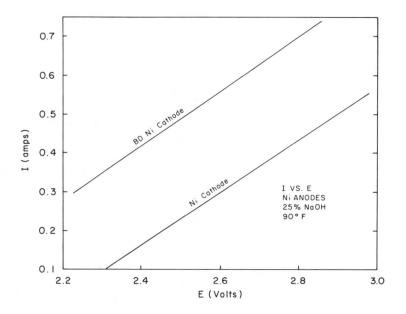

Figure 6.11 H_2, O_2 generation: BD nickel versus nickel

and activated nickel screen cathodes in 25% NaOH. Activated 90% Pt-10% Rh gauzes have shown promise in catalyzing the HCN reaction, and it is currently being pursued.

As of 1986, various representations of activated metals are being evaluated with success in many laboratories.

METHANOL SYNTHESIS

The methanol synthesis reaction is highly exothermic:

$$CO + 2H_2 \rightarrow CH_3OH \qquad -113 \text{ Kcal/mole.}$$

The state-of-the-art industrial catalysts used in the commercial synthesis are based on a coprecipitated ZnO, CuO, and Al_2O_3. This catalyst has inherently poor heat conductivity and suffers thermal degradation because of the exotherm. Conversion of CO + H_2 to CH_3OH is limited, since to minimize the exotherm, the feedstock, with less than stoichiometric CO, must be recycled several times. The simplicity of BD-activated Cu or Cu-Zn alloy as a screen, gauze, sheet, foam, tube, honeycomb, or foil, formed to any configuration, facilitates its placement in and removal from the reaction site. The configuration could be made in a form to achieve a low pressure drop and high heat dissipation in the system (for example, by activating the surface of heat exchange coils).

Initial tests at the University of Delaware, under the direction of A. B. Stiles, has shown a BD-treated coil of 8O Cu-20 Zn impregnated with metal salts to provide a methanol yield about equal to that of the state-of-the-art catalyst.

METHANATION REACTION

The methanation reaction ($CO + 3H_2 \rightarrow CH_4 + H_2O$) is extremely exothermic; past experience has shown that the temperature of the reaction must be maintained below 600°C in order to avoid destruction of the catalyst. This has, in the past, required costly recycling of off gas to the inlet so as to dilute the CO and H_2 content. Without such dilution, the reaction temperature could exceed 1100°C, at which temperature most catalysts would be destroyed. The equilibrium for methane is such that there would be large residual quantities of CO and H_2. The inside or outside surfaces of nickel or nickel alloy heat exchanger tubes could be activated in situ to form the catalytic support for impregnation with salts such as aluminum, cerium, chromium, and lithium as nitrates that, upon subsequent calcining, would leave residues of highly active oxides in the pores of the active nickel surfaces. The opposite untreated surface of the exchanger tube would contact a liquid heat exchange medium to which the heat of reaction would be rapidly and efficiently transmitted for subsequent recovery. Impregnation with a cocatalyst should add the the activity of the support, but the BD Ni support itself has been demonstrated to be very active and quite stable in the methanation reaction. Tests conducted at the Energy Research and Development Agency–Bureau of Mines on a 7 lap, 6 in. length BD Ni screen coil has shown it to display excellent and continued activity for 1600 hours of testing. Data relevant to this test are depicted in Figure 6.12. In the past, evaluation of a leached plasma-sprayed nickel aluminide coating on a metal tube or plate surface was evaluated by a few investigators. The major problem with this approach was the lack of uniformity and inconsistent adherence of the aluminide layer to the base metal surface. This resulted in detachment of the active layer during its preparation or in the course of the methanation reaction. The BD-activated nickel layer, on the other hand, is by nature in its synthesis very uniform and securely bonded by its intergranular penetration into the base metal surface during the deposition and diffusion reaction. Controlled and selective removal of the aluminum retains these excellent and necessary characteristics.

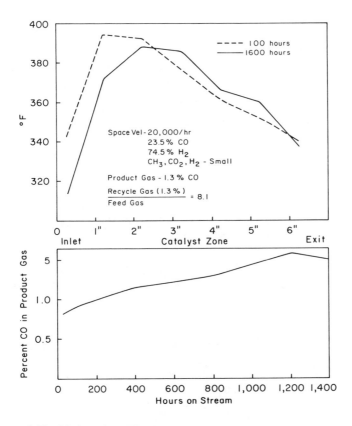

Figure 6.12   Methanation: BD nickel.

AUTOMOTIVE EXHAUST CATALYST

The ideal automotive exhaust catalyst should have the capability of catalyzing the reactions of NO_x reduction and carbon monoxide and propane oxidation. Tests by a large chemical company have found that BD-treated Pt-10%-Rh screens exhibit activity and thermal stability superior to those of conventional platinum on alumina supports. Their test results are shown in the graphs in Figures 6.13, 6.14, and 6.15. The low

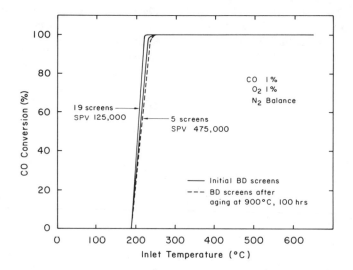

Figure 6.13 CO oxidation.

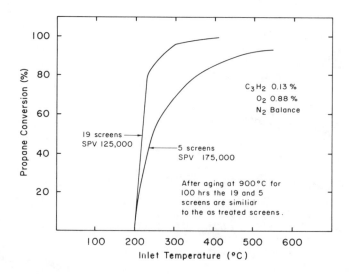

Figure 6.14 Propane oxidation: BD Pt-Rh Screens.

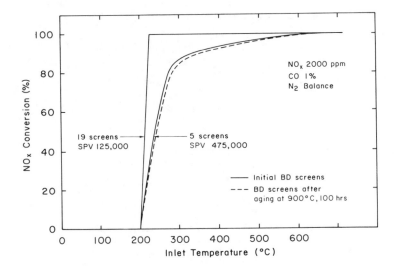

Figure 6.15   NO$_x$ reduction: BD-activated Pt-Rh screens.

light-off temperatures at the very high space velocities of 125,000 and 475,000 are particularly impressive before and after thermal aging for 100 hours at 900°C. Since the cost of platinum or platinum-rhodium screen base metal might be prohibitive, other approaches, such as activation of platinum-plated nickel-chromium base alloys or the cheaper base material itself with a cocatalyst impregnation, would be an interesting exploration to provide an advancement in the state-of-the-art of automotive exhaust catalysts.

NO$_x$ CONTROL

The abatement of nitrogen oxides is a major air pollution challenge. Graduate students of the Chemical Engineering Department of the University of Massachusetts have been evaluating various catalysts in the reduction of NO$_x$ with ammonia. The catalysis of the reduction of NO$_x$ by NH$_3$ by activated stainless steels in the presence of oxygen and water was recently investigated by R. J. Willey in his doctoral thesis from the University of Massachusetts [13]. He found that the most catalytically active metal was BD-430 stainless steel (17 Cr-Bal. Fe). Conversions were as high as 95%. With reactor space velocities of 60,000 hours -1, Willey observed that the BD surface was extremely rough, with BET surface area on the order of 30 m^2/g. The graphs in Figure 6.16 present some of the results of Willey's investigation. Impregnation of the active metal surface with chromates and other salts has improved the performance of the already active stainless steel support.

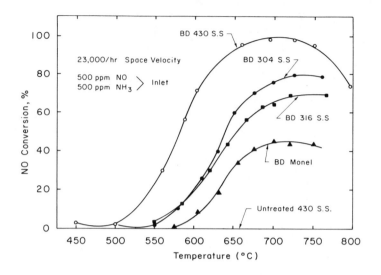

Figure 6.16   NO$_x$ reduction: BD-activated miscellaneous metals.

NO CONVERSION TO HNCO AND HN$_4$OCN

Voorhoeve and Trimble [12] of Bell Laboratories have conducted studies with BD-activated 90 Pt-10 Rh and NO conversion to ammonium cyanate. The following reactions were studied:

$$2NO + 3CO + 2H_2 \rightarrow NH_4OCN + 2CO_2;$$

$$2NO + 4CO + H_2 \rightarrow 2HNCO + 2CO_2;$$

$$2NO + 2NH_3 + 4CO + H_2 \rightarrow 2NH_4OCN + 2CO_2.$$

The authors state, "The yield of NH$_4$OCN in the first reaction was 97% over the Pt-10%-Rh catalyst. The best yield of HNCO in the second reaction was 75% over an unsupported iridium catalyst with an additional 22% of the NO reacting according to the first reaction for an overall NO $\rightarrow$ NCO conversion of 86%. The third reaction was carried out with a yield of 86% over the BD Pt-10%-Rh catalyst." The last equation shows that all of the NO is converted to NH$_4$OCN. According to the authors, the formation of isocyanate surface intermediates in the reaction of NO with CO is well established for a variety of supported catalysts, including Pd/Al$_2$O$_3$, Ir/Al$_2$O$_3$, Pt/Al$_2$O$_3$, and Rh/Al$_2$O$_3$. Their findings that a self-supporting BD Pt-10%-Rh catalyst can be used to synthesize NH$_4$OCN should be of great interest in manufacturing ammonium cyanate or its equivalent, urea, used as the main constituent in fertilizer and the production of plastics. Activated Pt plate on cheaper base materials with or without salt impregnation could be another interesting exploratory study to improve the economics of NH$_4$OCN synthesis.

OTHER REACTIONS CATALYZED BY ACTIVE METAL SUPPORTS

Immersion of activated Pt, Pt alloys, iridium, and palladium has caused rapid decomposition of hydrogen peroxide and/or hydrazine. BD-treated nickel, immersed in a triolein oil and subjected to elevated H_2 pressure at 150°F, converts it to a solid fat. Other reactions in which activated metal could have application include iron and iron-base alloys for ammonia synthesis, silver for ethylene oxide formation, manganese or alloys of Mn for hydrocarbon oxidation, and Iron-cobalt-ruthenium for CO hydrogenation (Fischer-Tropsch).

PYROTECHNICS

The BD activation treatment can be tailored to provide self-igniting (pyrophoric) metal surfaces in almost any form, including foils, sheets, screens, powders, and wafers. Once exposed to air, the surfaces oxidize and emit a great quantity of heat due primarily to the heat of formation of the oxide. The surfaces can be preserved or their spontaneity

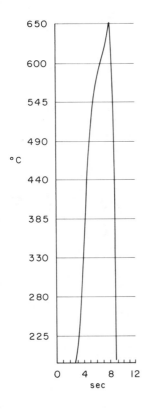

Figure 6.17 BD Fe: 3 mils thick, 3–5 μm emission.

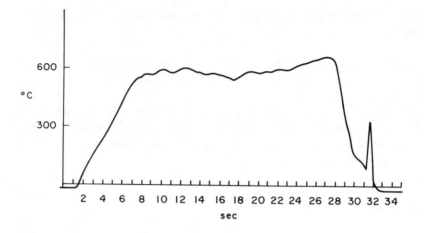

Figure 6.18 BD FeC: 15 mils thick, 2–3 μm emission.

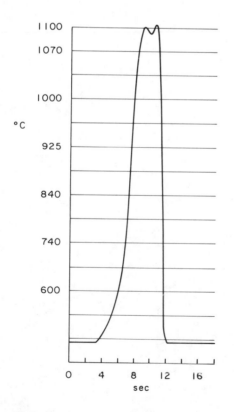

Figure 6.19 BDB Fe: 10 mils thick, 2–3 μm emission.

of ignition can be delayed for specific time periods by posttreating the active surface. The activated metals behave as a black body and radiate energy in the infrared region of the electromagnetic spectrum. We have measured the energy emitted at various wave lengths, including 2–3 μm, 3–5 μm, and 8–14 μm. Forty mil thick activated iron wafers sustained a temperature above 350°F on its surface for more than 5 minutes.

A 10 mil thick boron-containing material ignited to liberate intense heat developed a temperature over 2100°F on its surface. Activated steel foils having a thickness of only 3 mils attained a temperature of over 1200°F on their surfaces. Similar nickel foils reached even higher temperatures. Current testing indicates that there will be both military and industrial application for this phase of activated metals. Typical time versus temperature profiles are shown in Figures 6.17, 6.18, and 6.19 for, respectively, BD Fe, BD FeC, and BDB Fe modified with other elements.

CONCLUSIONS

Unlocking the energy on a metal-containing surface by the BD technology should be of paramount importance in the field of catalysis, pyrotechnics, and other endeavors. Our research has only scratched the surface of this discovery. The exploration that lies ahead in theory, synthesis, and application is boundless and thought provoking, and it will continue to be pursued with great vigor.

REFERENCES

1. Raney, M. U.S. patent 1,563,787 (1925).
2. Raney, M. U.S. patents 1,628,190 (1927); 1,915,473 (1933).
3. Baldi, A. L. U.S. patents 3,458,353 (1969); 3,622,391 (1971); 3,327,134 (1982).
4. Baldi, A. L., and Damiano, V. V. U.S. patents 4,154,705 (1979); Re 31,104, 4,292,208 (1981); 4,349,612 (1982).
5. Hansen, M. 1958. *Constitution of Binary Alloys.* 2d ed. New York: McGraw-Hill. Rhines, F. N. 1956. *Phase Diagrams in Metallurgy,* New York: McGraw-Hill. Shunk, F. A. 1969. *Constitution of Binary Alloys.* 2d supp. New York: McGraw-Hill.
6. Baldi, A. L. 1975. "The Key Elements in Diffusion Coatings to Combat High Temperature Corrosion." Presented at IV Inter-American Conference on Materials Technology, June 29–July 4. Southwest Research Institute, San Antonio, Texas.
7. Anderson, J. R. 1975. *Structure of Metallic Catalysts.* New York: Academic Press.
8. Stiles, A. B. 1983. *Catalyst Manufacture.* New York: Dekker.
9. Holtgren, R.; Deiai, P. D.; Hawkins, D. T.; Gleiser, M.; and Kelley, K. K. 1973. *Selected Values of the Thermodynamics Properties of Binary Alloys.* Metals Park, Ohio: American Society for Metals.
10. Oelsen, W., and Middel, W. 1937. *Mittkwi Eisenforschung, Dusseld* 19:1.
11. Freel, J.; Pieters, W. J. M.; and Anderson, R. B. 1970. The structure of Raney nickel. *J. Catal.* 14:247–25.
12. Voorhoeve, R. J. H., and Trimble, L. E. 1978. Conversion of NO to isocyanic acid and ammonium cyanate over Pt, Ir and Pt-10% Rh catalyst. *J. Catal.* 11:111.
13. Willey, R. J. 1984. The catalytic reduction of nitric oxide with ammonia on etched metal surfaces. Ph.D. dissertation, University of Massachusetts.

CHAPTER 7

Basic Principles of Catalysis by Functionalized Porous Organic Polymers: Theoretical Concepts and Considerations

Robert L. Albright

Attempts to catalyze reactions by synthetic organic ion exchange polymers (resins) were first explored in the 1940s [1, 2, 3]. These attempts to use organic polymers were a logical transition since naturally occurring zeolites were known to be effective heterogeneous catalysts [2, 3, 4]. The earliest investigations into catalysis by ionogenic cross-liked organic polymers were carried out with lightly cross-linked gel polymers, usually having less than 10 weight percent of the chemical cross-linker.

The rationale for using lightly cross-linked polymers is readily understood since the rate of reaction within the gellular polymer where the catalytic sites reside is dependent on the accessibility of the catalytic sites to the reactants. This accessibility is a function of the microporosity of the gel and the capacity of the matrix to swell or to be solvated by the reaction medium [5–8]. Increasing the density of the cross-linking decreases both the microporosity and the quantity of imbibed liquid. Although ion exchange rates are almost always controlled by diffusion or mass transport of the ions (reactants) rather than by the chemical reaction [9–12], resin catalysis is not so controlled [13]. Catalysis by gel resins appears to be controlled by the chemical reaction rather than by mass transfer of reactants [13–19], with the peripheral region of the polymer particle being the arena for the catalytic work [18, 20].

Macroporous resins were discovered during the 1950s [21–23] and during the 1960s were developed into useful substances by controlling the nature of the pore structure during synthesis [24–37]. It is the impact of the pore system capable of being built into the polymers that we wish to explore. There are boundary conditions imposed on the porous system by the physics, and it is these boundary conditions that dictate the selection of the appropriate matrix upon which to anchor a catalytic agent. Having laid out the internal structure of the polymers, we will then examine the chemistry of functionalized porous organic polymers as heterogeneous catalysts.

NATURE OF CROSS-LINKED POLYMERS

Cross-linked organic polymers are made in bead form (spheres) varying in diameter from about 1.20 mm (16 mesh U.S. Sieve Series) to 0.21 mm (70 mesh U.S. Sieve Series) by dispersion polymerization of their respective monomers [38]. Particle diameters outside this range can also be made by dispersion polymerization but are not commercial. Almost any monomer can be polymerized by dispersion techniques to produce spheres of cross-linked polymer [2, 39]. Of the common monomers being used, all but two polymerize to produce transparent spheres or beads. The two exceptions are acrylonitrile and methacrylic acid saturated with water. Both polymerize in aqueous dispersion to give opaque beads [40]. The transparent polymers are gellular in nature and are called gels because they have no porosity or permanent pores within the polymeric matrix. They do swell with miscible solvents and do have a microporosity, but they have no pores that are invariant with time. The opaque polymers have an internal structure distinctly different from the transparent polymers.

The most common cross-linked polymers in use today are polystyrene, polyacrylonitrile, polyacrylate esters, and polymethacrylate esters. These polymers are cross-linked with a polyfunctional monomer, the most prominent of which is divinylbenzene. The cross-linking monomer and its level of usage serve to give the resulting polymeric matrix the following properties:

1.   Insolubility of the polymer in miscible solvents,
2.   Controlled volume changes on swelling,
3.   Dimensional stability so that the resulting polymer is less susceptible to deformation under external force and more resistant to crack development.

In addition to the chemical cross-linker whose level is controllable, there is a concomitant cross-linking that arises during the formation of the polymer, and that cross-linking is chain entanglement [41]. The quantity of chain entanglement is not as readily controlled as the chemical cross-linker, but the level does vary with the conditions of synthesis. In general, faster rates of polymerization and higher temperatures during the polymerization produce more chain entanglement. These two cross-linkers are classified as primary cross-linking because they enter the polymer during its formation and are predominantly interchain cross-links. There are other types of cross-linking that can and do arise in polymers, such as those that arise during functionalization of the polymers and are classified as secondary cross-linking. They develop in an already-formed matrix, have a distinctly different impact on the nature of the polymer, have a short range of spatial influence, and are predominantly intrachain rather than interchain. Three such types of cross-linking are methylene bridging, nitrogen bridging, and disulfide linking.

NEED FOR A CONTINUOUS PORE SYSTEM
IN CATALYSIS

Catalysis by solvated functionalized gel polymers has been observed to be controlled by the chemical reaction rather than by mass transfer of the reactants into the catalytic sites [13, 14, 16, 17, 18, 42, 43]. The catalytic efficiency of functionalized gel polymers is very much dependent on the nature of the solvent or the reaction medium [5, 14, 16, 20, 44, 45] and the environment of the catalytic site [5, 46, 47]. Only in water have functionalized gel polymers been found to have catalytic efficiencies greater than the corresponding homogeneous catalysts [5, 14, 16, 44].

As the reaction medium is shifted to a more lipophylic nature, where particle swelling is less a result of poorer solvation of the polar functional group, the catalytic efficiency is diminished to a level below that of a corresponding homogeneous catalyst [14, 16, 44, 45]. Except in water or a suitable swelling solvent, the efficacy of gel polymers to perform catalytic work becomes questionable, though they have all the advantages of a heterogeneous system.

The deficiency of gel polymers rests with their particle size and the portion of the particle participating in the catalytic work. Only the peripheral region of the particle is the working arena [18, 20, 45]. The thickness of this peripheral region in aqueous media for strong acid resins, where hydration is optimum, can be estimated to be no greater than about 10,000 Å (1.0 micron or 1000 nm) from the kinetic data of Smith and Amundson [17]. For a spherical gellular catalyst particle of 0.50 mm diameter (30 mesh, U.S. Sieve Series), the working gel phase for catalysis therefore involves only 8.1% of the particle volume or total catalytic potential. For a spherical gellular particle of 0.841 mm diameter (20 mesh, U.S. Sieve Series), the working phase involves only 1.7% of the particle volume or total catalytic potential. In mixed aqueous-organic solvents or anhydrous organic liquids, the catalytically active region is reduced to an even smaller peripheral region [5, 14, 16, 44] of the bead and may reach a thickness of less than 1000 Å (0.1 micron). If the particle dimensions are reduced to expose more of the gel particle for catalytic work, the pressure drop (Δp) through a fixed bed of catalyst increases and becomes excessive as particle dimensions are made smaller and smaller. Obviously particle size reduction to expose more of the gellular particle for catalytic work is not the way to build a more effective catalyst. What is needed is a catalytically active polymer, 0.5 mm in diameter or larger, whose interior is accessible for catalytic work. Such a catalyst demands a continuous open-cell pore system.

INTRINSIC ELEMENTS OF CATALYSIS

A catalyst is an agent that enhances the overall rate of a reaction by reducing the activation energy of the rate-limiting step [48]. A good catalytic agent is one that not only increases the rate of the reaction but also is not destroyed during the reaction or by interaction with the products. As part of the overall scheme of employing a catalytic agent, it is necessary for the catalyst to be capable of separation or removal from the product. Most often it is economically attractive and practical to be able to separate the catalyst in a form to be reused or recycled. This last desired property of being able to separate for recycle is the attractive feature of heterogeneous catalysts. Many times, though, it is found that the heterogeneous counterpart is less effective than the homogeneous catalyst and that on continued recycle, efficiency continues to decline. In summary, then, a well-designed heterogeneous catalyst is one that is readily separated from the stream of reactants and products, is able to be recycled without losing efficiency, is equivalent to or better than the best homogeneous catalyst, and is specific for the desired reaction. Such systems do exist; they are enzymes specifically made to do just that. Porous polymers are not yet synthetic enzymes, but they are much closer to that target than their gel counterparts.

PHYSICAL STRUCTURE OF POROUS ORGANIC POLYMERS

Cross-linked polymers can be made porous with an open-cell or closed-cell pore system by the method of synthesis [21, 22, 23, 26, 30, 31, 39]. The closed-cell pore system will not be considered in this discussion because it is a discontinuous one lacking interconnecting channels; therefore, it does not provide the network for transport necessary for rapid ingress of reactants and egress of products.

The cross-linked porous polymers under scrutiny—as attested to by the electron micrographs of Figures 7.1, 7.2, and 7.3—are structurally composed of small microgel particles agglomerated together to form clusters. The clusters of microgel particles are fastened together at the interfaces and can be made to range in size in one dimension by a factor of about 1.5×10^3, from as small as 0.040 micron to as large as 60 microns. The geometry of the microgel tends toward spherical symmetry, as is seen in Figure 7.3, and the dimensions of the individual microgel particles can be made to vary by about the same factor of 1.5×10^3. The diameter of the microgel can be made as small as 0.010 micron (100 Å) to as large as 15 microns. These characteristics of shape and size can be observed in the electron micrographs of Amberlite IRA-938 polymer in Figures 7.1 and 7.3 and Amberlite XAD-4 polymer in Figure 7.2.

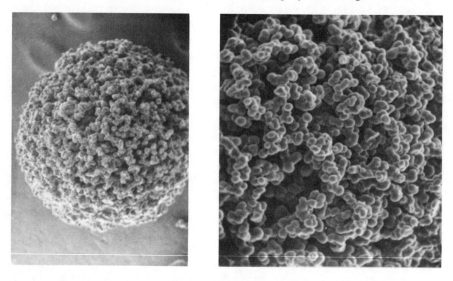

Figure 7.1   Scanning electron micrograph of Amberlite IRA–938.
Note: 100× magnification (left) and 300× magnification (right).

Figure 7.2   Amberlite XAD-4   (demonstrating smaller particle size).

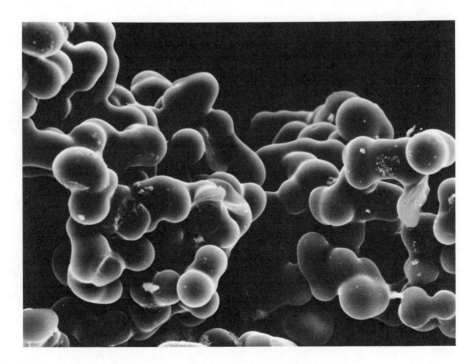

Figure 7.3   Amberlite XAD-4   (demonstrating larger particle size).

The porosity arises from the void spaces between and within the clusters, and the void region is a continuous open-cell system with essentially all the pores interconnected. The gel phase is also a continuum, so that the porous polymeric particle is constructed of two continuous phases: a continuous pore phase and a continuous gel phase. The surface area arises from the exposed surface of the microgel glued together into clusters.

The size of the clusters of microgel, rather than the microgel itself, accounts for the visual appearance of the porous polymers. Clusters larger than 2000 Å—one-half of the wavelength of the shortest frequency of the visible part of the electromagnetic spectrum—scatter the light waves (Mie scattering) [49] as light passes through the porous matrix and produces opacity. Clusters smaller than 2000 Å are not of sufficient size to induce the same type of light scattering. Polymeric beads or particles made up of the smaller clusters appear translucent. The translucency results from Rayleigh scattering [49] of the photons as they pass through the alternating sequence of pores and clustered microgel. Nonporous gel resins appear transparent since there is no internal structure of significant size to perturb the flow of photons passing through. The lack of significant internal structure in a gel polymer can be seen in Figure 7.4, where the electron micrograph of a gel and a porous polymer are compared.

The absence or the presence of a system of pores within a bead of polymer can not always be correctly assessed by visual appearance. The photomicrographs of Figure 7.5 show the visual contrast among a gel polymer that appears transparent, a porous polymer with moderately sized clusters (Amberlite XAD-2 polymer) that appears opaque, and a porous polymer with very small clusters (Amberlite XAD-4 polymer) that appears translucent. The transparent gel polymer and the translucent porous polymer may appear the same, and it is for this reason that porosity must be assessed by the appropriate measurement rather than by visual appearance. Porosity is readily ascer-

Figure 7.4   Electron micrographs of gel and macroreticular structures.

Figure 7.5 Depiction of contrast between gel polymer (transparent) and polymer comprising clusters (opaque).

Note: Gel Copolymer (top), Amberlite XAD-2 (left), and Amberlite XAD-4 (right).

tained by the measurement of the apparent and the skeletal densities, followed by application of the equation [50],

$$P_v = 1 - \frac{d_a}{d_s}, \tag{7.1}$$

where P_v is porosity in ml of pore per ml of porous polymer; d_a is apparent density in gm/ml of polymer particle; and d_s is skeletal density in gm/ml of polymer mass. With a nonporous polymer, the values for both the apparent and the skeletal densities are the same within experimental error. The porosity can also be measured accurately by a nitrogen adsorption isotherm [51, 52].

The intrinsic, detailed nature of the pore system making up the porosity is best visualized and understood from the electron micrographs and the graphs of the pore size distributions. Pores varying from 20 Å to 500,000 Å in diameter may be formed, and distributions of pore sizes can be made to range from narrow with a sharp mode (peak) to very broad with no mode or peak. The pore size distributions given in figures 7.6, 7.7, 7.8, and 7.9 show these features of variation in pore size distribution for the same polymer composition: that of Amberlite XAD-4 polymer. Figure 7.10 presents the pore size distribution of an all-aliphatic porous polymer, Amberlite XAD-7 resin, having a moderately high specific surface area of about 500 m²/gm. The electron micrographs in Figures 7.2 and 7.3 reveal the extremes in intrinsic features of the microgel, the clusters, and the pores. All the internal characteristics of porous polymers are set or established by the composition of the monomers, the porogen or the phase-separating liquid, and the environment during the polymerization.

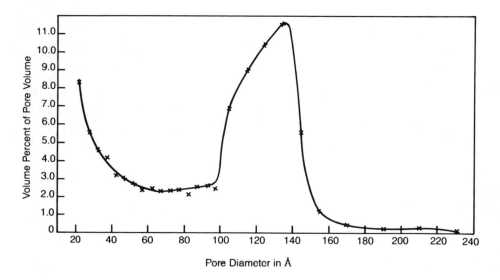

Figure 7.6 Pore size distribution by nitrogen desorption isotherm of Amberlite XAD-4, sample A.

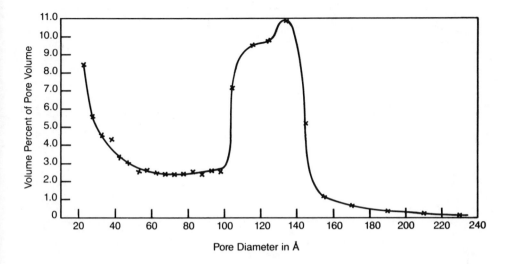

Figure 7.7   Pore size distribution by nitrogen desorption isotherm of Amberlite XAD-4, sample A, after heat treatment at 130°C for 3.0 hours.

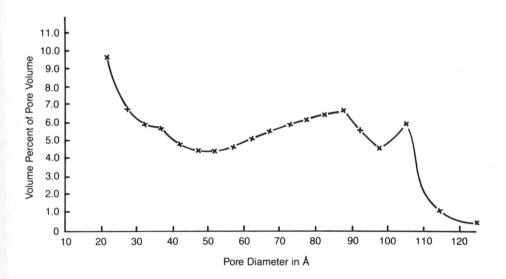

Figure 7.8   Pore size distribution by nitrogen desorption isotherm of Amberlite XAD-4, sample C.

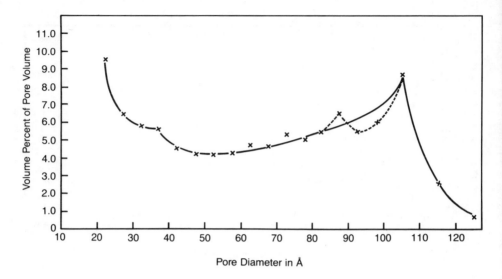

Figure 7.9   Pore size distribution by nitrogen desorption isotherm of Amberlite XAD-4, sample D.

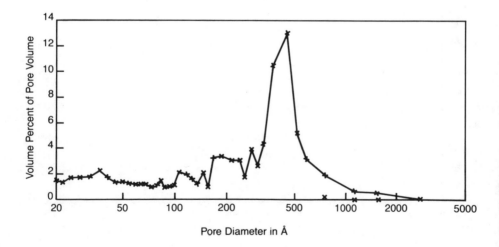

Figure 7.10   Pore size distribution by nitrogen desorption isotherm of Amberlite XAD-7.

The surface area of porous polymeric beads arises from the internal and not the external surface, where the diameter of the porous beads is 10 microns or larger. Porous polymers have been prepared with internal specific surface areas as large as 1000 m^2/gm and with as little specific surface area as 0.1 m^2/gm. For a spherically symmetrical system, the relationship of particle diameter to total specific surface, $\bar{S}$, is given by the equation,

$$\bar{S} = \frac{6 \times 10^{-4}}{d_s D},$$
(7.2)

where $\bar{S}$ is in units of m^2/gm, d_s is the skeletal density of the particle mass in gm/ml, and D is the diameter in cm of the element (microgel) providing the surface. This relationship, graphically displayed in Figure 7.11, reveals that the specific surface area contributed by the exterior of a porous bead whose diameter is 10 microns or greater is less than 1.0 m^2/gm when the skeletal density is 1.0 gm/ml (the actual value is 0.6 m^2/gm). Figure 7.12 shows the relationship of total specific surface that results from a system of random-close-packed microspheres of poly(divinylbenzene) as a function of the diameter of the microspheres where the skeletal density of the polymer is 1.105 gm/ml [53, 54]. Since the relationship of specific surface to the skeletal density is inverse, the specific surface area will decrease as the polymer skeletal density increases. For this reason, functionalized carbon polymers with larger skeletal densities than 1.105 gm/ml [53, 55] and porous silicate polymers with skeletal densities of about 2.2 gm/ml will have smaller specific surface areas, $\bar{S}$, than the corresponding hydrocarbon polymers having the same microgel dimensions (for example, see the silicate polymers in *The Chemistry of Silica*) [56]. Because of this inverse relationship, the comparison and the selection of polymers as substrates for anchoring catalytic agents are better done by use of the surface area per skeletal volume rather than the surface area per gm ($\bar{S}$). The interconversion of one quantity into the other is according to the equation,

$$(\bar{S}, \, m^2/gm) \, (ds, \, gm/ml) = \bar{S}_v, \, m^2/ml,$$
(7.3)

where $\bar{S}_v$ is the specific surface per skeletal volume of polymer in m^2/ml and d_s is the skeletal density in gm/ml.

Questions arise as to what quantity of total specific surface area can be built into the interior of a porous polymer whose fundamental building unit has spherical symmetry. What is the impact of having a large internal surface? What is the relationship of pore size to total specific surface area? What size pore will allow entrance of what size molecule? What surface capacity can be constructed into the interior of a porous polymeric bead? In summary, what are the boundary conditions imposed by the physical constraints of such a system?

To appreciate these physical constraints, we need to consider some models. For example, a monolayer of polydivinylbenzene has a specific surface area of 2313 m^2/gm

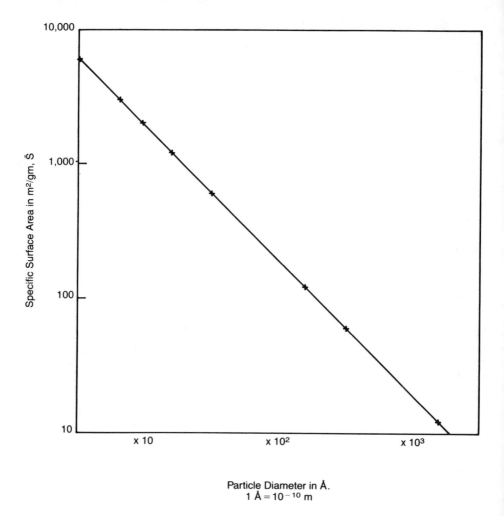

Figure 7.11   Specific surface area, $\overline{S}$, as a function of microsphere diameter.

for each side of the monolayer film at a packing density of aromatic rings of 1.0 and a surface area per aromatic ring of 50 Å^2 [57]. For both sides of the monolayer film, the total specific surface is 4626 m^2/gm. A packing fraction or packing density of aromatic rings of, say, 0.60, which may be more realistic than 1.0, gives a specific surface area of 3855 m^2/gm for one side, or for both sides of the monolayer film gives 7710 m^2/gm.

To estimate the specific surface of a monolayer of aromatic rings of poly-divinylbenzene on the basis of spherical geometry and the skeletal density of the polymer, one can calculate a value of 7538.9 m^2/gm for both sides of the monolayer film (see the Appendix at the end of this chapter for calculations). As can be seen, the agreement between the two values calculated from two different bases is very good. Table 7.1 has been constructed to display the relationship of microgel diameter

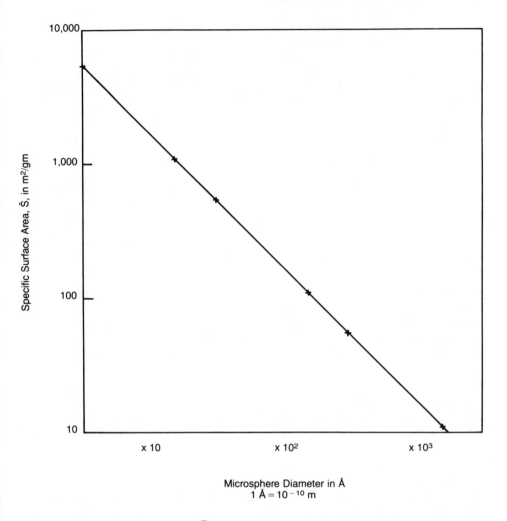

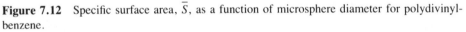

Microsphere Diameter in Å
$1 \text{ Å} = 10^{-10} \text{ m}$

Figure 7.12   Specific surface area, $\bar{S}$, as a function of microsphere diameter for polydivinyl-benzene.

to the following elements in the assembly of a porous bead from microgel spheres of polydivinylbenzene:

- Surface area of each sphere of microgel,
- Specific surface ($\bar{S}$) for 1 gram of spheres,
- Volume of each sphere of microgel,
- Number of spheres of microgel per equivalent of polymer,
- Number of divinylbenzene rings per sphere of microgel.

The information and the equations for calculating the values tabulated in Table 7.1 are given in the Appendix at the end of this chapter.

Table 7.1   Relationship of Various Quantities to the Diameter of Spherical Particles of Polydivinylbenzene

Diameter of Sphere		Area of Surface of Each Sphere m²	Specific Surface Area, $\bar{S}$, of One Gm. of Spheres m²/gm	Volume of Each Sphere ml	Number of Spheres per Equiv. of Polymer	Number of DVB Rings per Sphere
mm.	Angstrom Å					
1.00	10^7	3.14159×10^{-6}	5.4299×10^{-3}	5.236×10^{-4}	2.250×10^5	2.676×10^{18}
0.50	5×10^6	7.8540×10^{-7}	1.0860×10^{-2}	6.545×10^{-5}	1.800×10^6	3.3456×10^{17}
0.10	10^6	3.1416×10^{-8}	5.4299×10^{-2}	5.236×10^{-7}	2.250×10^8	2.676×10^{15}
0.05	5×10^5	7.8540×10^{-9}	1.0860×10^{-1}	6.545×10^{-8}	1.800×10^9	3.3456×10^{14}
0.01	10^5	3.1416×10^{-10}	5.4299×10^{-1}	5.236×10^{-10}	2.250×10^{11}	2.676×10^{12}
5×10^{-3}	5×10^4	7.8540×10^{-11}	1.0860	6.545×10^{-11}	1.800×10^{12}	3.3456×10^{11}
10^{-3}	10^4	3.1416×10^{-12}	5.4299	5.236×10^{-13}	2.250×10^{13}	2.676×10^9
5×10^{-4}	5×10^3	7.8540×10^{-13}	1.0860×10	6.545×10^{-14}	1.800×10^{15}	3.3456×10^8
10^{-4}	10^3	3.1416×10^{-14}	5.4299×10	5.236×10^{-16}	2.250×10^{17}	2.676×10^6
5×10^{-5}	5×10^2	7.8540×10^{-15}	1.0860×10^2	6.545×10^{-17}	1.800×10^{18}	3.3456×10^5
10^{-5}	10^2	3.1416×10^{-16}	5.4299×10^2	5.236×10^{-19}	2.250×10^{20}	2.676×10^3
5×10^{-6}	5×10	7.8540×10^{-17}	1.0860×10^3	6.545×10^{-20}	1.800×10^{21}	3.3456×10^2
10^{-6}	10	3.1416×10^{-18}	5.4299×10^3	5.236×10^{-22}	2.250×10^{23}	2.676
7.2×10^{-7}	7.2	1.6286×10^{-18}	7.5415×10^3	1.9543×10^{-22}	6.02867×10^{23}	0.9990
7.20245×10^{-7}	7.20245	1.6297×10^{-18}	7.53891×10^3	1.9563×10^{-22}	6.02252×10^{23}	1.00

As an approximation for the pore size, it can be assumed for random-close-packed spheres of uniform size that the pore size is equivalent to the size of the spheres whose assemblage forms the voids [58]. From this approximation and the knowledge that a slightly less than perfect packing of classified or monodisperse spherical particles has a void fraction between 0.37 and 0.40 [59], it is possible to estimate the pore diameter of a porous polymer directly from the measured specific surface, $\bar{S}$. From a plot of specific surface area versus microgel diameter, such as in Figure 7.12, the estimated pore diameter can be read directly off the abscissa by locating the value of the measured surface area on the curve. This approximation works for porous polymers whose porosities fall within the range of 0.39 ± 0.05 ml of pores per ml of porous polymer. A plot of specific surface area versus microgel diameter is readily constructed from the skeletal density of the polymer and the application of equation 7.2.

For porous polymers whose porosities lie outside the void fraction range of 0.34 to 0.44, the following equation can be used to obtain a less accurate estimate of pore size, but nevertheless, an estimate that usually falls within a factor of 3 of the predominating pore size as measured by a nitrogen desorption isotherm,

$$ADP = \frac{(40,000) \, P_{wt}}{\bar{S}}, \tag{7.4}$$

where APD is the average pore diameter in Å; P_{wt} is the porosity in ml of pore per gm of polymer; and $\bar{S}$ is the specific surface area in m²/gm of porous polymer measured by the Brunauer, Emmett, and Teller method [60].

The following equation relates the porosity in pore volume per volume of porous polymer to the porosity expressed in pore volume per weight of porous polymer:

$$P_{wt} = \frac{P_v}{d_a}, \tag{7.5}$$

where P_{wt} is the porosity in ml of pore per gm of porous polymer; P_v is the porosity in ml of pore per ml of porous polymer; and d_a is the apparent density of the porous polymer in gm/ml.

For the most accurate assessment of the pore size and the distribution of pore sizes, the application of the Kelvin equation to the nitrogen desorption isotherm is necessary [60]. This technique works well for measuring pore sizes within the range of 20 Å to 500 Å, and possibly up to 2000 Å pores with the newer instruments that utilize more sensitive pressure transducers [61, 62] but is not applicable for measuring pores larger in diameter than 2000 Å. Mercury porosimetry has been used to measure distributions of pore sizes on rigid, hard materials having porosity [60] but is not applicable to porous organic polymers where deformation rather than mercury penetration occurs [63]. Only for porous organic polymers, such as Amberlite IRA-938 polymer, with very large pores—greater than 10,000 Å—does mercury porosimetry appear to provide pore size distributions congruent with the information from electron micrographics (see Figures 7.1, 7.3, and 7.13). For porous organic polymers having

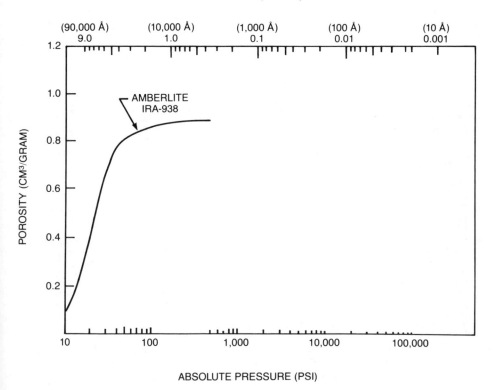

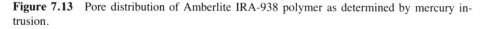

Figure 7.13   Pore distribution of Amberlite IRA-938 polymer as determined by mercury intrusion.

pore sizes within the region of 2000 to 10,000 Å, it appears that the new technique of size-exclusion chromatography [64] may be the only one that will provide an accurate assessment of pore sizes without polymer deformation [65, 66].

From this technique of size-exclusion chromatography it is possible to obtain the information desired to relate pore size to the molecular size that will enter that pore. In Table 7.2 and Figure 7.14 taken from the data of Halasz and Martin [65] are tabulated and graphed, respectively, the calculated molecular dimensions of a series of molecules increasing in size and the respective pore sizes entered freely by each in the liquid state. From this correlation of pore size and molecular entrance, it can be derived that the size relationship between the pore and the entering molecule is such that the pore diameter must be 2.5 times the diameter of the molecule for unhindered entrance of the pore by the molecule [65].

In the selection of a porous polymer upon which to anchor a catalytic agent, this relationship of pore size to molecular size for unhindered entrance is important and is fundamental to designing a successful, functioning catalyst. Elementary but fundamental to reaction physics and to the functioning of a catalyst is the accessibility of the reactants to the catalyzing agent, followed by the movement of the products from the catalytic site. The pore dimensions therefore have to be at least 2.5 times the size of the largest molecule involved in the reaction, whether it is the reactants or the products. Most often the size of the product or products to be made will dictate

Table 7.2 Pore Diameter, ϕ, Assigned to Standard Sample Molecules via Size Exclusion Chromatography

Molecule	Molecular Weight	ϕ_d in Å^3	ϕ in Å^2
Benzene	78.046950	3.189	7.4
Ethylbenzene	106.078250	3.819	8.5
Butylbenzene	134.109551	4.384	10.9
Hexylbenzene	162.277268	4.905	13.4
Octylbenzene	190.331458	5.387	15.9
Dodecylbenzene	246.439839	6.271	20.8
Pentadecylbenzene	288.521124	6.88	24.4
PS[1] 600	600	10.58	26.7
PS 2,100	2.1×10^3	22.12	55.9
PS 4,000	4.0×10^3	32.31	81.6
PS 10,000	1×10^4	55.385	140.0
PS 20,800	2.08×10^4	85.21	215.0
PS 36,000	3.6×10^4	117.66	297.0
PS 111,000	1.11×10^5	228.19	576.0
PS 200,000	2.0×10^5	322.63	815.0
PS 498,000	4.98×10^5	551.78	1400.0
PS 867,000	8.67×10^5	764.55	1930.0
PS 2,610,000	2.61×10^6	1,462.00	3700.0
PS 3,700,000	3.70×10^6	1,795.15	4530.0

1. PS = polystyrene and the number indicates the molecular weight; $\bar{M}_w/\bar{M}_n = 1.1$

2. ϕ (Å), the exclusion value, is the diameter of the smallest pore which is accessible for the molecule of that molecular weight; $\phi = 0.62 \, (\bar{M}_w)^{0.588}$

3. ϕ_d (Å) is the calculated coil diameters for polystyrenes in tetrahydrofuran solution; $\phi_d = 0.2457 \, (\bar{M}_w)^{0.588}$

Reference: I. Halasz and P. Vogtel, Angew. Chem. Int. Ed. Engl., 19, 24-28 (1980)
I. Halasz and K. Martin, "Pore Size of Solids," Angew. Chem. Int. Ed. Engl., 17, 901-908 (1978)
M. E. Kreveld and N. van den Hoed, J. Chromatography, 83, 111 (1973)

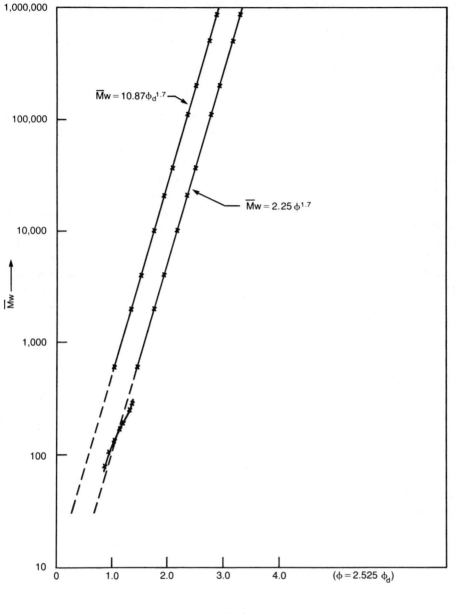

Figure 7.14 Molecular size ($\overline{\mathrm{M}}$w) as assessed by the calculated diameter of the random coil (ϕ_d) of the molecule and by the pore diameter (ϕ) of size sufficient for entrance of the molecule in size exclusion chromatography.

the selection of the proper internal dimensions—pore size, pore volume, and specific surface area—of the porous polymer upon which to build the catalyst.

CHEMISTRY OF FUNCTIONALIZED POROUS POLYMERS

The continuous pore system makes a macroporous resin suitable as a substrate for anchoring catalytic sites and makes it superior to that of a nonporous gel polymer. Comparisons between gel and porous polymers of equivalent levels of chemical cross-linker clearly show the enhanced catalytic effectiveness of the porous over the non-porous gel polymer [5]. It is misleading, however, to judge the suitability of a polymer simply by measuring the porosity and the specific surface of the pore system, for within the confines of polymer physics, porosity brings its own limits and its own constraints. The interrelation among porosity, pore size, pore size distribution, specific surface, and internal geometry has been presented and discussed. But there is one element about porosity that has not been given sufficient recognition with porous organic polymers. In order to develop porosity into organic polymers so as to have large internal specific surfaces, the cross-linking density of the polymer must be significantly increased. This change affects the intrinsic nature of the gel phase by making it less penetrable and less effective as the working arena. These concomitant changes of a greater number of pores, more internal specific surface, and a less penetrable gel phase (microgel) can lead to wrong expectations.

What does a catalyst seek to do? A catalyst speeds up a chemical reaction by lowering the barrier of the activation energy. But preceding this act and fundamental to having anything happen is the accessibility of the reactants to each other and to the catalytic site. Having pores in the polymeric matrix is good but not an elixir. The following example of wrong expectations will help to clarify. When porous polymers were discovered, it was initially thought that since rates of ion exchange are controlled by mass transfer, resins with pores would exhibit much better rates of ion exchange. The rate curves in Figure 7.15 show the rates of cation exchange in the exchange of Na^+ for H_3O^+ by a series of cross-linked resins of polystyrene/sulfonic acid with increasing cross-linking and increasing surface area. The specific surface of the resins under comparison increases in the following order:

- Amberlite IR-120 ($\bar{S}$ 0.1 m^2/gm),
- Amberlite 252 ($\bar{S}$ = 43 m^2/gm),
- Amberlite 200 ($\bar{S}$ = 55 m^2/gm),
- Amberlite XE-284 resin ($\bar{S}$ = 615 m^2/gm).

The cross-linking levels increase in the same order, but the rate of ion exchange decreases correspondingly [67], even though the surface area and the number of pores per unit volume is increasing. The trend of decreasing rate of ion exchange with increasing cross-linking density no longer applies with Amberlite XE-284 resin [67]. This resin contains the highest level of cross-linking density of the entire group of

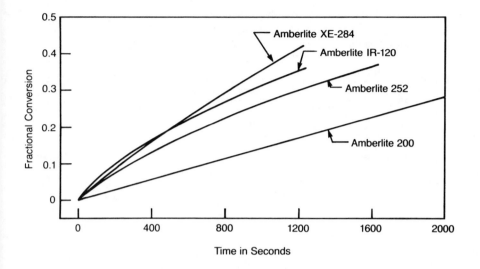

Figure 7.15   Rates of cation exchange for Amberlite resins.
Note: Data obtained via nuclear magnetic resonance [67].

resins at 95% divinylbenzene and has a rate of cation exchange equivalent to Amberlite IR-120 resin, which is a hydrated gel polymer. The reason for this reversal in the kinetic trend results from a shift in the working arena. For Amberlite XE-284 resin, the working phase for cation exchange is no longer the gel phase, as with all the other resins in this group, but is the surface phase. All of the functional groups in Amberlite XE-284 resin lie either on the internal surface or only one monolayer deep into the gel phase; 69.4% of the sulfonated aromatic rings are positioned in these two layers.

The important question, therefore, is, What is the working phase? The fact of porosity, interconnecting pores, and surface area may be of only minor significance if the working phase is still the gel phase. For a particular system, the working phase can be determined experimentally by examining the kinetics at three levels of specific surface ranging from low (100 m²/ml) to high (800 m²/ml) at a pore size large enough to allow ingress of reactants and egress of products. If the gel phase remains the working phase as the surface area is being increased, the rate of catalysis will decrease until that point is reached where the surface phase capacity becomes significant in the overall catalytic work. This relationship is a constraint of the porous polymer physics and arises from the nature of pore formation; for in order to increase the internal surface of a porous organic polymer particle (bead), the cross-linking density must be increased. The increasing cross-linking density in the gel phase is reducing the mass transfer in the working catalytic arena—the gel phase—much faster than the increasing surface phase is approaching a level of significance in the catalytic activity. The kinetic results given in Figure 7.15 are a clear witness to this relationship.

A second question arises from this observation. At what point or level of specific surface does the cross-over occur, where the surface phase takes over from the gel

Table 7.3   Intrinsic Properties of a Family of Sulfonated Porous Aromatic
Polymers: The Relationship of Surface Capacity, Specific Surface
Area, Cross-linking Density, and the Working Catalytic Arena

Sulfonated Porous Polymer	Theory Weight Capacity, meq./gm.	Measured Weight Capacity, meq./gm.	Rings on Internal Surface, No. %	Calculated Theory Wt. Cap on Int. Surf., meq./gm.	Cross-linking Density, Wt. % DVB	Specific Surface Area		Working Phase in Catalysis
						Ŝ m²/gm	Ŝ$_v$ m²/ml	
Amberlyst XN-1008[1]	5.299	5.26	2.76	0.146	12	40	60	gel phase
Amberlyst 15	5.210	5.00	3.72	0.197	20	55	82	gel phase
Amberlyst XN-1005[2]	4.854	3.50	11.95	0.683	50	120	180	gel phase
Amberlyst XN-1010	4.749	3.60	33.50	1.827	85	615	850	surface phase

1. Amberlyst XN-1008 is no longer marketed commercially. It has been replaced by Amberlyst 16 which is very similar in specific surface but is slightly more porous.
2. Amberlyst XN-1005 is no longer commercially available.

phase as the working arena? The answer to this question is not as accessible as the prior one either experimentally or theoretically. The data in Table 7.3 provide information on the sulfonated porous aromatic polymers derived from styrene, ethylvinylbenzene, and divinylbenzene where the varying levels of specific surface area, surface site capacity, and cross-linking density are compared. Only with Amberlyst XN-1010 resin is the surface site capacity a significant portion of the total weight capacity. The total weight capacity for this resin is accounted for by the sites on the surface and by those one monolayer deep. Only with Amberlyst XN-1010 resin is acid catalysis a true surface-phase event. The other three acid catalysts all function with the gel phase as the working arena. The relationship of their kinetic effectiveness for a given system is as represented below and decreases as the level of cross-linking within the gel phase increases:

- Amberlyst XN-1008,
- Amberlyst 15,
- Amberlyst XN-1005.

Amberlyst XN-1008 and XN-1005 are not commercially available.

CONCLUSIONS

Although not all the necessary knowledge is available to allow for an accurate selection of the right porous polymer on which to anchor the catalytic site for the reaction desired, it is possible to lay down some guidelines for the selection. The following statements and guidelines are presented as just that—guidelines. These guidelines are not cast in granite, and as additional kinetic properties are gathered, it will be necessary to modify the guidelines.

1. Identify the working phase for the reaction to be catalyzed.
2. Remember that aromatic polymers are very stiff and much less elastic and less

penetrable than aliphatic polymers. If the gel phase is the working phase in the porous polymer being chosen, a porous aliphatic polymer may be a more effective matrix on which to anchor the catalytic site than a porous aromatic polymer.

3. Porous polymers are usually more highly cross-linked than nonporous gel polymers and therefore have a less penetrable gel phase.

4. The advantage of the porous over the nonporous polymers where the working arena is the gel phase lies in the smaller dimensions of the gel domain and the increased accessibility of the gel domain.

5. For reactions of small molecules (molecular weights of 400 or less), the gel phase has sufficient penetrability for moderately cross-linked porous polymers (up to 30% cross-linker for aromatic and up to 50% for aliphatic polymers) to act as the working arena. Porous polymers with specific surface areas $(\overline{S}_v)$ within the range of 20 to 300 m^2/ml fall within this category and will serve well as supports.

6. For reactions whose products have intermediate molecular weights within the range of 400 to 800, more lightly cross-linked porous polymers (20% or less cross-linker for aromatic and up to 35% cross-linker for aliphatic polymers) will have gel phase penetrability sufficient to provide suitable rates of catalysis, where the specific surface areas $(\overline{S}_v)$ fall within the range of 20 to 300 m^2/ml.

7. For reactions whose reactants and (or) products exceed 800 molecular weight, gel phase penetrability becomes very sluggish with porous aromatic polymers and with moderately cross-linked aliphatic polymers (cross-linking greater than about 20%), and the working phase for acceptable rates of catalysis must be shifted from the gel phase to the surface phase.

8. For acceptable surface phase rates of catalysis, the specific surface area $(\overline{S}_v)$ of the porous polymer must be 500 m^2/ml or greater.

9. For porous aromatic polymers, such as the cross-linked polystyrene-type polymers, the specific surface area $(\overline{S}_v)$ reaches the minimum of 500 m^2/ml (540 m^2/gm at a skeletal density of 1.080 gm/ml) when about 25% of the aromatic rings lie on the internal surface.

10. For porous polymers with very large specific surface areas—$\overline{S}_v$ greater than 800 m^2/ml—pore dimensions begin to narrow and may become restricting to the entrance of the reactants into the pore surface for catalytic work or to the exiting of the products from the pore after catalytic work. For such porous polymers, the pore size distribution measurement—pore dimensions—becomes the significant element in the rate of catalytic work.

Appendix to Chapter 7

**EQUATIONS FOR CALCULATING THE
RELATIONSHIP OF VARIOUS QUANTITIES TO THE
DIAMETER OF SPHERICAL PARTICLES OF
POLYDIVINYLBENZENE**

Quantity:

1. Surface area of each sphere,
2. Specific surface area $(\overline{S})$ for 1 gm of spheres,
3. Volume of each sphere,
4. Number of spheres per equivalent of polymer,
5. Derivation of number of divinylbenzene rings per sphere.

Let:

V = volume of each sphere in ml;

D = diameter of sphere in cm;

d = skeletal density of gel polymer;

S = surface area per sphere in cm^2;

N = Avagadro's number or number of repeating monomer units per equivalent of polymer = 6.02252×10^{23} repeating monomer units per gram equivalent of polymer;

$\overline{M}$ = equivalent weight in gm of repeating monomer unit in polymer;

$\overline{V}$ = molar volume in ml of repeating monomer unit in polymer;

$\overline{S}$ = specific surface area in m^2/gm of polymer.

Given:

$$V = 1/6 \ \pi \ D^3;$$

$$S = \pi \ D^2;$$

$$d = 1.105 \text{ gm/ml for polydivinylbenzene};$$

$$\overline{M} = 130.1907 \text{ gm/eq for polydivinylbenzene;}$$

$$\overline{V} = 117.8196 \text{ ml/eq for polydivinylbenzene.}$$

Equations:

$$\frac{\overline{V}}{V} = Y = \text{number of spheres per equivalent of polymer;}$$

$$\left(\frac{V}{\overline{V}}\right) N = X = \text{number of aromatic rings from divinylbenzene per sphere;}$$

$$\frac{\overline{M}}{\overline{V}} = d;$$

$$\overline{S} = (\pi D^2) \left(\frac{\overline{V}}{V}\right) \left(\frac{1}{\overline{M}}\right)^{10^{-4}} \text{m}^2/\text{gm} \qquad \text{since} \quad \frac{\overline{V}}{M} = 1/d \;;$$

$$\overline{S} = \left(\pi D^2\right) \left(\frac{1}{d}\right) \left(\frac{1}{V}\right) 10^{-4} \text{ m}^2/\text{gm};$$

$$\overline{S} = \left(\pi D_2\right) \left(\frac{1}{d}\right) \left(\frac{10^{-4}}{1/6 \; \pi \; D^3}\right) \text{m}^2/\text{gm};$$

$$\overline{S} = \frac{6 \times 10^{-4}}{d \, D} \text{ m}^2/\text{gm};$$

$$\overline{V} = (Y)(1/6 \; \pi \; D^3) = 5.235988 \times 10^{-1} \; Y \, D^3 \;;$$

$$D^3 = \frac{\overline{V}}{5.235988 \times 10^{-1} Y} \;;$$

$$D = \left(\frac{\overline{V}}{5.235988 \times 10^{-1} \; Y}\right)^{1/3} \qquad \text{since} \quad X = \frac{N}{Y} \quad \text{and} \quad Y = \frac{N}{X} \;;$$

$$D = \left(\frac{\overline{V}}{5.235988 \times 10^{-1} \; (N/X)}\right)^{1/3} \;;$$

$$D = \left(\frac{X \, \overline{V}}{5.235988 \times 10^{-1} N}\right)^{1/3} \;;$$

$$D = \left(\frac{X \, \overline{V}}{3.153384 \times 10^{23}}\right)^{1/3} = \left(\frac{X \; 1.178196 \times 10^2}{3.153384 \times 10^{23}}\right)^{1/3} \;;$$

$$D = 7.20245 \times 10^{-8} \; (X) 1/3 \text{ cm.}$$

(This equation relates the diameter of the sphere of microgel to the number of aromatic rings per sphere.)

Surface area per sphere $= \pi D^2$ where d is in cm,

Surface area per sphere in m^2 $= (10^{-4}) \pi D^2$,

Surface area per sphere in m^2 $= (3.141593 \times 10^{-4}) D^2$.

Let:

S_{sp} = Surface area per sphere in m^2 ;

$$\bar{S} = (S_{sp})\,(Y)\left(\frac{1}{\overline{M}}\right) = (3.141593 \times 10^{-4})(D^2)(Y)\left(\frac{1}{\overline{M}}\right);$$

$$\bar{S} = (3.141593 \times 10^{-4})\left(\frac{V}{\overline{V}}\right)\left(\frac{1}{\overline{M}}\right)(D^2);$$

$$\bar{S} = \frac{(3.141593 \times 10^{-4})\,D^2\,\overline{V}}{V\,\overline{M}}.$$

SURFACE AREA CALCULATED FOR A MONOLAYER OF POLYDIVINYLBENZENE

Given:

Mol. Wt. of divinylbenzene = 130.1907,
Surface area of one DVB molecule = 50 $Å^2$,
Number of molecules per mole = 6.02252×10^{23}/gm mol,
Packing fraction of rings on the monolayer surface = 0.60.

$$\bar{S} = \frac{(50\ Å^2/\text{molecule})(6.02252 \times 10^{23}\ \text{molecule/mol})(10^{-20}\text{m}^2/Å^2)}{(130.1907\ \text{gm/mol})(0.60)} ;$$

$\bar{S}$ = 3,854.93 m^2/gm per monolayer side;

$\bar{S}_2$ = (3,854.93 m^2/gm)(2) = 7,709.87 m^2/gm for both
sides of monolayer.

AGREEMENT WITH $\bar{S}_2$ CALCULATED FROM DIAMETER OF SPHERE HOUSING ONE DVB RING

$$\bar{S}_2 = \pi D^2 = \frac{\pi D^2 (10^{-20}\ \text{m}^2/Å^2)(6.02252 \times 10^{23}\ \text{molecule/mol})}{130.1907\ \text{gm/mol}} ;$$

$$\bar{S}_2 = \frac{(3.141593)(7.20245\ Å)^2(6.02252 \times 10^{23}\ \text{molecule/mol})(10^{-20}\text{m}^2/Å^2)}{130.1907\ \text{gm/mol}} ;$$

$\bar{S}_2$ = 7,538.91 m^2/gm.

CALCULATION OF THE SURFACE AREA OF A MONOLAYER OF POLYDIVINYLBENZENE AT VARYING PACKING FRACTIONS FOR THE AROMATIC RINGS

Given:

$$\text{Surface area, one side, of divinylbenzene ring} = 50 \text{ Å}^2.$$

1. At a packing fraction of 1.0

$$\bar{S}_1 = \frac{(50 \text{ Å}^2)(6.02252 \times 10^{23} \text{ molecules/mol})(10^{-20} \text{Å}^2/\text{m}^2)}{130.1907 \text{ gm/mol}};$$

$$\bar{S}_1 = 2,312.961 \text{ m}^2/\text{gm (one side)};$$

$$\bar{S}_2 = (2,312.961)(2)\text{m}^2/\text{gm} = 4,625.922 \text{ m}^2/\text{gm};$$

$$\bar{S}_2 = 4,625.922 \text{ m}^2/\text{gm (two sides)}.$$

2. At a packing fraction of 0.6136060, which is obtained from the ratio of 100 Å^2—the surface area for two sides of a DVB ring—and the surface area of the sphere housing one DVB ring of 162.971 Å^2

$$\bar{S}^1 = 2,312.961/0.6136062 \text{ m}^2/\text{gm};$$

$$\bar{S}_1 = 3,769.456 \text{ m}^2/\text{gm (one side)};$$

$$\bar{S}_2 = 7,538.91 \text{ m}^2/\text{gm (two sides)}.$$

3. At a packing fraction of 0.60

$$\bar{S}_1 = 3,854.9348 \text{ m}^2/\text{gm (one side)};$$

$$\bar{S}_2 = 7,709.870 \text{ m}^2/\text{gm (two sides)}.$$

SOME CALCULATED QUANTITIES FOR A HOMOPOLYMER OF DIVINYLBENZENE

1. Diameter of sphere housing one aromatic ring

$$D = 7.20245 \text{ Å}.$$

Based upon this value for the diameter of the sphere

$$\bar{S} = 7,538.91 \text{ m}^2/\text{gm}.$$

Table 7A.1 Percentage of Aromatic Rings on the Internal Surface of Porous Polymers of Divinylbenzene as a Function of the Internal Specific Surface at Different Packing Fractions

Specific Surface Area, Ŝ, in m²/gm	Packing Fraction of the Aromatic Rings on the Internal Surface					
	1.0	0.90	0.80	0.70	0.60	0.613606
	%	%	%	%	%	%
100	4.323	3.891	3.459	3.026	2.594	2.653
300	12.970	11.673	10.376	9.079	7.782	7.959
500	21.617	19.456	17.294	15.132	12.970	13.265
700	30.264	27.238	24.211	21.185	18.159	18.570
900	38.911	35.020	31.129	27.238	23.347	23.876
1000	43.235	38.911	34.588	30.264	25.941	26.529
1100	47.558	42.802	38.046	33.291	28.535	29.182
1300	56.205	50.585	44.964	39.344	33.723	34.488
1500	64.852	58.367	51.882	45.396	38.911	39.794
1700	73.499	66.149	58.799	51.449	44.099	45.099
1900	82.146	73.931	65.717	57.502	49.287	50.405
2000	86.469	77.822	69.175	60.528	51.882	53.058
2100	90.793	81.713	72.634	63.555	54.476	55.711
2300	99.440	89.496	79.552	69.608	59.664	61.017

2. And the surface area per molecule with the assumption of spherical symmetry is

$$S/molecule = \pi D^2 = (3.14159)(7.20245 \text{ Å})^2 ;$$

$$S/molecule = 162.971 \text{ Å}^2.$$

3. For a porous homopolymer of divinylbenzene, Table 7A.1 is a tabulation of the percentage of the aromatic rings lying on the surface as a function of specific surface area and the packing density or packing fraction of the rings lying on the surface.

REFERENCES

1. C. L. Levesque and A. M. Craig. 1948. *Ind. Eng. Chem.* 40:96.
2. R. Kunin. 1972. *Ion Exchange Resins*, pp. 247–59. Huntington, N.Y.: Robert E. Krieger Publishing Co.
3. F. G. Helfferich. 1962. *Ion Exchange*, pp. 519–49. New York: McGraw-Hill.
4. H. S. Sherry. 1969. *In: Ion Exchange*, vol. 2. J. A. Marinsky, ed. New York: McGraw-Hill.
5. H. W. Heath, Jr., and B. C. Gates. 1972. *Am. Inst. Chem. Eng. J.* 18:321–26.
6. F. G. Helfferich. 1962. *Ion Exchange*, pp. 104–13. New York: McGraw-Hill.
7. H. P. Gregor. 1948. *J. Am. Chem. Soc.* 70:1293. H. P. Gregor. 1951. *J. Am. Chem. Soc.* 73:642.
8. H. P. Gregor, F. C. Collins, and M. Pope. 1951. *J. Colloid Sci.* 6:304.
9. G. E. Boyd, A. W. Adamson, and L. S. Myers, Jr. 1947. *J. Am. Chem. Soc.* 69:2836.
10. B. A. Soldano and G. E. Boyd. 1953. *J. Am. Chem. Soc.* 75:6099–104.
11. G. E. Boyd and B. A. Soldano. 1953. *J. Am. Chem. Soc.* 75:6091–99.
12. F. G. Helfferich. 1962. *Ion Exchange*, pp. 538–49. New York: McGraw-Hill.
13. F. G. Helfferich. 1983. *In: Mass Transfer and Kinetics of Ion Exchange*, pp. 157–79. L. Liberti and F. G. Helfferich, eds. The Hague: Martinas Nijhoff Publishers.

14. V. C. Haskell and L. P. Hammett. 1949. *J. Am. Chem. Soc.* 71:1284.
15. S. A. Bernhard and L. P. Hammett. 1953. *J. Am. Chem. Soc.* 75:1798.
16. S. A. Bernhard and L. P. Hammett. 1953. *J. Am. Chem. Soc.* 75:5834.
17. N. L. Smith and N. R. Amundson. 1951. *Ind. and Eng. Chem.* 43:2156.
18. S. Bhatia, K. Rajamoni, P. Rajkhowa, and M. G. Rao. 1973. *Ion Exch. and Membranes* 1:127.
19. J. Klein and H. Widdecke. 1979. *Chem.-Eng. Tech.* 51:560–68.
20. G. G. Thomas and C. W. Davies. 1947. *Nature* 159:372.
21. E. F. Meitzner and J. A. Oline. U.S. patent application 749,526, filed July 18, 1958; issued U.S. patent 4,221,871 to Rohm and Haas Co., September 9, 1980.
22. E. F. Meitzner and J. A. Oline. U.S. patent application 749,526, filed July 18, 1958; issued U.S. patent 4,224,415 to Rohm and Haas Co., September 23, 1980.
23. E. F. Meitzner and J. A. Oline, U.S. patent application 156,004, filed June 3, 1980; issued U.S. patent 4,382,124 to Rohm and Haas Co., May 3, 1983.
24. Anon. 1966. *Chem. and Eng. News* 44:54.
25. R. L. Gustafson, R. L. Albright, J. Heisler, J. A. Lirio, and O. T. Reid, Jr. 1968. *Ind. Eng. Chem., Prod. Res. and Dev.* 7:107.
26. R. L. Albright, U.S. patent 3,663,467, assigned to Rohm and Haas Co., May 16, 1972.
27. R. L. Albright, U.S. patent 3,767,600, assigned to Rohm and Haas Co., October 23, 1973.
28. R. Kunin, E. F. Meitzner, and N. Bortnick. 1962. *J. Am. Chem. Soc.* 84:305.
29. R. Kunin, E. F. Meitzner, J. A. Oline, S. A. Fisher, and N. Frisch. 1962. *Ind. Eng. Chem., Prod. Res. and Dev.* 1:140–44.
30. K. A. Kun and R. Kunin. 1967. *J. Poly. Sci.* C 16:1457–69.
31. K. A. Kun and R. Kunin. 1968. *J. Poly. Sci.* A 16:2689–701.
32. F. T. Fang. 1965. *In: Proceedings of the Third International Congress on Catalysis*, pp. 901–13. W. M. H. Sachtler, G. C. A. Schuitt, and P. Zwietering, eds. Amsterdam: North-Holland Publishing Co.
33. T. Alfrey and W. G. Lloyd. U.S. patent 3,322,695, assigned to Dow Chemical Co., May 30, 1967; W. G. Lloyd and T. Alfrey. 1962. *J. Poly. Sci.* 62:301.
34. J. R. Millar, D. G. Smith, W. E. Marr, and T. R. E. Kressman. 1963. *J. Chem. Soc.*: 218–25.
35. J. R. Millar, D. G. Smith, W. E. Marr, and T. R. E. Kressman. 1963. *J. Chem. Soc.*: 2779–84.
36. J. R. Millar, D. G. Smith, W. E. Marr, and T. R. E. Kressman. 1964. *J. Chem. Soc.*: 2740–46.
37. J. R. Millar, D. G. Smith, and T. R. E. Kressman. 1965. *J. Chem. Soc.* :304–10.
38. J. Lieto, D. Milstein, R. L. Albright, J. V. Minkiewicz, and B. C. Gates. 1983. *Chemtech* 13:46–53.
39. D. C. Sherrington. 1980. *In: Polymer Supported Reactions in Organic Synthesis*, pp. 1–82. P. Hodge and D. C. Sherrington, eds. New York: John Wiley.
40. F. W. Billmeyer, Jr. 1971. *Textbook of Polymer Science*. 2d ed., pp. 413–14. New York: John Wiley.
41. R. S. Porter and J. F. Johnson. 1966. *Chem. Reviews* 66:1–27.
42. K. M. Dooley, J. A. Williams, B. C. Gates, and R. L. Albright. 1982. *J. Catal.* 74:361–72.
43. R. B. Diemer, Jr., K. M. Dooley, B. C. Gates, and R. L. Albright. 1982. *J. Catal.* 74:373–87.
44. C. W. Davies and G. G. Thomas. 1952. *J. Chem. Soc.* :1607.
45. S. Affrossman and J. P. Murray. 1968. *J. Chem. Soc.* B :579.

46.   S. A. Bernhard, E. Garfield, and L. P. Hammett. 1954. *J. Am. Chem. Soc.* 76:991.
47.   P. Riesz and L. P. Hammett. 1954. *J. Am. Chem. Soc.* 76:992.
48.   E. A. Moelwyn-Hughes. 1971. *The Chemical Statics and Kinetics of Solutions*, pp. 340–80. New York: Academic Press.
49.   E. B. Brown. 1965. *Modern Optics*, pp. 111–17. New York: Reinhold Publishing.
50.   W. S. Schumb and E. S. Ritter. 1943. *J. Am. Chem. Soc.* 65:1692.
51.   S. J. Gregg and K. S. W. Sing. 1982. *Adsorption Surface Area, and Porosity*. 2nd ed. New York: Academic Press.
52.   S. J. Gregg and K. S. W. Sing. 1976. *In: Surface and Colloid Science*, vol. 9, pp. 231–360. E. Matijevic, ed. New York: John Wiley.
53.   D. C. Miles and J. H. Briston. 1965. *Polymer Technology*, p. 190. New York: Chemical Publishing.
54.   R. L. Albright. Measurements on polymers from my own research.
55.   D. C. Miles and J. H. Briston. 1965. *Polymer Technology*, p. 221. New York: Chemical Publishing.
56.   R. K. Iler. 1979. *The Chemistry of Silica*, p. 241. New York: John Wiley.
57.   R. L. Albright. Value calculated from bond lengths and bond angles for a molecule of styrene.
58.   S. J. Gregg and K. S. W. Sing. 1976. *In: Surface and Colloid Science*, vol. 9, pp. 263–68. E. Matijevic, ed. New York: John Wiley.
59.   G. D. Scott. 1960. Void fraction of random-close-packed system. *Nature* 188:908. J. D. Bernal and J. Mason. 1960. Void fraction of random-close-packed system. *Nature* 188:910.
60.   S. J. Gregg and K. S. W. Sing. 1967. *Adsorption, Surface Area, and Porosity*, pp. 121–94. New York: Academic Press.
61.   Micromeritics. 1982. "DigiSorb™ 2600." Norcross, Ga.: Micromeritics Instrument Corporation.
62.   Omicron. 1984. "Omnisorp™ 360 Analyzer." Berkeley Heights, NJ: Omicron Technology Corporation.
63.   R. L. Albright. Measurements on porous organic polymers from my own research.
64.   W. W. Yaw, J. J. Kirkland, and D. D. Bly. 1979. *Modern Size—Exclusion Liquid Chromatography*. New York: John Wiley.
65.   I. Halasz and K. Martin. 1978. *Angew. Chem. Int. Ed. Engl.* 17:901.
66.   I. Halasz and P. Vogtel. 1980. *Angew. Chem. Int. Ed. Engl.* 19:24.
67.   Data from L. S. Frankel, Private communication; L. S. Frankel. 1970. *Anal. Chem.* 42:1638.

CHAPTER 8

Specific Reactions Catalyzed by Functionalized Porous Organic Polymers: Reactions Catalyzed by Polymers with Acidic Functional Groups

Ignac J. Jakovac

Strongly acidic ion exchange resin catalysts have been employed in lieu of homogeneous acids in a host of chemical reactions including esterification, alkylation, olefin hydration/alcohol dehydration, olefin etherification, olefin dimerization, and condensation. The catalytic performance of ion exchange resins is controlled by a number of factors different from those that control homogeneous systems.

ELEMENTS AFFECTING CATALYTIC ACTIVITY

Cross-Linking Level

The effect of cross-linking on catalyst activity has received considerable attention. The catalytic activities for different levels of cross-linking have been measured for a variety of processes, including esterification and hydrolysis of aliphatic compounds [1-8], Claisen condensations of aromatic aldehydes [9], Prins reactions [10, 11], reaction of acetone and iodine [12], reaction of phenol with acetone [13], inversion of saccharose [14], alkylation of benzene with lower olefins [15, 16], and dehydration reactions [17, 18]. In general, it was concluded from the studies that the rate of reaction for gellular resins decreases with increased cross-linking. For macroporous (MR) resins, however, the rate was found to change only to a small degree with variations in cross-linking degree. At the same level of cross-linking, macroporous resins were always associated with faster reaction rates than those observed with a corresponding gel resin.

Surface Area and Porosity

The degree of cross-linking affects the surface area of a macroreticular polymeric catalyst. The greater is the degree of cross-linking, the larger is the surface area and porosity. A larger surface area is accompanied by the direct availability of a greater number of sulfonic acid groups. At the same time, however, the accessibility of active groups within the polymeric mass decreases.

It has been established that the rates of a variety of reactions in both liquid and gas phases are not proportional to the surface area of the catalysts [1, 7, 8, 17]. Therefore the catalytic activity of a macroporous resin is dependent on both surface sulfonics and on groups within the gellular portion of the matrix.

It has been concluded [7] that sulfonics in the gellular portion of a macroporous resin are in fact more active than those on the surface of the catalyst. That is, the environment within the gel portion gives rise to a higher Hammett acidity (Ho) with respect to that found on the surface of the catalyst. Therefore a catalyst that has the largest number of easily accessible interior sites might be expected to be the most catalytically active species.

Particle Size

The study of initial reaction rates of both gas- and liquid-phase transesterification of ethyl acetate with I-propanol has revealed that the catalyst particle size does not strongly influence the reaction rate [1]. Three particle sizes were studied—0.50–0.31 mm, 0.31–0.16 mm, and approximately 0.05 mm—with a variety of catalysts ranging from 2% to 60% divinylbenzene. A moderate increase in reaction rate was observed for gellular beads. The particle size did not affect the reaction rate when macroreticular resins were employed.

A similar rate increase was observed for the liquid-phase esterification of acetic acid with ethyl alcohol [21] and sucrose inversion [22] when smaller particle gel resins were used. In these cases, however, the rate enhancement was attributed to faster diffusion of substrates and products through smaller gellular particles.

Concentration of Catalytic Sites

It is well documented that the catalytic activity of styrene-DVB sulfonic acid catalysts is proportional to the concentration of "active" groups for a variety of reactions [16, 19, 20, 28, 29]. For example, if a resin is partially neutralized so that the SO_3H groups are partially replaced with SO_3Na groups uniformally throughout the whole polymeric mass, the catalytic activity will decrease [20]. If the concentration of SO_3H group remains constant in a given area—for example, by partial sulfonation—the activity docs not change, at least when considering the reesterification of ethyl acetate [19]. The rate does drop, however, when less than 50% of the resin is sulfonated. In the case of 2-propanol dehydration, it was shown that the rate fell to less than half by neutralizing only about 20% of the hydrogen ions [28].

Acidity to Superacidity

Superacid catalysts such as Nafion® (du Pont), a perfluorosulfonic acid polymer, have been used successfully in reactions where materials of lower acidity such as simple organic sulfonic acids showed little conversion of starting materials to products [39]. Klein and Widdecke [37] showed that Nafion® catalyzed the alkylation of benzene with propylene about three times faster than did a macroreticular sulfonic acid resin. However, when they fluorinated the sulfonic resin, they obtained a perfluorinated resin that catalyzed the same reaction about three times faster than did Nafion®. This rate enhancement was attributed not only to the increased activity of the catalyst but also to the higher degree of porosity associated with the ion exchange resin.

Another approach taken to increase catalytic activity by increasing the acidity of the catalyst is to introduce Lewis acids into sulfonic resin catalysts. The combination of Lewis acids with sulfonic resin Bronsted acids led to highly active catalysts. This was accomplished by reacting the catalyst with gaseous BF_3 or gaseous $AlCl_3$ [40, 41]. The isomerization and cracking of alkanes was possible with such catalysts and was not possible using commercial sulfonic resins. Klein and Widdecke [37, 42] have demonstrated that a polystyrene matrix itself is well suited to incorporate Lewis acids. For example, it was shown that polystyrene resins when reacted with $PCl_3/AlCl_3$ mixtures were effective catalysts in the alkylation of benezene with olefins [37].

THERMAL STABILITY OF ION EXCHANGE
RESIN CATALYSTS

Ion exchange resins (IERs) are prone to thermal degradation. The thermal degradation of aromatic sulfonic acids has been extensively investigated and proceeds by the well-documented [27, 34] mechanism shown in Figure 8.1.

For Rohm and Haas's commercial resins, we recommend a maximum operating temperature of 120°C in order to ensure a reasonable catalyst life. However, many processes, such as the hydration of lower olefins, proceed much more rapidly or selectively at elevated temperatures (circa 150°C). This, of course, considerably shortens the catalyst life to the point of making an ion exchange catalyst unattractive from a commercial viewpoint.

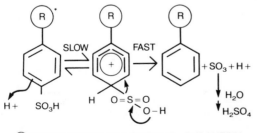

Ⓡ ˙CORRESPONDS TO A STYRENE—DVB MATRIX

Figure 8.1   Thermal degradation of aromatic sulfonic acids.

It has been demonstrated [27] for a variety of aromatic sulfonic acids that the desulfonation rate is affected by a number of factors:

1.   Temperature: The general rule of thumb is that the desulfonation rate increases 2.5–3.5 times for every 10°C rise in temperature.
2.   Acid Concentration: The reaction is acid catalyzed. In general, the rate of desulfonation increases 2.5 to 3.5 times for every 1N increase in acid concentration.
3.   Charge Density: Electron-rich sulfonic acids are less thermally stable than electron-poor ones.

The generation of thermal desulfonation data has been accomplished primarily in sealed apparatus in water [27, 30–33]. However, in the case of a sealed system, the rates of decomposition are affected by the sulfuric acid's being formed during desulfonation, and the rate can be significantly increased [33]. In order to eliminate the effect of sulfuric acid, we and others [43] have generated data using a continuous-flow system. Thus, 30 ml of resin are packed into a stainless steel tube enclosed in an oven. Water is pumped through the system at a flow rate of 4 BV/hr. The temperature is adjusted to 155°C, and the pressure in the system is 150 psi. The effluent is periodically collected and titrated for acid with standardized sodium hydroxide. Typical data for some of our commercial resins as well as some of our developmental resins are shown in Figures 8.2 and 8.3.

As the temperature decreases, so does the rate of desulfonation, and the difference in thermal performance between resins becomes less pronounced. At temperatures below 100°C, there is little or no difference in thermal desulfonation rates between resins for many hundreds, even thousands, of hours because all are on the initial fast desulfonation portion of the curve. Only at elevated temperatures are the thermal differences between IERs apparent.

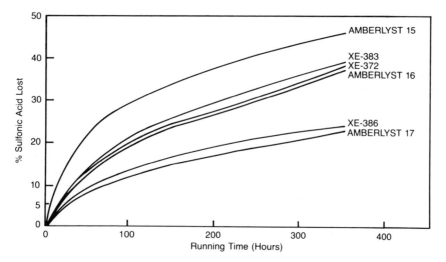

Figure 8.2   Thermal stability: Percentage capacity lost versus time 155°C, 4BV/hr 150 psi.

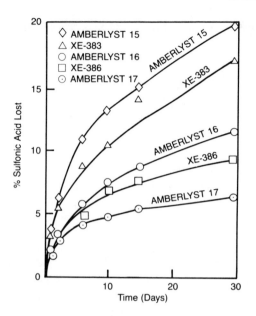

Figure 8.3   Thermal stability (130°C).

It has been shown that the kinetics of the desulfonation reaction can be described by an H^+- ion catalyzed elimination of -SO₃H groups, resulting in an overall second-order reaction [33, 34] dependent on sulfonic acid group concentration.

The shape of the decomposition curve for styrene-divinylbenzene resins is informative. There is an initial fast desulfonation followed by a slower rate. We agree with Petrus and coworkers [34] that at least three types of species are desulfonating. A small number of groups (approximately 3%) decompose quickly. These have been attributed to sulfate esters. They can be formed by the sulfonation of unpolymerized olefinic units from either end groups or the double bond of a divinylbenzene unit. The most stable sulfonic groups are those attached at the para position of styrene units [27]. Less stable units are those attached to divinylbenzene and ethylstyrene moieties. Dialkyl-substituted aromatics make the aromatic ring electron rich compared to styrene and thus give rise to a faster desulfonation rate. This argument implies that more highly cross-linked resins are less thermally stable. The data shown in Figure 8.1 support the hypothesis. That is, Amberlyst 15 is more highly cross-linked than Amberlyst 16, and the former is clearly less thermally stable.

If one were to decrease the electron density in the aromatic sulfonic acids, one might expect thermally more stable materials. A number of electron-withdrawing substitutes have been introduced into the polymeric matrix of styrene-DVB resins, including nitro [35], chloro [35, 36], and fluoro [37]. The corresponding sulfonic acids are all claimed to be more thermally stable than those without electron-withdrawing groups associated with them.

Finally, it has been demonstrated that aliphatic sulfonic acids attached to styrene-divinylbenzene matrices are more thermally stable than aromatic sulfonic acids because the aliphatic materials are not accessible to the same type of hydrolysis reaction [37, 38].

EXAMPLES OF RESIN-CATALYZED PROCESSES

Tert-Butyl Alcohol Dehydration

The dehydration of t-butanol has been investigated extensively [23–25]. It was determined that the reaction rate increased with temperature for both gel and macroporous resin catalysts. A series of resins was then evaluated with respect to cross-linking level, water effects, particle size, and active site concentration in the dehydration of t-butanol. Increasing the level of cross-linking in gel resins decreased the rate of reaction. (The cross-linking level in macroporous resins was not evaluated.) This was thought to be a result of swelling rates. That is, a 12% divinylbenzene resin was said to have a tighter gel network than a 2% resin and would thus swell less readily. The number of active catalytic sites is lower in a nonswollen material than in a swollen one. Mass transport was also impeded with increasing particle size so that the rate decreased with larger resin particles.

It was determined that water initially accelerated the reaction but then inhibited it as water concentration increased. The interpretation was that water initially served to swell the polymer and thus allowed for faster mass transfer by reducing intraparticle resistance. Inhibition by water was said to indicate a competition between water and t-butanol for the catalytic sites. There was no initial rate acceleration for a macroporous resin such as Amberlyst 15 because interior sulfonic acid groups are accessible. Conversely, there was no induction period for Amberlyst 15, but there were induction periods for every gel catalyst tested. Under identical conditions, Amberlyst 15 catalyzed the dehydration of t-butanol at a faster rate than a more lightly cross-linked gel.

The rate of t-butanol dehydration was proportional to acid concentration in both gel and macroporous resins. This was demonstrated by neutralizing the sulfonic acid units with Na, K, or Rb.

We have screened a number of macroreticular resins in t-butanol dehydration using the technique of Heath and Gates [24]. The results are outlined in Figure 8.4. Physical properties of the catalysts are listed in Table 8.1.

The wide range of catalytic performance is not directly proportional to surface area/porosity. Furthermore, the rate is not directly proportional to acid capacity; Amberlyst 17 has a roughly 30% lower capacity than Amberlyst 16 but gives rise to a faster dehydration rate than Amberlyst 16.

Amberlite XE-386 is more lightly cross-linked than Amberlyst 15, and Amberlite XE-383 has similar cross-linking to Amberlyst 15. The catalytic performance of these materials is, however, significantly different.

We have modified the structure of our ion exchange catalysts in a way that allows for the observed rate enhancement.

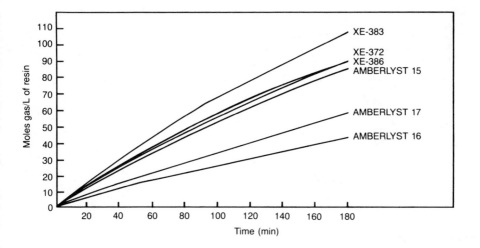

Figure 8.4   t-BuOH dehydration: 75.5 ± 0.5°C 400g. 95% t-BuOH/5% H_2O 5 g of −20 + 30 mesh catalyst.

Bisphenol "A"

Bisphenol "A" is produced by condensing 2 moles of phenol with 1 mole of acetone, as outlined in Figure 8.5. The Bisphenol "A" can be condensed with phosgene to produce polycarbonates or with epichlorohydrin to form epoxy resins. These are the two major high-volume uses for Bisphenol "A" [43].

The catalysts used initially for producing Bisphenol "A" were either sulfuric or hydrochloric acid. However, the use of homogeneous acids required a neutralization procedure and also a distillation of the resulting Bisphenol "A" because of the many by-products formed during the reaction under the highly acid conditions. Furthermore, the mineral acids employed caused corrosion problems, accounting for a significant amount of downtime.

Strongly acidic ion exchange resins have been used to carry out the condensation of acetone and phenol; however, the rate of reaction is slower than that seen for mineral acids. The presence of mercaptans was found to accelerate the reaction to where it

Table 8.1   Surface Area/Porosity Data

Catalyst	Porosity (cc/g)	Surface area (BET m^2/gm)
AMBERLYST 15	0.40	58
AMBERLYST 16	0.15	39
AMBERLYST 17	0.14	37
XE 372	0.36	45
XE 386	0.20	35
XE 383	0.36	44

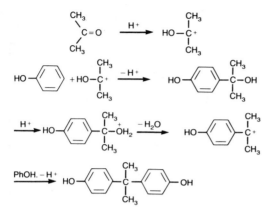

Figure 8.5   Bisphenol "A" production.

became commercially viable [44–49]. Presumably a sulfonium ion is formed that is prone to reaction with phenol.

Catalysts containing both the mercapto and sulfonic acid groups have appeared in the patent literature. These have included strongly acidic ion exchange resins that were partially neutralized with mercaptoamines [44], partially esterified with a mercaptoalcohol [45], partially neutralized with thiazolidines [46], partially reduced to thiophenols [47], and partially amidated to produce sulfonamide mercaptans [48, 49]. The last is claimed to be the most active and most selective, and the catalyst least susceptible to chemical degradation of the types of resins evaluated.

This author is unaware of any published study that compares the use of various ion exchange resin catalysts in Bisphenol "A" production. The patent literature [44] speaks of gellular and macroreticular resins interchangeably; thus, diffusion may not be an issue. Finally, 5–25 mole percent of the available strong acid sites were modified with an appropriate mercaptan species in the cited examples. Thus, a high-capacity resin would clearly be desirable in this application in order to have a reasonable quantity of free sulfonic acid units available.

Methyl tert-Butyl Ether (MTBE)

MTBE has gained wide acceptance as an environmentally safe octane improver for gasoline. Macroporous strong acid resins have been the catalysts of choice for preparing MTBE.

A number of reports have recently been published detailing the performance of commercial catalysts in the production of MTBE [50–54], along with similar etherification reactions, including the reaction of conjugated dienes with lower alcohols [55], isoamylene with methanol to produce t-amyl methyl ether (TAME) [56], and mixtures of C-4 and C-5 iso-olefins with lower alcohols [57].

For macroporous materials such as Amberlyst 15 [51, 53, 54], KU-2FPP [50],

and an unnamed material similar to Amberlyst 15 [52], it was determined that conversion of isobutylene to MTBE increased with increasing temperatures [50–54],
decreased with decreasing mole ratios of methanol to isobutylene [50–52], and increased with longer contact times [52]. The selectivity of the reaction for MTBE
decreased when the mole ratio of methanol to isobutylene dropped below 1.0 [52].

A detailed study was carried out in conjunction with Ladisch and Voloch (Purdue
University) to evaluate the performance of Amberlyst 15 and other strong acid ion
exchange resins in the preparation of MTBE [57, 58]. A bench scale plug flow reactor
was employed using the feed composition outlined in Table 8.2 with a methanol-to-
isobutylene mole ratio of 1.24:1. The conversion of isobutylene and selectivity for
MTBE was measured at two different flow rates with respect to temperature. The data
are presented in Figure 8.6. As outlined in the literature [50–54], the conversion to
MTBE increased with increasing temperature and decreasing flow rate. The increase
in conversion with lower flow rates indicates the reaction to be kinetically controlled
over the range of conditions examined. It was further observed that selectivity for
MTBE increased with increasing temperature and decreasing flow rate. Finally, using
Amberlyst 15, there was no apparent particle size effect on either conversion or
selectivity. The conversion and selectivity of a number of other materials was then
examined at one flow rate, 97.5 lbs/ft^2/hr (4.02 g/min), and two steady-state temperatures, 40°C and 60°C. The results are outlined in Table 8.3.

The only gellular material examined (IR-132C) had very low conversion, presumably because of diffusion difficulties. The selectivity for MTBE, however, was
excellent, even at 40°C. The rest of the resins are macroporous and catalyze the
etherification efficiently at 60°C. There does not appear to be a strong correlation
between porosity and surface area except to say that a good range may be .20–.40
cc/g for porosity and 40–60 m^2/gm for surface area.

The cross-linking levels are of the order:

$$XN-1010 > Amberlyst\ 15 \approx XE-383 > Amberlyst\ 16 \approx XE-386 > XE-397.$$

There is no direct relationship to level of cross-linking, but a favored range is 12–
20% (the first four resins in Table 8.3 fall into this range).

Finally, Amberlyst 15 and Amberlite XE-383 are the resins of choice for MTBE
synthesis under our conditions because even at lower temperatures (40°C), the selec-

Table 8.2 Analysis of Feed Mixture[a]

Compound	Wt. %	Mole %
Methanol	12.0	19.7
Isobutylene	17.0	15.9
Isobutane	35.5	31.6
n-Butane	35.5	31.6
Propane	0.5	0.6
n-Pentane	0.5	0.4

[a]Supplied by Matheson Co., Joliet, Ill.

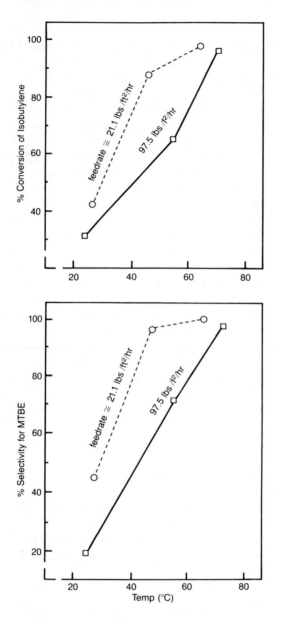

Figure 8.6   Conversion and selectivity as a function of temperature at two flow rates using Amberlyst 15 as a catalyst.

Table 8.3 Comparison of Resin Performance in MTBE Preparation

Resin	% IB Conversion		% MTBE Selectivity		Porosity (cc/g)
	60°C	40°C	60°C	40°C	
Amberlyst 15	95	47	100	80	0.40
Amberlyst 16	86	48	91	38	0.11
Amberlite XE-383	97	69	98	100	0.36
Amberlite XE-386	93	74	90	65	0.20
Amberlyst XN-1010	79	16	100	46	0.34
Amberlite IR-132C	30	11	100	100	—
Amberlite XE-397	84	21	99	64	0.65

tivity of isobutylene conversion to MTBE remains high. The by-products are dimers and polymers of isobutylene, which may foul the resin and decrease its useful life.

HYDRATION OF OLEFINS

Strongly acidic IER catalysts have been used to hydrate primarily C2-C5 olefins [59–69] to provide the corresponding alcohols. However, there also exist examples where more complex olefins such as bicyclo (2.2.1) heptenes, as well as related nortricyclenes, have also been hydrated to the corresponding alcohols [70]. Hydration of lower olefins is commercially important in that corresponding alcohols constitute intermediates in the production of various ketones (such as, acetone and methyl ethyl ketone) and other organic compounds. Furthermore, lower alcohols such as isopropyl alcohol (IPA) have become important in the fuel sector when the alcohol may be used as an octane number booster and a cosolvent for methanol [61].

Classical olefin hydration using sulfuric acid proceeds in two stages. First, the olefin reacts with the acid to form a mono- or dialkyl sulfate, and the sulfate is then hydrolyzed to produce the alcohol. In order to alleviate the well-known handling and processing difficulties of sulfuric acid, Deutsche Texaco has commercialized a process that uses a strong acid resin to catalyze the direct hydration of olefins such as propylene (in water) to produce the corresponding alcohol [59–61]. Although direct hydration appears to be the most commonly practiced procedure, there are instances where lower olefins are hydrated in a two-step process involving a dialkyl ether intermediate [69] or hydrating in the presence of a cosolvent such as acetone [66], a glycol diether [67], or hydroxy acids and derivatives [68].

Both gellular and macroporous resins have been used as olefin hydration catalysts. Macroporous materials are preferred because they tend to foul less readily than gels in long-term tests [61]. The activity of any given catalyst was found to be proportional to the concentration of sulfonic acid units [60, 61] and the activity was found to decrease with time because at the operating temperature (130–160°C), desulfonation occurred. The rate was found to be proportional to temperature, pressure, and acid concentration and level of cross-linking in the catalyst [61]. Thus, the ideal catalyst was identified as one containing 8–12% cross-linker [61]. This range of cross-linking was identified as being desirable because the desulfonation rate was acceptable and mechanical stability was ensured. Finally, it was observed that resins that were highly cross-linked catalyzed the hydration of, for example, propylene at a slower rate than some lightly cross-linked materials because of steric hindrance [60].

CONCLUSIONS

Ion exchange resins offer these advantages:

1. They are easy to handle.
2. They reduce or eliminate waste disposal problems.
3. They may improve product purity and yield.
4. They may cost less then homogeneous acid.
5. They eliminate or significantly reduce corrosion.

Their use is becoming increasingly important in chemical processing and catalysis on an industrial scale.

REFERENCES

1. Rodriguez, O., and Setinek, K. 1975. *J. Catal.* 39:449.
2. Andrianova, T. I. 1964. *Kinet. Katal.* 5:927.
3. Goldstein, L. M., and Friedlin, G. N. 1965. *Zh. Prike. Khin.* 38 (Leningrad) :1345.
4. Davini, P., and Tartarelli, R. 1972. *Chim. Ind.* 54 (Milan) :133.
5. Kebre, S. Y., and Ras Gopala, M. 1969. *Trans. Indian Inst. Chem. Eng.* :115.
6. Polyanskii, N. G., and Gorbunov, G. V. 1972. *Zh. Prike. Khim.* 45 (Leningrad) :2282.
7. Dooley, K. M.; Williams, J. A.; Gates, B. C.; and Albright, R. L. 1982. *J. Catal.* 74:361.
8. Beranek, L. 1979. *Acta Polymerica* 30:774.
9. Czuros, Z.; Deak, G.; Haraszty-Papp, M; and Prihradny, L. 1968. *Acta Chim. Acad. Sci. Ung.* 53:41.
10. Kuruser, Y. 1972. *Bull. Chem. Soc. Jap.* 45:211.
11. Bobylev, B. N.; Tepenitsyna, E. P.; and Farberov, M. I. 1969. *Neftkhimiam* 1:71.
12. Bafna, S. L., and Bhale, V. M. 1959. *J. Phys. Chem.* 63:1971.
13. Verkhovskaya, A. N.; Klimenko, M. Y.; Vystavkina, L. B.; Zaleskaya, E. M.; and Markarova, L. N. 1968. *Khim. Prom.* 7:490.
14. Bodamer, G., and Kunin, R. 1951. *Ind. Eng. Chem. Int. Ed.* 43:1082.
15. Mobil Oil Corp. British patent 1,023,426 (1966); *Chem. Abstr.* 65:20053F.
16. Klein, J., and Widdecke, H. 1979. *Chem. Ing. Tech.* 51:560.
17. Prokop, Z., and Setinek, K. 1974. *Collect. Czech. Chem. Commun.* 39:1253.
18. Martinec, A.; Setinek, K.; and Beranek, L. 1978. *J. Catal.* 51:86.
19. Setinek, K. 1979. *Collect. Czech. Chem. Commun.* 44:502.
20. Jarabek, K. 1979. *Collect. Czech. Chem. Commun.* 44:2611.
21. Kunin, R. 1972. *Amber-Hi-Lites*, no. 127.
22. Kunin, R. 1951. *Amber-Hi-Lites*, no. 13.
23. Frilette, V. J. U.S. patent 3,256,250 (1969).
24. Heath, H. W., Jr., and Gates, B. C. 1972. *AIChE J.* 18:321.
25. Gates, B. C.; Wisnourkas, J. S.; and Heath, H. W., Jr. 1972. *J. Catal.* 24:320.
26. Gates, B. C., and Rodriguez, W. 1973. *J. Catal.* 31:27.
27. Gilbert, E. E. 1965. *Sulfonation and Related Reactions*, pp. 427–42. New York: Interscience Publishers.

28. Sivanand, S. P.; Singh, R. S; and Chakrabarty, D. K. 1983. Proc. Indian Acad. Sci. Chem. Sci. 3:227.
29. Prokop, Z., and Setinek, K. 1982. Collect. Czech. Chem. Commun. 47:1613.
30. Hall, G. R.; Klaschka, J. T.; Nellestyn, A.; and Streat, M. 1970. Ion Exc. Process, Ind. Pap. Conf., pp. 62–70.
31. Marinsky, J. A., and Potter, W. D. 1954. U.S. Atomic Energy Commission Keyport AECU:3348.
32. Tulupor, P. E., and Creben, V. P. 1972. J. Phys. Chem. 46:689.
33. Bothe, N.; Doscher, F.; Klein, J.; and Widdecke, H. 1979. Polymer 20:850.
34. Petrus, L; Stamhuls, E. J.; and Joosten, G. E. H. 1981. Ind. Eng. Chem. Prod. Res. Div. 20:366.
35. Frilette, V. J., and Eriton, N. J. U.S. patent 3,256,250 (1966).
36. Costin, C. R. U.S. patent 4,269,943 (1981).
37. Klein, J., and Widdecke, H. 1983. Erdol, und Kohle-Erdgas-Petrochemie vereinift mit Brennstoff-Chemie 1:307.
38. Doscher, F.; Klein, J.; Pohl, F.; and Widdecke, H. 1980. Makromol. Chem., Rapid Commun. 1:297.
39. Kapura, J. M., and Gates, B. C. 1973. Ind. Eng. Chem. Res. Prod. Div. 12:62.
40. Magnotta, V. L., and Gates, B. C. 1977. J. Catal. 46:266.
41. Weitkamp, J. 1980. Compendium 80/81, Erganzungsband der Zeitschrift Erdol und Kohle Erdgas-Petrochemie : 71.
42. Klein, J., and Widdecke, H. 1982. Chem. Ing. Tech. 54:595.
43. Wiseman, P. 1972. Industrial Organic Chemistry, pp. 194, 266–78. London: Applied Science Publishers.
44. McNutt, B. W., and Gammill, B. B. U.S. patent 31,394,089 (1968).
45. Apel, F. N.; Conte, L. B.; and Bender, H. L. U.S. patent 3,153,001 (1964).
46. Gammill, B. B.; Ladewig, G. R.; and Ham, G. E. U.S. patent 3,634,341 (1972).
47. Wagner, R. B. U.S. patent 3,172,916 (1965).
48. Heydenreich, F. European patent appl. 80,104,231.8 (1981).
49. Faler, G. R., and Loucks, G. R. U.S. patent 4,424,283 (1984).
50. Stryakhileva, M. N. 1981. "Sb. Nauch. Tr. NII Monomerov dlya Sintetich, Kauchuka," p. 88.
51. Gicguel, A., and Torck, B. 1983. J. Catal. 83:9.
52. Muja, I. 1982. Revista de Chimie 33:903.
53. Humski, K.; Jendrickso, J.; Milnovic, I.; and Simoncic, V. 1982. Kem. Ind. 31:403.
54. Smith, L. A. U.S. patent 4,336,407 (1982).
55. Wood, H. J.; Chase, J. D.; and Buenaventura, B. G. U.S. patent 4,204,077 (1980).
56. Sweeney, W. M., and Herbstman, S. U.S. patent 4,356,001 (1982).
57. Lacisch, M. R., and Voloch, M. Unpublished results.
58. Beasley, G. H., and Jakovac, I. J. 1984. Ion exchange technology. Soc. of Chem. Ind. :440.
59. Brandes, G.; Neier, W.; Wollner, J.; and Webers, W. U.S. patent 4,340,769 (1982).
60. Neier, W., and Woeliner, J. Chemtech:95.
61. Neier, W. 1984. Ion exchange technology. Society of Chemical Industry:360.
62. Gupta, V. P., and Douglas, W. J. M. 1967. AIChE J. 13:833.
63. Bowman, W. G., and Stadig, W. P. U.S. patent 4,087,471 (1978).
64. Odioso, R. C.; Henke, A. M.; Stauffer, H. C.; and Frech, K. J. 1961. Ind. and Eng. Chem. 53:209.
65. Hudson, F., and Pennington, J. British patent 1,374,368 (1974).
66. Giles, J. H.; Stultz, J. H.; and Pickle, J. D. U.S. patent 4,183,920 (1980).

67. Braithwaite, D. G., and Pickle, J. D. U.S. patent 4,424,388 (1984).
68. Okumura, Y.; Sakakibara, T.; and Kansko, K. European patent 55522 (1982).
69. Bezman, S. A. U.S. patent 4,352,945 (1982).
70. Tinsley, S. W.; MacPeck, D. L.; and Starcher, P. S. U.S. patent 3,345,419 (1967).

CHAPTER 9

The Spillover Phenomenon of Adsorbed Species

Sargis Khoobiar

The phenomenon of spillover was first noticed in the 1950s [1] when Kuriacose observed that the decomposition of GeH_4 on a Ge film was increased by contact with a Pt wire. Taylor proposed that the wire provided a ''porthole'' for the recombination of H atom to H_2 molecule. This was a reverse spillover and will be discussed later in the chapter.

EARLY WORK

The existence of hydrogen spillover and its importance in heterogeneous catalytic reaction was recognized in my first catalytic study in the late 1950s [2] and early 1960s [3]. An outstanding catalytic discovery made in the 1950s had a dramatic effect on the petroleum industry. The catalyst was Pt/Al_2O_3, which is used in the reforming process. Pt/Al_2O_3 is used universally for the improvement of octane ratings of motor fuels. High octane rating is essential to the improvement of engine performance.

Cyclohexane Dehydrogenation over Pt/Al_2O_3

The dehydrogenation of cyclohexane to benzene over Pt/Al_2O_3 was chosen as a model reaction since cyclohexane is an important component of natural naphtha. The aim of this study, done at Illinois Institute of Technology, was to develop a kinetic model for catalytic reforming reaction. To obtain a reliable model, it was necessary to have an isothermal reactor and to obtain low conversion, which would simplify the kinetic study.

    The reactor was 1 1/2" schedule 80 pipe, sectionally heated and fitted with several fixed thermocouples evenly placed in the catalyst bed. The reactor was charged with $1/16 \times 1/8"$ extruded catalyst and was diluted with small particles of inert alumina. An attempt was made to distribute the catalyst and alumina evenly in the bed. The ratio of inert alumina to the catalyst varied from 80:1 to 5000:1. To ensure isothermality of the reactor, heating was adjusted so that all thermocouples had similar temperature

201

readings. Dehydrogenation, the reaction being studied, was effected at 800°–900°F and 250–500 psig pressure. The hydrogen-to-cyclohexane ratio was 2–6 mole ratio. Liquid hourly space velocity (LHSV)—weight of cyclohexane per weight of catalyst per hour—varied from 10 to 800. The feed rate was 2.96 mole/hr and was kept constant, and to achieve the variation in space velocity, the catalyst weight was varied. The total inert weight was varied from 0.5–3 kg. The reactor height was 10 ft and was equipped with a preheater for the inlet fluids. The thermocouple readings were identical, which indicated approximate isothermality of the bed.

Figure 9.1 presents some experimental data. It appears that as the catalyst concentration increased, conversion reached pseudo-equilibrium, which was below the calculated thermodynamic value. At pseudo-equilibrium, the catalyst concentration for all runs was approximately 0.002 wt/wt., and LHSV was 100. There were 2.4 gm of catalyst diluted in 1.2 kg of inert support. The 2.4 g catalyst particles were very small, amounting numerically to approximately 450 diluted in 1200 cc of support. Each catalyst particle had as its neighbor 2.6 cc of inert alumina support.

In another experiment, catalyst particle size was reduced from 1/16″ to 20–30 mesh size. Table 9.1 shows the results for these two particle sizes. Conversion increased from 20 to 40% by decreasing the catalyst particle size. The 20–30 mesh fraction comprised approximately doubled the number of 1/16″ catalyst particles for the same weight. These data indicate the reaction rate was extremely rapid: 2.5 gm of catalyst diluted in 1200 cc of inert alumina yields 50–60% conversion when the feed is 2.9 gm mole/hr. There was significant bypass, as shown by the pseudo-equilibrium's being significantly below thermodynamic equilibrium (Figure 9.1). This was predictable

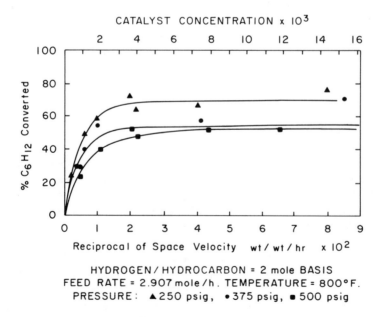

Figure 9.1   Conversion versus catalyst concentration.

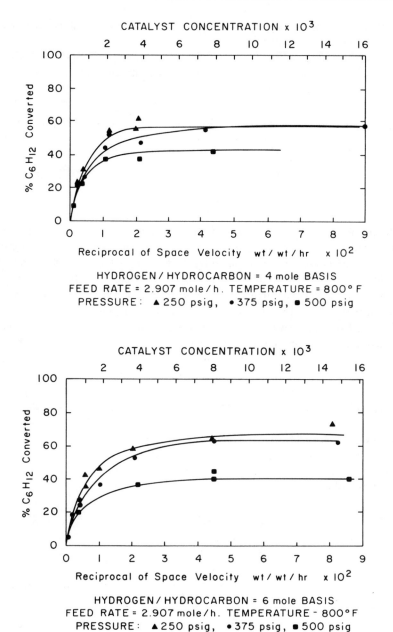

Figure 9.1   (continued)

Table 9.1　Difference in Conversion Attributable to the Condition of the Catalyst Whether in Pellet or Pulverized Form

Mol H_2 Mol C_6H_6 in Feed	Pressure (psig)	$\dfrac{Wt.\ C_6H_6\ in\ Feed}{Wt.\ of\ Cat/Hr.}$	Temperature (°F)	Catalyst Concentration $=4.7\times10^{-4}$ % Conversion Ground Catalyst, Mesh 24-28	Cat Full Size, 1/16" Pellet
4	250	400	800	50.00	23.60
4	375	400	800	42.12	21.40
4	500	400	800	37.93	17.6

because of the reactor length (L) to catalyst particle diameter (Pd) ratio of L/Pd 3–4. The preferred L/Pd ratio is 100 or more. Cyclohexane dehydrogenation is highly endothermic. The maximum rate is controlled by the rate of heat influx in the catalyst particle, assuming that heat transfer in the catalyst particle is rate controlling. A simple heat transfer calculation indicates that a small portion of observed conversion takes place on catalyst particles, and the remainder takes place somewhere else.

To explain the results, it was proposed that each catalyst particle activates the surrounding inert alumina. The volume of activated inert alumina is much larger than the catalyst particle volume. Reaction takes place on the catalyst and on activated alumina. This will satisfy heat transfer and pseudo-equilibrium. It is important to mention that the support without Pt/Al_2O_3 was completely inert, as shown in appropriate tests. To explain the results, the following kinetic step was hypothesized:

1.　Hydrogen dissociates over Pt/Al_2O_3 and migrates to surrounding inert alumina.
2.　The migrating hydrogen atom activates the inert alumina in its path.
3.　The hydrogen atom on the surrounding activated alumina dehydrogenates cyclohexane as follows:

$$H_2 \underset{}{\overset{Pt}{\rightleftarrows}} 2\overset{\cdot}{H}$$

$$2\overset{\cdot}{H} \underset{}{\overset{Al_2O_3}{\rightleftarrows}} 2H^+ + 2\bar{e}$$

$$n\overset{\cdot}{H} + M \quad \langle \rangle \rightleftarrows \langle \rangle \rightleftarrows \langle \rangle \rightleftarrows \langle \rangle \quad + (n + 6m)\overset{\cdot}{H}$$

$$2\overset{\cdot}{H} \overset{Pt}{\rightleftarrows} H_2 \quad gas .$$

This hypothesis increased effective catalyst volume from 0.0038 cc per particle to a significantly larger volume. Disclosure of these results created interest and skepticism since these hypotheses contradicted Langmuir and Hinshelwood's theory, which states that active species chemically adsorbed on surface sites are stationary and do not migrate on the catalyst surface. After chemical reaction, they desorb to the gas phase without migration.

Dissociation and Migration of H Atom

A literature survey at Exxon in 1959 and 1960 indicated that H_2 gas dissociated with electric discharge to atomic H, that WO_3 and MoO_3 are efficient chemical traps for atomic H [4], and that the color of WO_3 changes from yellow to blue when WO_3 traps atomic H. The hypothesis was that H2 dissociates to atomic H on Pt/Al_2O_3 and migrates from Pt to inert alumina. To elucidate this hypothesis, the following experiment was performed: Three groups of mechanically mixed granules were prepared. The first mixture was Pt/Al_2O_3 and WO_3 in equal weight. The second mixture was Al_2O_3 and WO_3 in equal weight. The third material was simply granules of WO_3. All three mixtures were placed in a Pyrex tube and separated by glass wool. Hydrogen was passed through the Pyrex tube over all three mixtures at room temperature [3].

The color of the mixture containing Pt changed rapidly from yellow to blue in 1 to 2 minutes, which indicated the reduction of WO_3 or, simply, hydrogen bronze formation, which is blue in color. Hydrogen flow was continued for several hours. No color change was observed in the other two mixtures. This experiment did prove the hypothesis: Hydrogen dissociates on Pt/Al_2O_3 and migrates to surrounding support.

Publication of these results created extensive interest in hydrogen migration and became known as hydrogen spillover. Since that time, over 400 papers on spillover, as well as four excellent review articles, have been published [5–8], and one International Congress (on the spillover phenomenon) was held in 1983 [9].

Two other hypotheses—the migrating of atomic H activating the inert support in its path and the dehydrogenation of cyclohexane by atomic H over activated alumina—were proved by others and will be presented later in this chapter. The spillover phenomenon was extended to O_2, CO, NO, and some hydrocarbons; however, the majority of the work was done on H_2 spillover.

Spillover Phenomenon

When a surface site (primary site) creates an ionic or radical active species, these active species migrate to the other sites (secondary sites), chemically adsorb or induce activity, or undergo a chemical reaction. The secondary sites cannot create significant active species without primary sites. This phenomenon is known as spillover.

There are at least two prerequisites for a spillover phenomenon to take place: (1) a primary source for the spilling species and (2) an acceptor, which is the secondary site, to accept the split species. The primary sources are group VIII and IB elements such as Pt, Pd, Ru, Rh, Ni, and Cu. The acceptors are most oxides, zeolites, and active carbon. In hydrogen spillover, the active species maintain equilibrium with other adsorbed gases, catalyst surfaces, and bulk. The spillover is a chemical reaction that is reversible and obeys the following thermodynamic rules:

$$H_2 \overset{Pt}{\rightleftarrows} 2H^\cdot$$
$$2H^\cdot \overset{Al_2O_3}{\rightleftarrows} 2H^+ + 2\bar{e}$$
$$\text{ionized doner } (Na^+) + P^+ = \text{ionized acceptor } (Na^-) + \bar{e}$$
$$H^+ + P^+ = \bar{O} + \bar{e}.$$

The adsorbed H_2 molecule, $H^{\cdot}$, H^+, $\bar{e}$, P^+, maintain [10] thermodynamic equilibrium between the gas phase, surface, and bulk of catalyst, where $\bar{e} + P^+$ are negative electrons and positive holes. Thermodynamic equilibrium occurs when there is no chemical reaction. When chemical reaction takes place, the concentration of $H^{\cdot}$, H^+, and other active species depends on partial pressure of H_2, the rate of splitting H_2 molecules, the rate of diffusion, the rate of chemical reaction of the active species, the chemical nature of the accepting support, the existence of impurities on the surface, the ease of transfer from particle to particle in pelleted or extruded catalyst, the existence of an active center for trapping H, and the temperature of operation.

HYDROGEN SPILLOVER AND ASSOCIATED PHENOMENA

The kinetic of spillover involves characterizing the species that adsorb and spill over, the transformation occurring on the surface or throughout the solid, the specific nature of the active site created on the support surface by spillover species, and the catalyst reaction taking place on these surfaces. Since over 90% of the studies that have been made have been on hydrogen spillover, the kinetics and mechanism of hydrogen spillover is better understood than other spillover species.

Electrical Conductivity of Al_2O_3 Under O_2 or H_2 at 500–600°C

The catalyst surface contains a mixture of H_2, $H+$, $H^{\cdot}$, and H-S, which are adsorbed hydrogen molecules, ionic hydrogen, radical hydrogen, and bound hydrogen, respectively. Several studies have attempted to generalize hydrogen spillover as one of these four types of species. This author proposed, in early work, that H_2 dissociates as a radical species and then donates an electron to the support as follows:

$$H_2 \overset{Pt}{\rightleftarrows} 2H^{\cdot}$$

$$2H^{\cdot} \overset{Al_2O_3}{\rightleftarrows} 2H^+ + \bar{e}.$$

Oxide supports are basically nonstoichiometric insulators with excessive impurities. Their electronic properties are similar to semiconductors, but they have large energy gaps between the conducting band and the valence band. There is thermodynamic equilibrium between all ionized impurities and $\bar{e}$, P^+ (electrons and holes) density. H^+ is a donor-ionized impurity. When H^+ migrates on the surface, the $\bar{e}$ tunnel in bulk follows the H^+ to maintain solid charge neutrality.

We studied the electronic properties of powdered Al_2O_3 [10], pressed at high pressure between two electrodes. The electronic properties were measured under O_2 and H_2 at 500–600°C. Figures 9.2, 9.3, and 9.4 show the results. The data indicate that conductivity increased severalfold under increasing pressure of either O_2 or H_2

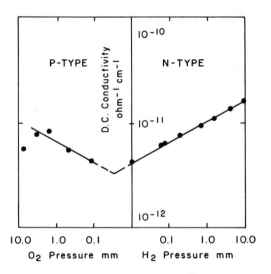

Figure 9.2   DC Conductivity of etaAl_2O_3 versus O_2 and H_2 pressure measured at 600°.

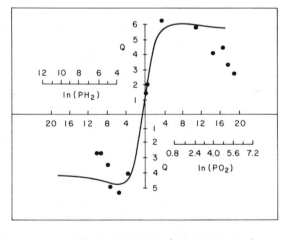

Figure 9.3   Thermoelectric power (Q) for etaAl_2O_3 at 600°C as a function of H_2 and O_2 pressure.

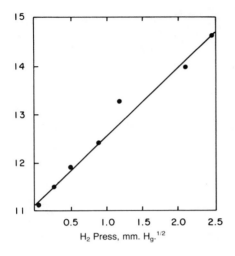

Figure 9.4   Dielectric constant of Al_2O_3 versus square root of H_2 pressure measured at 600°.

from a minimum conductivity in vacuum. Thermoelectric power changed direction on switching from H_2 to O_2, or the reverse. The dielectric constant was directly proportional to 0.5 H_2 partial pressure. The data indicated that the electronic properties of the Al_2O_3 changed depending on whether the environment was H_2 or O_2. It was assumed that this change was due to the effect of H^+, $\overline{O}$, $\overline{e}$, P^+ on nonstoichiometric aluminum oxide. H^+ and O^- are produced by ionization of H_2 and O_2 on the surface of Al_2O_3 at 500–600°C.

The concentration ratio of $H^{\cdot}$ and H^+ and their individual contribution to surface migration and chemical reaction is not clear; however, several outstanding studies have contributed significantly to the understanding of spillover. The first work was by Sinfelt and Lucchesi [11]. They hydrogenated C_2H_4 with Pt/SiO_2 catalyst, diluted with inert SiO_2 or Al_2O_3. The rate of reaction was severalfold higher when the diluent was Al_2O_3 versus SiO_2 under identical conditions.

Later, several workers [12, 13, 14] attempted to test the hypothesis that Pt/Al_2O_3 particles would activate surrounding inert surfaces and create active areas, much larger than the Pt/Al_2O_3, particles themselves under spillover conditions.

Sixty mg of Pt/Al_2O_3 catalyst were placed in a pan. The pan was covered with 100 mg aerogel alumina. After sample evacuation at 10^{-5} torr and 430°C for 17 hrs, 700 torr of H_2 was introduced for 6 hrs. The temperature was maintained at 430°C, a temperature in the spillover range. Then the temperature was reduced to 180°C for catalytic reaction. Using an accepted procedure, the Pt/Al_2O_3 catalyst was totally removed from aerogel alumina. Various tests included neutron activation, which indicated that no trace of Pt was left behind. A mixture of 700 torr of H_2 and 60 torr of ethylene was introduced into the reactor. The ethylene hydrogenated totally to ethane. The ethylene doses were repeated several times. Figure 9.5 shows the result.

Two blank experiments were conducted. In the first blank experiment, the alumina support ''activation'' at 430°C was performed with He instead of H_2. In the second experiment, support activation was performed with H_2 but without the Pt/Al_2O_3

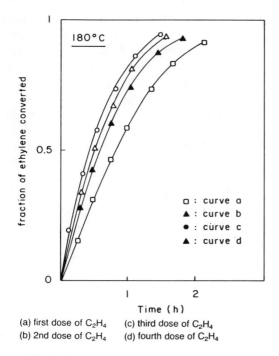

(a) first dose of C_2H_4 (c) third dose of C_2H_4
(b) 2nd dose of C_2H_4 (d) fourth dose of C_2H_4

Figure 9.5   Hydrogenation of ethylene.

catalyst. The hydrogenation was conducted as described. No ethylene hydrogenation was observed in either blank experiment. These experiments directly proved that aerogel alumina, activated with spillover hydrogen, successfully catalyzed the ethylene without the presence of Pt/Al$_2$O$_3$. Other independent measurements indicated that spillover hydrogen adsorbed per gm of Al$_2$O$_3$ is 1.4–1.5 cc [15] which is too small to account for all hydrogenation. This experiment proves the hypothesis that hydrogen spillover activates surrounding inert surfaces and those surfaces become catalytic for the hydrogenation of ethylene. The third hypothesis—that atomic H, on an activated support, dehydrogenates cyclohexane—was demonstrated by Sermon et al. [16] by analogy to dehydrogenation of other hydrocarbons.

Kinetics of Hydrogen Spillover

The data presented prove that H$_2$ dissociates over Pt; H$^{\cdot}$, H$^+$ migrates to surrounding areas or inert support and activate the support; and H$^{\cdot}$, H$^+$ of active region react with cyclohexane and initiate a dehydrogenation reaction. Now our attention will be turned to the effect of hydrogen spillover on catalytic reactions. It is believed that there is a thermodynamic equilibrium between H$_2$ in the gas phase and H$^{\cdot}$ and H$^+$ when the chemical reaction is rate controlling. H$^{\cdot}$ or H$^+$ may initiate reaction on the catalyst surface; that is, they may react with the support and reduce it, or they may get trapped in vacancies or in interstitial positions of the support. They may react with impurities on the surface and react with other present organic species. The effect of hydrogen spillover on the rate of catalytic reaction is a function of (1) the rate of dissociation of H_2 on the primary source (noble metals), (2) the rate of diffusion from primary source to support, (3) the rate of diffusion on support, (4) the rate of interparticle diffusion in pellet or extruded catalyst, or (5) the nature of support and ease of its activation for catalytic reaction. The group VIII and IB metals have been shown to be the primary elements for hydrogen spillover. Metals used extensively are Pt, Pd, Ir, Ru, Rh, Ni, Cu, and others. Many workers in the field believe that diffusion from primary source to acceptor support or surface migration is rate controlling.

Figure 9.6 shows H_2 uptake at 300°C on Pt/C at hydrogen pressure of 600, and 300 torr [17]. Figure 9.7 shows H_2 uptake on Pt/Al$_2$O$_3$ at 250–400°C [18]. As the example shows, activated carbon, metal oxides, and zeolites are acceptable supports for hydrogen spillover. Table 9.2 shows H/metal atomic ratio. If there was no spillover, the H/m ratio would be below 1. Several studies have tried to determine the concentration of hydrogen spillover over various supports. The following are some values of H concentration:

Metal and Support	Temperature	H_2 Concentration/Unit Area
Pt/Aerogel Al$_2$O$_3$	300° C	10^{12}/cm^2
PT/Al$_2$O$_3$	400° C	2×10^{12}/cm^2
	710 torrs	
Pt/SiO$_2$	25° C	1.5×10^{12}/cm^2
Pt/C	25° C	10^{13}–10^{16}/cm^2
Pd/Al$_2$O$_3$	25° C	10^{12}/cm^2

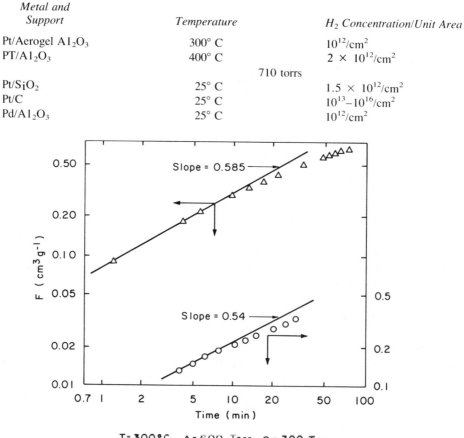

T= 300°C, Δ = 600 Torr, O = 300 Torr

Figure 9.6   Hydrogen uptake versus time on Pt/C.

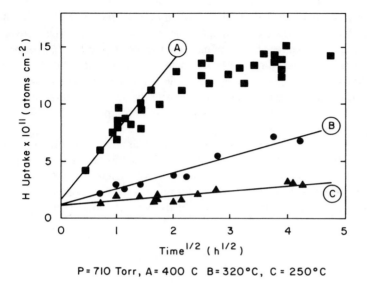

P = 710 Torr, A = 400 C B = 320°C, C = 250°C

Figure 9.7   Hydrogen uptake versus time on Pt/Al$_2$O$_3$.

Table 9.2   Maximum Values of n_H/n_M Measured for Some Supported Metals by Hydrogen Adsorption

Metal	Support	Maximum n_H/n_M	Temperature of Adsorption (°C)	Hydrogen Pressure (cm Hg)
Pd	SiO$_2$	(4.0)	−196	40
Pd	Al$_2$O$_3$	5.0		
Pd	Al$_2$O$_3$	3.2	25	
Pt	SiO$_2$	1.35	20	0.1
Pt	SiO$_2$	(1.5)	−196	
Pt	SiO$_2$	(1.6)	−196	$10^{-3} - 10^{-6}$
Pt	Al$_2$O$_3$	2.44	250	12
Pt	Al$_2$O$_3$	2.19	250	12
Pt	Al$_2$O$_3$	2	300	
Pt	Al$_2$O$_3$	1.5	200	0.9
Pt	Al$_2$O$_3$	> 1	200	0.9
Pt	Al$_2$O$_3$	10.0		
Pt	C	75	250	60
Pt	Zeolite	1.4	21	
Pt	Zeolite	2	100	
Pt	Zeolite	2	200	$5 - 20$
Pt		1.92	250	< 25
Rh	Al$_2$O$_3$	1.39	25	0

Source: After P. A. Sermon and G. C. Bond [5, 8].

The surface density of support oxide is about 10^{15} unit cells; therefore, 10^{12} is small. It corresponds to 0.1% of surface coverage. On carbon, however, hydrogen coverage is an order and magnitude larger than alumina. Some workers in the field assume that surface diffusion is rate controlling. They estimate the surface diffusion coefficient and the activation energy value as shown in Table 9.3. The value of the diffusion coefficient, measured on different supports, varies significantly depending on various techniques of measurement, preparation, and source of supports. Table 9.3 is an indication of the different values.

Excellent work was done to measure the distance that deuterium migrates versus the time from a single point source (Pd) on surface of SiO_2, by infrared spectroscopy [22]. Figures 9.8 and 9.9 show deuterium gradient versus distance for different time intervals at 200°C. These data indicate that deuterium migrates a distance of 8–9 mm from Pt primary source to acceptor support. The estimated diffusion coefficient is 10^{-5} cm^2/S.

Table 9.3 Estimated Surface Diffusion Parameters [8]

Surface	Temperature (°C)	D_{eff} (cm^2/s)	Distance (Å)	E_a (Kcal/mole)
Al_2O_3	400	10^{-15}	2000	28.5
WO_3	50	10^{-16}		
MO_3	50	10^{-13}		
C or SiO_2	100	10^{-14}	2000	15.5
C	2000	10^{-12}	1000	21.0
C	119	10^{-17}		39.2
Ce/Y-Zeo.	20	10^{-10}		

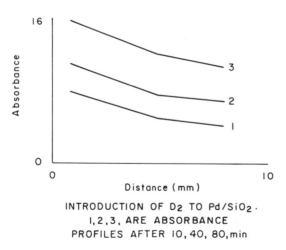

INTRODUCTION OF D2 TO Pd/SiO2.
1,2,3, ARE ABSORBANCE
PROFILES AFTER 10, 40, 80, min

Figure 9.8 Deuterium gradient versus distance (in millimeters).

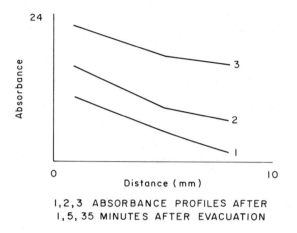

1,2,3 ABSORBANCE PROFILES AFTER
1,5,35 MINUTES AFTER EVACUATION

Figure 9.9 D_2 concentration gradient versus time.

HYDROGEN SPILLOVER EXTENDED ACTIVITY

Studying the dehydrogenation of cyclohexane to benzene in 1959, we observed a pseudo-equilibrium significantly below thermodynamic equilibrium. (Refer to Figure 9.1 at pseudo-equilibrium.) The concentration of the catalyst was 1×10^{-3}, and the weight hourly space velocity (WHSV) of hydrocarbon was 1×10^2. Catalyst weight was 2.43 gm, and support was 1.2 kg. The average catalyst size was 1.5×2.5 mm. There were approximately 450 catalyst particles diluted with 1.2 liters of inert support. If the catalyst particles activated the total inert volume, then hydrogen spillover should migrate and activate 7–8 mm radius from each catalyst particle. However, the observed pseudo-equilibrium indicated a significant bypass that reduced active distance from catalyst particle to under 7–8 mm. The migration distance for spillover deuterium on active alumina was determined as 7–8 mm [22].

More recently, Antonricci et al. [23] hydrogenated benzene to cyclohexane diluted with inert alumina. Hydrogenation was performed at 100–250°C. Figures 9.10 and 9.11 show the results. The data indicate that increasing catalyst dilution increases the reaction rate by a factor of eight for the same platinum loading compared to undiluted catalyst. Assuming that the concentration of $\overset{.}{H}$ atoms decreases proportionately as the distance increases from a point source and the rate of reaction is directly proportional to $\overset{.}{H}$ concentration, then for the same catalyst, $\overset{.}{H} = c\,e\,-\,kL$ or $R = c\,e\,-\,kL$. The data in Figure 9.12 approximate such an exponential equation. We predicted this hypothesis in our original work. Total concentration of H spillover will decrease with distance from the source (L). Pt/SiO₂ catalyst (0.05% Pt) diluted with Al_2O_3 at a ratio of 1–9 was seven times more active in the hydrogenation of ethylene than the undiluted catalyst [24].

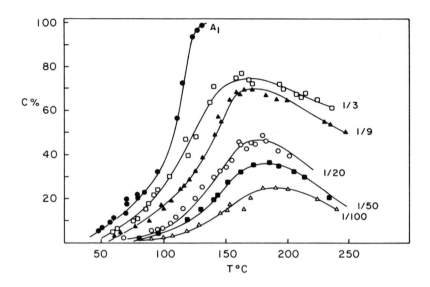

Figure 9.10   Hydrogen spillover and benzene hydrogenation with A_1 catalysts (Antonricci et al. experiment results).

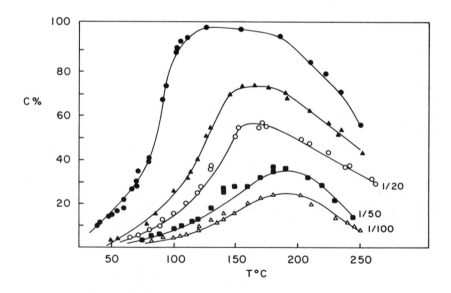

Figure 9.11   Hydrogen spillover and benzene hydrogenation with A_4 catalysts (Antonricci et al. experiment results).

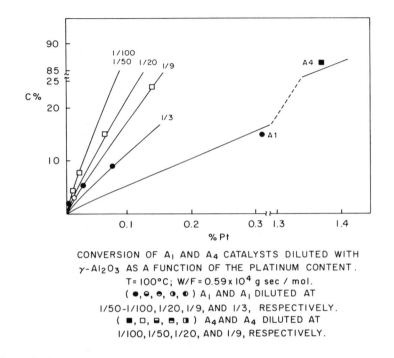

CONVERSION OF A_1 AND A_4 CATALYSTS DILUTED WITH
γ-Al_2O_3 AS A FUNCTION OF THE PLATINUM CONTENT.
T= 100°C; W/F = 0.59 x 10^4 g sec / mol.
(●, ◒, ◓, ◔, ◕) A_1 AND A_1 DILUTED AT
1/50-1/100, 1/20, 1/9, AND 1/3, RESPECTIVELY.
(■, ◻, ◨, ◧, ◩) A_4 AND A_4 DILUTED AT
1/100, 1/50, 1/20, AND 1/9, RESPECTIVELY.

Figure 9.12 H atom concentration decreasing proportionately away from point source while rate of reaction is directly proportionate to H concentration.

Effect of Hydrogen Spillover on Acceptor Support and Bronze Formation

Atomic hydrogen in a free radical H˙ form or ionic form, H^+, is an extremely active species. Each will react at much lower temperatures than molecular hydrogen with oxide supports. It has been well documented that the addition of a trace quantity of Pt or Pd to various oxide catalysts or supports [5, 6, 25] lowers their reduction temperatures much below the level attained by molecular H_2. This is observed on such oxides as CO_2O_3, V_2O_5, UO_3, Fe_2O_3 [26, 27, 28, 5], MoO_3, WO_3, Re_2O_7, CeO_2, NiO, CuO, Cu_2O, ZnO, SnO_2, and TiO_2. The degree of reduction is a function of temperature and the nature of the oxides. H atoms also react with oxides of V, W, and Mo at room temperature and create hydrogen bronzes without reduction. Formation of $H_{0.4}WO_3$ (tungsten bronze) by Pt/Al_2O_3 under H_2 flow was first proof of hydrogen spillover [3], as the color of WO_3, yellow, changed to blue, $H_{0.4}WO_3$. Later [23] $H_{1.6}$ MoO_3 and $H_{3.3}V_2O_5$ (molybdenum bronze) was observed. Kunimori et al. [29] used temperature programmed oxidation (TPO) and temperature programmed reduction (TPR) to study oxidation and reduction of a support. The experiment was performed at 400–500°C. They found that the support reduces, as shown in Table 9.4.

Table 9.4   Information on the SMSI State Estimated from the Consumption Measurements of Pt/Al_2O_3 and Pt/TiO_2 Catalysts

Catalyst	Degree of Reduction	N_0[a]	Local Structure[b]
5%Pt/Al_2O_3	Al_2O_{3-x} ($x = 0.03$)	ca. 4×10^{13}	$(Pt \cdot Al_2O_2)_n$ or $(PtAl_{2/3})_n$ etc.
1%Pt/TiO_2	TiO_{2-x} ($x = 0.01$)	ca. 1×10^{14}	$Pt_n(Ti_4O_7)_{2n}$ etc.

[a]Number of O atoms (per cm^2) eliminated from the oxide surface.
[b]The number of Pt atoms of each crystallite in the normal state is given as n.

Strong Metal Support Interaction (SMSI)

It was observed that the reduced support interacts so strongly with noble metal that it lowers the precious metals H_2 chemi-adsorption capacity at room temperature.

Figure 9.13 shows the result of reduction or oxidation of Pt-supported on TiO_2 at 400–550°C under hydrogen or oxygen atmosphere. It is evident that as TiO_2 reduces, the H_2 uptake decreases; as reduced TiO_2 is oxidized, the H_2 uptake increases. This is also observed for Pt/Al_2O_3 reduced and oxidized at 400–550°C in hydrogen or oxygen atmosphere, respectively. When Pt/Al_2O_3 or Pt/TiO_2 are reduced at high temperatures, the hydrogen adsorption capacity for Pt is greatly reduced. This is known as the SMSI phenomenon (strong metal support interaction). There are two explanations for SMSI:

1.   Pt alloys itself with reduced aluminum or titanium and loses its hydrogen adsorption capacity.
2.   The reduced titanium or aluminum oxide becomes an n-type electrical conductor (semiconductor or insulator) and transfers electrons to Pt. This reduces the hydrogen uptake capacity of Pt.

The latter explanation is preferred.

In another study [30], three samples were prepared by impregnation of TiO_2 with Pt, Rh, and Ni. A fourth sample was prepared without any metal. The electrical conductivity of the four samples was measured under the following conditions: catalyst treatment at 200°C temperature, 250 torr H_2 pressure, then evacuation at 400°C, followed by reducing the temperature to 25°C, and finally introducing H_2 at 50, 100, and 150 torr pressure.

The data indicate that TiO_2, after evacuation, behaved as a degenerate semiconductor with low activation energy. However, metal, which is the primary source of hydrogen spillover, partially reduces the TiO_2 under hydrogen atmosphere. The hydrogen donates electrons to TiO_2 and increases conductivity. After evacuation at 400°C, the reverse takes place, and TiO_2 loses electrons, thus reducing conductivity due to reverse spillover. Reducing the temperature from 400°C to 25°C reduces con-

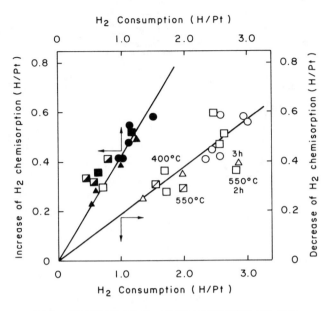

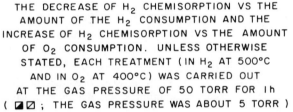

THE DECREASE OF H_2 CHEMISORPTION VS THE
AMOUNT OF THE H_2 CONSUMPTION AND THE
INCREASE OF H_2 CHEMISORPTION VS THE AMOUNT
OF O_2 CONSUMPTION. UNLESS OTHERWISE
STATED, EACH TREATMENT (IN H_2 AT 500°C
AND IN O_2 AT 400°C) WAS CARRIED OUT
AT THE GAS PRESSURE OF 50 TORR FOR 1h
(◪◩ ; THE GAS PRESSURE WAS ABOUT 5 TORR)

Figure 9.13 Result of reduction of oxidation of Pt supported TiO_2 at 400°–550°C under hydrogen or oxygen atmosphere.

ductivity by an order of magnitude. This is an activating process with activation energy of 8 Kcal/mole. The addition of H_2 increases the conductivity at 25°C. Hydrogen behaves as a donor impurity and converts to H^+, which accounts for the increased conductivity.

In the evacuation step at 400°C, hydrogen is removed by reverse spillover,

$$H^+ + \bar{e} \rightleftharpoons H^{\cdot}$$

$$2H^{\cdot} \overset{Pt}{\rightleftharpoons} H_2 \, ,$$

and TiO_2 conductivity decreases (see Figure 9.14). The reduced Pt/TiO_2 has high electron density and low hydrogen uptake capability. The reverse is true with an oxidized catalyst. This indicates that SMSI is due to increased electron density of TiO_2 and, possibly, the transfer of electrons to Pt crystallites.

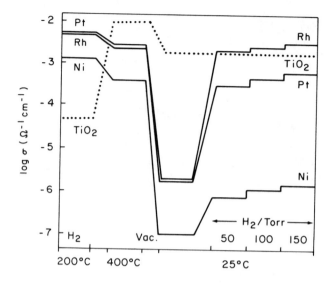

Figure 9.14   Electrical conductivity of TiO_2 and of Pt, Rh, and Ni/TiO_2 under indicated conditions.

Figure 9.15 shows Rh/TiO_2 conductivity versus H_2 (lower scale) and H_2 1/2 (upper scale) partial pressure. The data confirm the theory that adsorbed H donates electrons to Rh/TiO_2. It has been shown that TiO_2 is reduced by a beam of H atoms generated by a microwave discharge or by hydrogen spillover produced by Rh. In both cases, the TiO_2 surface is reduced. Reduced titanium oxide behaves as n-type semi-

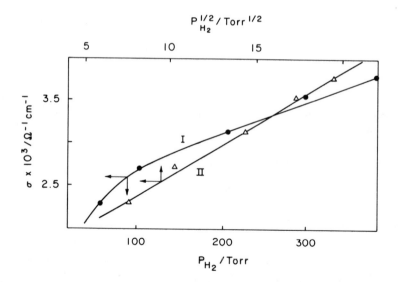

Figure 9.15   Rh/TiO_2 conductivity isotherm as a function of P_{H_2}(I) and linear transform (II).

conductor with increased electropotential (Fermi energy). The increase of electro-potential and transfer of electrons to noble metal prevents the noble metal from adsorbing H at room temperature. This condition is favorable for the creation of SMSI between metal and TiO_2. SMSI has been observed between Pt/Al_2O_3, $Pt/ZnAl_2O_3$, and others.

Strong metal support interaction was reported in 1978 [31] for Pd/TiO_2. The catalyst was reduced at 500°C in a hydrogen atmosphere. After evacuation, the catalyst was cooled to room temperature. It was found that Pd catalyzed the reduction of TiO_2 with the result that there was a significant loss of H_2 or CO uptake capability. This property is also known as SMSI. However, the SMSI does not affect catalytic activity significantly. The SMSI is normally associated with partial reduction of oxides and increases their electron density of semiconductor or insulator oxides. SMSI occurs with other noble metals and most oxides and zeolites.

In the presence of spillover hydrogen, stoichiometric metal oxides reduce to a nonstoichiometric oxidation state. Some oxides lose all their oxygen and reduce to a metallic state. This depends on the temperature of reduction and the specific oxide. Hydrogen spillover lowers the reduction temperature of oxides significantly [5, 6, 25]. Pt and Pd are most effective in this case. A large number of metal oxides have been reduced by spillover from Pt or Pd, at a much lower temperature than is the case when the reductant is molecular H_2. The metals are CO_3O_4, V_2O_5, VO_3, Fe_2O_3, WO_3, Re_2O_7, CrO_4, Ni_3O_4, MnO_2, NiO, CuO, Cu_2O, ZnO, SnO_2, and Ag_2O. SMSI takes place between many metals and metal oxides. They usually do not lose their catalytic activity, but they may lose CO and H_2 uptake capability. It is important to mention that reduced metal oxides have oxygen vacancies, and their SMSI property frequently is reversed with oxidation.

SOME HYDROCARBON REACTIONS AND HYDROGEN SPILLOVER

Spillover also takes place with O_2, CO, NO, and some hydrocarbons. Following are a few examples of hydrocarbon reactions that are explained by hydrogen spillover.

Naphtha Reforming

J. M. Parero et al. [32] studied reforming catalyst with the intent of gaining further evidence of spillover phenomena. They coked Al_2O_3 support with methylcyclopentane and naphtha under various conditions. In a set of experiments, Al_2O_3 was coked at 500°C for 2 or 12 hrs with a stream of hydrogen and methylcyclopentane at a 2:1 ratio. Coking was also done with naphtha at 515°C with a H_2-to-naphtha ratio of 4:1. In another set of experiments, a mixture of Al_2O_3 support and Pt/Al_2O_3 was coked under the same conditions; then the Pt/Al_2O_3 was separated from the coked Al_2O_3. It was found that the Al_2O_3 mixed with Pt/Al_2O_3 had a higher coke level than the unmixed Al_2O_3. A portion of the isolated coked Al_2O_3 was then mixed with Pt/Al_2O_3. The mixed and unmixed portions of coked Al_2O_3 were oxidized to determine their carbon levels by TPO (Total Product Oxidation). The oxidation was done with a thermal differential analyzer, raising the temperature 20°C/min and passing a flow of 50 ml/min of oxygen over a 20 mg sample. The TPO was done to determine the presence of carbon on the support and also the temperature of oxidation of that carbon. The higher the required oxidation temperature is, the more graphitic the carbon is. The TPR (Total Product Reduction) was performed to remove the easily removable carbon from the Al_2O_3 surface by hydrogenalysis of nongraphitic carbon. In a set of TPR experiments, it was found that Al_2O_3 that was coked by passing naphtha, or methylcyclopentane, for a short period of time produced a coke that could be partially eliminated by hydrogenation and completely eliminated if hydrogenation was performed in the presence of Pt. These experiments indicated that hydrogen spillover from Pt increased the rate of coke removal by the hydrogenalysis of coke. In a set of TPO experiments, it was found that coked Al_2O_3 oxidized at a lower temperature when mixed with Pt/Al_2O_3 catalyst. The explanation is that Pt causes oxygen to dissociate and migrate to coked Al_2O_3, thus oxidizing coke at a much lower temperature than molecular oxygen. This set of experiments indicates that hydrogen spillover is playing an important role in naphtha reforming or coke removal. It is commonly accepted by the petroleum industry that H_2 reduces coke formation by the avoidance of graphitic carbon.

Isopentane and Cyclohexane Dehydrogenation on Activated Carbon: Reverse Spillover

It has been observed that the addition of noble metals or IB metals of the periodic tables to a dehydrogenation catalyst increases the rate of dehydrogenation. It is assumed that hydrogen produced during the dehydrogenation process is first in the atomic form and then migrates and combines on Pt to H_2 molecules which desorb as molecular H_2. These experiments below are examples of reverse spillover.

One series of experiments [34] clearly shows that reverse spillover controls the rate of most dehydrogenation reactions. It was found that the dehydrogenation of isopentane on an active carbon is accelerated by the addition of a hydrogen acceptor molecule, such as O_2, NO, or C_2H_4, where the acceptor molecules react with the derived atomic hydrogen. Also observed was that the catalytic activity of carbon generally is increased by the addition of transition metals, such as Co, Ni, Fe, Cu. These two sets of experiments point out that the increase in the reaction rate when transition metals are added to the dehydrogenation catalyst is due to reverse spillover, where hydrogen atoms combine on the surface of metal and then desorb as the less reactive molecular H_2. The rate of combining two hydrogen atoms on metal is much higher than on the carbon support. The following experiments are semiquantitative but tend to augment the spillover concept.

Several catalysts were prepared from steam activated carbon with 1200 m^2/gm of surface area. Activated carbon was impregnated with transition metals Co, Ni, Fe as well as Cu at various concentration levels. The catalysts were reduced with hydrogen; then the rate of H_2 adsorption and temperature program desorption (TPD) were performed on all reduced catalysts. Subsequently dehydrogenation experiments were done in a flow system. Figure 9.16 shows the amount of hydrogen uptake versus time. The rate of adsorption is the amount of uptake at zero time. Table 9.5 shows the result for isopentane and cyclohexane dehydrogenation at constant conditions. Figure 9.17 shows the initial rate of hydrogen uptake versus the rate of dehydrogenation of cyclohexane for various metal loadings.

These experiments indicate that transition metals increase the rate of hydrogen uptake, as well as the rate of cyclohexane dehydrogenation. Total hydrogen uptake for the support is independent of metal loading. The metal only increases the rate of hydrogen uptake. A similar experiment indicates that the metal loading increases the rate of hydrogen desorption. These experiments show that metals are a gate for adsorption and desorption of H_2, which facilitates dehydrogenation activity. These explanations will apply to any metal-supported catalyst.

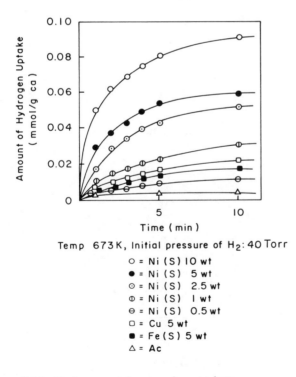

Temp 673 K, Initial pressure of H_2: 40 Torr

O = Ni (S) 10 wt
● = Ni (S) 5 wt
⊙ = Ni (S) 2.5 wt
Φ = Ni (S) 1 wt
⊖ = Ni (S) 0.5 wt
□ = Cu 5 wt
■ = Fe (S) 5 wt
△ = Ac

Figure 9.16   Hydrogen uptake on carbon catalysts.

Table 9.5 Dehydrogenation of Isopentane and Cyclohexane on Various Activated Carbon Catalysts

Catalyst	Reactant	Conversion (mol%)	Dehydrogenation Selectivity
C		3.5	0.93
C-Cr		31.0	0.80
C-Mn		18.4	0.94
C-Fe		23.4	0.94
C-Co	Isopentane	21.5	0.91
C-Ni	(723K)	21.3	0.91
C-Cu		15.4	0.94
C-Th		23.7	0.87
C-Mo		27.7	0.80
C		4.7	0.99
C-Co		31.7	0.97
C-Cu		12.4	0.99
C-Th	Cyclohexane	9.6	0.99
C-Mi(S)	(693K)	30.2	0.96
C-Fe(S)		11.3	0.99
C-Co(S)		20.5	0.98

Note: W/F $=$ 24 g $-$ cat $\cdot$ hr/mol, Promoter 5wt % Metal on Carbon Isopentane/N_2 = 0.2, Cyclohexane/N_2 = 0.086

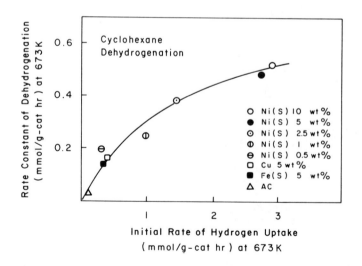

Figure 9.17 Catalytic activity versus initial rate of hydrogen spillover.

SPILLOVER OF SPECIES OTHER THAN HYDROGEN

O_2 Spillover

There is strong evidence that the spillover phenomenon applies not only to hydrogen but is widespread. O_2, CO, NO, and hydrocarbons all show the spillover phenomenon. The existence of oxygen spillover is reported in the oxidation of coke on Pt/Al_2O_3 reforming catalyst. A well-studied system is oxidation of carbon [35]. The technique used for this study is etch decoration/transmission electron microscopy technique (ED-TEM). The EDTEM technique, described in detail by Herning, consists of cleaving single crystals of natural graphite to a thickness of a few hundred angstroms and etching the graphite in a gas (O_2 in argon). This expands the surface vacancy and creates a pit, one atom layer deep; the edge of the pit is "decorated" with gold nuclei, which are examined by Transmission Electron Microscopy. The radius of the pit is proportional to the time of etching. The graphite atoms on the edge of the pit are the active sites and react readily with O atoms. From the pit growth rate, it is possible to calculate the rate of removal of carbon atoms at 650°C or turnover frequency of oxygen atoms directly proportional to the atoms of carbon removed. Impregnating carbon with metal increases the rate of carbon oxidation. Oxidation by metal on carbon creates pits or channels on the carbon surface. In this study, catalysts were chosen that created only hexagonal pits, which were easy to follow by TEM. For the uncatalyzed carbon-oxygen reaction, there is a linear relationship between time of oxidation and the radius of the pit, an indication that the turnover frequency is constant during oxidation. The rate of increase of the pit radius R (dR/dt) was calculated from a single experiment. The turnover frequency is:

$$r\left(\frac{\text{atom gasified}}{\text{edge atom sec}}\right) = \frac{\rho 0001}{\rho 11\bar{2}0} \frac{2\,R dR/dt}{2T1RH},$$

where $\rho 0001$ is $0.377 C/A^2$, $\rho 11\bar{2}0$ is $0.140 C/A^2$, and H is step height $- 3.35\ A^2$.

The catalysts used in the following experiments were metal carbides impregnated or coated on carbon crystals. The preparation was as follows. The crystallites of the metal carbides were slurried in water. Their size was 0.2 μm, and their concentration was 0.1 m-mol. The metal carbides were impregnated on a cleaved single crystal and dried in argon gas at 650°C for 10 hrs. Then a stream of 20% O_2 and the balance argon was passed over the graphite crystals, and the change of the radius of the hexagonal pit was measured versus time. The experiments were conducted for 10 to 25 minutes. Table 9.6 shows the calculated turnover frequency and Tamann temperature for various metal carbides.

The addition of small but unreported amounts of transition metal carbides to graphite increases the turnover frequency significantly. Because the amounts of metal carbides were not reported, there is no quantitative relationship between metal carbide and turnover frequency.

Table 9.6 Overall Turnover Frequencies for Carbon Oxidation (over 7–10 min reaction time) in 0.2 atm O_2 at 680°C Catalyzed by Transition Metal Carbides and Oxides

Catalyst	Overall Turnover Frequency (s^{-1})	Tamann Temperature (°C)
WC	6.2	1325
TaC	12.5	1887
Mo_2C	12.5	1266
WO_3	15.6	635
Cr_2O_3	4.7	1135
Ta_2O_5	3.1	804
MoO_3	Formed channels	282
None	0.7–1.17	—

CO and O_2 Spillover

Bond et al. [36] oxidized carbon monoxide on SnO_2 and Pd/S_1O_2 catalysts separately. They then mixed SnO_2 and Pd/SiO_2 in a simple mix (SM) or grinding mix and obtained these results:

Catalyst	% CO Conversion
Pd/SiO_2	0.03
SnO_2	0.23
SM. Pd/SiO_2 and SnO_2	0.33
Grinding mix Pd/SiO_2 and SnO_2	3.75

These data indicate that grinding the simple mix increases the rate of CO oxidation on SnO_2 by a factor of $3.75/0.23 = 16$. Bond et al. measured the rate of reduction and the rate of oxidation of SnO_2 commercial oxide as a catalyst mixed with Pd/SiO_2 and without. It was found that the rate of reduction and oxidation of SnO_2 increases directly with Pd content up to 4–5% Pd. These data indicate that CO and O_2 adsorb rapidly on Pd/SiO_2 but react slowly. However, CO and O react rapidly on SnO_2 but adsorb and desorb slowly. The grinding mix increases the rate of CO oxidation by a factor of 16. This clearly indicates that CO and O adsorb rapidly on Pd/SiO_2, migrate to SnO_2, and react to CO_2 on SnO_2 surface and then desorbs.

Reaction of NO and CO on Rh

Rh is an active catalyst for the reaction of CO and NO_x in automotive exhaust gases [37]:

$$CO + NO \xrightarrow{\text{Rh}} CO_2 + N_2.$$

When Rh is alloyed with Sn, the reaction temperature is lowered significantly, as evidenced from the following experiment. The chemisorption of O_2 reduced the rate of NO adsorption on Rh as follows:

$$Rh$$
$$NO \rightleftarrows N + O$$
$$O_2 \rightleftarrows 2\ O.$$

Therefore removal of O will increase the rate of NO decomposition.

It was shown in the previous study that Sn is a scavenger for O atoms and oxidizes to SnO_2. Then SnO_2 is rapidly reduced by CO:

$$Sn + O \rightleftarrows SnO + SnO_2$$
$$SnO_2 + \rightleftarrows CO_2 + SnO.$$

Rh increases the rate of NO dissociation and O migration; Sn increases the rate of CO oxidation and O removal. Therefore an alloy of Rh and SnO_2 increases the reaction of CO with NO. It is believed that CO adsorbs on Rh and migrates to SnO_2, while NO adsorbs on Rh and dissociates to N and O. O migrates to SnO_2 and reacts with CO. The resultant, CO_2, desorbs to a gas phase. 2N combine on a Rh surface and produce N_2 molecules and desorb to gas phase. This is a good example of NO and CO spillover.

THE SPECIFIC EFFECT OF H SPILLOVER OVER VARIOUS SUPPORTS

The heterogeneous catalysis system is extremely complex. A simple assumption or explanation usually is shown to be oversimplification and even misleading. In this study, the hydrogen spillover phenomenon was used to explain these simple hydrogenation reactions; however, it immediately became apparent that although hydrogen spillover plays an important role, the system still is quite complex. In this subsequently described study, Al_2O_3, SiO_2, and MgO were individually activated with Pt/Al_2O_3 at 430°C under H_2 atmosphere for a period of 12 hours [38]. Then the Pt/Al_2O_3 was totally removed, and the activated support was left behind without exposure to air. Ethylene, benzene, 1,3 cyclohexadine, and 1,4 cyclohexadine were hydrogenated individually at low temperatures (50–170°C) on activated supports. After activation, a portion of each sample was treated with O_2 at 430°C or NH_3 at 200°C to determine whether O_2 or NH_3 would poison the activated support. The inhibition effect of O_2 or NH_3 was determined by conducting hydrogenation after exposure to these gases. In some experiments, feed was passed over the activated support without H_2 (using inert He). The experimental result for each oxide is described briefly.

H Spillover Effect on Al$_2$O$_3$

Al$_2$O$_3$ oxide is an extremely stable oxide and is difficult to reduce. It was shown in Table 9.3 that the surface layer of Al$_2$O$_3$ loses some oxygen in the presence of hydrogen spillover at 430°C and that there is also an uptake of the H atoms by Al$_2$O$_3$. Table 9.7 shows the hydrogen spillover concentration, determined by physical and chemical means. This is contrary to the widespread assumption that Al$_2$O$_3$ does not reduce.

Ethylene, benzene, 1,3 cyclohexadine, and 1,4 cyclohexadine were hydrogenated on activated Al$_2$O$_3$ in a hydrogen atmosphere. Data indicate that ethylene hydrogenates to ethane at 110–150°C and that O$_2$ and NH$_3$ do not inhibit the hydrogenation reaction. Benzene hydrogenates to cyclohexane. Neither O$_2$ nor NH$_3$ inhibits this reaction either. 1,3 and 1,4 cyclohexadines are hydrogenated to cyclohexane, and neither O$_2$ nor NH$_3$ inhibits this hydrogenation (Table 9.8).

These data indicate that O$_2$ and NH$_3$ do not poison the hydrogenation properties of activated Al$_2$O$_3$. SiO$_2$, under the above conditions, is similar in some reactions to Al$_2$O$_3$ and different in others.

H Spillover Effect on SiO$_2$

Ethylene was hydrogenated to ethane over activated SiO$_2$ in an H$_2$ atmosphere at 170–280°C. Neither O$_2$ nor NH$_3$ inhibits the hydrogenation reaction. Benzene hydrogenates destructively (hydrogenalysis), in an H$_2$ atmosphere to ethane and in He atmosphere to acetylene. Both O$_2$ and NH$_3$ inhibit this hydrogenolysis of benzene. The hydrogenation properties of silica are similar to Al$_2$O$_3$, but the hydrogenalysis is different. Activated SiO$_2$ in an H$_2$ atmosphere destructively hydrogenates 1,3 cyclohexadine to ethane and 1,4 cyclohexadine to acetylene (Table 9.9). Al$_2$O$_3$ does simple hydrogenation. Hydrogen spillover adsorbed on the surface of activated SiO$_2$ hydro-

Table 9.7 Titration of the Split-Over Hydrogen by Direct Adsorption and Addition Reactions

Titration of H_{sp} by	Temperature	Volume $(cm^3 STP \ g^{-1} \ SiO_2)$ of H_{sp} Adsorbed
1. Volumetry	200°C	1.40
2. Induction period in $C_2H_4 + H_2$	200°C	~1.00
3. $C_6H_{10} + H_2 \rightarrow C_6H_{12}$	170°C	0.58
4. $C_6H_6 + 2 H_2 \xrightarrow{NH_3} C_6H_{10}$	170°C	0.91
5. $C_6H_6 \quad \begin{array}{l} + 2 H_2 \rightarrow C_6H_{10} \\ + 3 H_2 \rightarrow C_6H_{12} \end{array}$	170°C	1.51
6. 1,3 $C_6H_8 \quad \begin{array}{l} + 2 H_2 \rightarrow C_6H_{12} \\ + H_2 \rightarrow C_6H_{10} \end{array}$	170°C	1.54
7. 1,4 $C_6H_8 \quad \begin{array}{l} + 2 H_2 \rightarrow C_6H_{12} \\ + H_2 \rightarrow C_6H_{10} \end{array}$	170°C	1.49

Table 9.8 Al_2O_3 Activated by Pt/Al_2O_3 at 430°C H_2 Atmosphere for 12 Hours

Reactants	Temperature (°C)	Product	Inhibition O_2 430°C	NH_3 200°C
$C_2H_4 + H_2$	110–150	C_2H_6		
$C_6H_6 + H_2$	160	C_6H_{12}	No	No
+ He	160	No conversion	No	No
+ H$_2$	160	C_6H_{12}	No	No
1,3 CHD				
+ He	160	No conversion		
+ H$_2$	160	C_6H_{12}	No	No
1,4 CHD				
He	160	No conversion		

genated 1,3 and 1,4 cyclohexadine to cyclohexane without hydrogen gas. Hydrogen spillover, adsorbed on the surface of activated Al_2O_3, does not hydrogenate 1,3 and 1,4 cyclohexadine, in contrast to SiO_2.

H Spillover Effect on MgO

The effect of hydrogen spillover over MgO is quite different from Al_2O_3 and SiO_2. MgO has no hydrogenolysis properties under conditions similar to those effective for

Table 9.9 SiO_2 Activated with Pt/Al_2O_3 at 430°C and H_2 for 12 Hours

Reactants	Temperature (°C)	Product	Inhibition O_2 430°C	NH_3 200°C
C_2H_4	+ H$_2$	170–280	C_2H_6	No	No
	+ H$_2$	170	C_2H_6	Yes	Yes
	+ He	170	C_2H_4	Yes	Yes
C_6H_{12}					
	+ HSP[a]	170	$C_6H_{10} + C_6H_{12}$	Reaction of addition	
	+ H$_2$	170	C_2H_6	Yes	Yes
1,3 CHD					
	+ He	170	C_2H_2	Yes	Yes
	+ HSP[a]	170	C_6H_{10} & C_6H_{12}	Yes	Yes
	H$_2$	170	C_2H_6		
	+ He	170	C_2H_2	Yes	Yes
1,4 CHD					
	+ HSP[a]	170	$C_6H_6 + C_6H_{12}$	Addition Reaction	

[a]Hydrogen spillover.

Table 9.10　MgO Activated with Pt/Al$_2$O$_3$ at 430°C and H$_2$ for 12 Hours

| | | | Inhibition | |
Reactants	Temperature (°C)	Product	O_2 430°C	NH_3 200°C
C$_2$H$_4$ + H$_2$	50	C$_2$H$_6$	No	Yes
	50–130	C$_2$H$_6$	No	Yes
	130	C$_2$H$_6$	No	No
C$_2$H$_4$ + H$_2$	130	C$_2$H$_6$		
C$_6$H$_6$ + H$_2$	170 (low activity)	C$_6$H$_{12}$	No activity without Pt	
1,3 & 1,4 + H$_2$ CHD	170 (Activity with Pt at 430°C)	C$_6$H$_{12}$	No	Yes
1,3 & 1,4 + H$_2$ CHD	Activity at 30°C without Pt	C$_6$H$_{12}$	Yes	No C$_6$H$_{10}$ as transient

Note: MgO activated at 430°C and H$_2$ without Pt/Al$_2$O$_3$ for 12 hours.

SiO$_2$ and Al$_2$O$_3$. Activated MgO in an H$_2$ atmosphere hydrogenates ethylene, benzene, and 1,3 and 1,4 cyclohexadiene to the corresponding saturated products. NH$_3$ inhibits these reactions, and O$_2$ has no effect. MgO was activated by H$_2$ gas at 430°C without Pt/Al$_2$O$_3$. The activated MgO was able to hydrogenate ethylene and 1,3 and 1,4 to cyclohexadene cyclohexane but had no activity for the conversion of benzene. O$_2$ inhibits these properties and NH$_3$ has no effect. The activation of MgO, without Pt.Al$_2$O$_3$, is different from Al$_2$O$_3$ and SiO$_2$ (Table 9.10).

Readers can readily see that hydrogen spillover affects each oxide differently, and each oxide has a different catalytic activity for different hydrocarbons. This is expected for heterogeneous catalysis because each catalyst has its own specific properties.

Hydrogen uptaken by a support may be as adsorbed species or trapped in vacancies or interstitial positions or combined with O, as an −OH group, but it usually can be removed by evacuation or chemical reaction. Table 9.7 shows concentration to H spillover 0.9-1.5 cc/gm of support corresponding to Ca 10^{12} atoms of H/cc of support.

CONCLUSIVE REMARKS AND OUTLOOK

Solid catalyst surfaces are by their nature heterogeneous steps, offsets, and edges, and structurally they are microcrystalline, not amorphous. Each individual crystallite has cations or anion vacancies. There are also impurities, which may be on the surface or trapped in vacancies or interstitial positions. The heterogeneities, crystal defects, and impurities together create an infinite number of different structures situated at various locations of the surface. Some of these locations, or sites, are those catalytically active at reaction conditions.

The Langmuir-Hinshelwood mechanism assumed that the number of active sites, initially present or induced by the reactants, is fixed and that the reacting species adsorb and interact at the isolated sites. It was assumed that there was no mobility from site to site of the adsorbed species across the surface. By contrast, the spillover phenomenon has shown that adsorbed species are mobile on the surface. Experimentally, the phenomenon has not been proved for all adsorbed species, but where it does apply, the Langmuir and Hinshelwood mechanism should be adjusted to take the spillover phenomenon into account.

Spillover phenomenon does add to the complexity of heterogeneous catalysis; at the same time, it increases the understanding of heterogeneous catalytic reactions. Spillover species migrate significant distances—up to several mm. The migrating species are chemically active, and they may interact with other species in their path. They may react with the support and chemically or electronically change the support. They may be trapped by the support, without chemical reaction, by simply occupying vacancies or interstitial positions. They may react with inorganic impurities on the surface. The combination of the steps may or is likely to develop a new catalytic structure, significantly different from the original catalyst. The new complex structure is in equilibrium with the gas phase during chemical reaction and is changing continuously with time during the catalyst life. This transition state manifests itself during the catalyst life by continuous change of activity and selectivity. The rate of structural change is initially rapid, then slows down, and continues throughout the catalyst life at a slower rate.

One of the most significant advances in catalysis has been the spillover phenomenon. It has broad applications in most catalytic reactions and explains many catalytic phenomena not previously understood. Some examples are the high rate of dehydrogenation reactions in catalytic reforming, coke formation on the whole catalyst pellet instead of on the Pt alone, coke burnout of the entire pellet at lower temperature, coke burnout on a support without Pt, and the high rate of sulfur removal in the hydrodesulfurization catalyst, due to mixed oxides of Co and Mo compared to individual oxides. Other examples are catalytic coal gasification with steam, H_2, and oxygen when compared to noncatalytic, the high rate of CO and H_2 reaction in alcohol synthesis with mixed oxides compared to the almost noncatalytic individual oxides, the Fischer-Tropsche synthesis of hydrocarbons, and the high rate of CO oxidation on Pt/SnO_2 catalyst. Additionally, one can cite the high rate of CO and NO reaction on Rh and Sn mixed oxide system when compared to the individual oxides and the high reaction rate of NH_3 synthesis on mixed oxide catalyst.

The spillover phenomenon applies similarly to many partial oxidation reactions where one oxide oxidizes hydrocarbon and is itself reduced. The gas phase oxygen dissociates on the second oxide and migrates and replaces the extracted oxygen. There are many reactions in this group: oxidation of propylene to acrolein and acrolein to acrylic acid, ammoxidation of propylene and ammonia to acrylonitrile, and oxidation of isobutylene to methacrolein and methacrolein to methacrylic acid.

Another important group of industrial catalysts are bimetallic or multimetallic alloy catalysts. In this group, hydrogen spillover causes the SMSI effects in which Pt maintains its catalytic activity but is sharply curtailed in its coke formation property. One could go on and cover most catalytic reactions.

The spillover phenomenon increases our fundamental understanding of catalysis. At the same time, it highlights the complexity of the heterogeneous catalysis systems and reveals that the catalyst is in a state of continuous transition, which is a function of temperature, catalyst composition, adsorbed gases, and the environment in general. In the future, we must further examine kinetic models, developed up to now on the basis of Langmuir-Hinshelwood's mechanism, and develop a new kinetic model that includes the existence of the spillover phenomenon. It became apparent that active species in the hydrogenation reaction may not be the H atom alone but a mixture of $H^{\cdot}$, H^+, H_2, or H_2^+, H^-. The same line of reasoning applies to the oxidation reaction: that active species are $O^{\cdot}$, O^-, O^{--}, or O_2^-. This will apply to other heterogeneous reactions as well.

The spillover phenomenon increases our knowledge of heterogeneous catalysis and catalytic systems generally. It gives new tools to design new experiments and enables us to understand more fully complex chemical systems. One could subdivide a complex reaction system into many elementary species and determine which species are migrating and which are relatively immobile; whether migrating species are radical or ionic; whether they react with the catalyst or become trapped in vacancies or interstitial positions. It is important to distinguish between sites responsible for spillover and those responsible for chemical reaction. It is essential to study the catalyst structural and electronic changes occurring during the rapid and slow transition stage and to study the deactivators and determine whether they poison the primary source of spillover, poison the sites for catalytic reaction, or block the path of migrating species. One could use this information to tailor-make, that is, to develop catalysts that achieve high selectivity and activity or to increase catalyst stability and life, the most difficult problems in catalytic research. This analysis points out that catalysts, particularly supported catalysts, are more complicated than previous workers assumed. Future workers will discover that heterogeneous catalysis generally is more complex than suspected. The spillover phenomenon has increased our chances of conducting meaningful research in basic and fundamental studies; however, trial and error undoubtedly will still be, not the preferred way, but realistically the only way for industrial or applied research. The fundamental study is necessary to solve specific problems after a promising catalyst has been invented.

REFERENCES

1. Kuriacose, J. *Ind. J. Chem.* 1957. 5:646.
2. Khoobiar, S.; Peck, R. F.; and Reitzer, B. J. 1964. Mechanism of naphthene dehydrogenation. Presented at the 3d Intern. Cong. of Catal., Amsterdam.
3. Khoobiar, S. 1964. Particle to particle migration of hydrogen atoms on platinum-alumina catalysts from particle to neighboring particles. *J. Phys. Chem.* 68:411.
4. Melville, H. W., and Robb, J. C. 1956. *Proc. Roy. Soc.* (London): A:pp. 196–445.
5. Sermon, P. A., and Bond, G. C. 1973. *Catal. Rev.* 8:211.
6. Dowden, D. A. 1980. *Catalysis, VIII*, Chap. 6. London: Chemical Society.
7. Bond, G. C. 1983. (See ref. 9, p. 1.)
8. Conner, W. C., Jr.; Pajonk, G. M.; and Teichner, S. J. 1985. Spillover of adsorbed species. *Adv. in Catal.* vol. 34.

9. *Spillover of Adsorbed Species. Proceedings of the Int. Symp., Lyon-Villeurbanne, September 12–16, 1983*. Amsterdam: Elsevier.

10. Khoobiar, S.; Carter, J. L.; and Lucchesi, P. J. 1968. The electronic properties of aluminum oxide and chemisorption of water, hydrogen and oxygen. *J. Phys. Chem.* 72:1682.

11. Sinfelt, J. M., and Lucchesi, P. J. 1963. *J. Am. Chem. Soc.* 85:3365.

12. Beck, D. D., and White, J. M. 1984. *J. Phys. Chem.* 88:2764.

13. Hilaire, P. 1963. French Atomic Ener. Comm. Paris, reprint no. 2260. Hilaire, P. 1963. thesis, Lyons.

14. Pajonk, G. M.; Teichner, S. J.; and Germain, J. E., eds. 1983. *Proc. of the 1st Int. Symp. on the Spillover of Adsorbed Species,* Amsterdam: Elsevier; and Pajonk, G. M.; Teichner, S. J.; and Germain, J. E., eds. 1984. volume of discussions. University of Claude Bernard-Lyon 1, Villeurbanne.

15. Keren, E., and Soffer, A. 1977. *J. Catal.* 50:43.

16. Sermon, P. A., and Bond, G. C. 1976. *J. Chem. Soc. Trans. Farad.* 2:745.

17. Robell, A. J.; Ballou, E. V.; and Boudart, M. 1964. *J. Phys. Chem.* 68:2748.

18. Kramer, R., and André, M. 1979. *J. Catal.* 58:287.

19. Bianchi, D.; Gardes, G. E. E.; Pajonk, G. M.; and Teichner, S. J. 1975. *J. Catal.* 38:135.

20. Boudart, M.; Aldag, A. W.; and Vannice, M. A. 1970. *J. Catal.* 18:46.

21. Gadgil, K., and Gonzalez, R. D. 1975. *J. Catal.* 40:190.

22. Conner, W. C., Jr.; Cevallos-Candau, J. F.; Shah, N.; and Haensel, V. 1983. (See ref. 9, p. 31.)

23. Antonucci, P.; van Truong, N.; Giordano, N.; and Maggiore, R. 1982. *J. Catal.* 75:140.

24. Carter, J. L.; Lucchesi, P. J.; Sinfelt, J. H.; and Yates, D. J. C. 1965. *Proc. 3d Int. Congr. Catal.*, p. 644. Amsterdam: North-Holland Pub.

25. Il'Chenko, N. I. 1972. *Rus. Chem. Rev.* 41:47.

26. Ekstrom, A.; Batley, G. E.; and Johnson, D. A. 1974. *J. Catal.* 34:106.

27. L'Homme, G. A.; Boudart, M.; and D'Or, L. 1966. *Bull. Acad. Roy. Belg. Cl. Sci.* 52:1206–49.

28. Bond, G. C., and Tripathi, J. B. P. 1976. *J. Chem. Soc. Trans. Farad.* 72:933.

29. Kunimori, K., and Uchijima, T. 1983. (See ref. 9, p. 197.)

30. Resasco, D. E., and Haller, G. L. 1983. *J. Catal.* 82:279.

31. Tauster, S. J.; Fung, S. C.; and Garten, R. L. 1978. *J. Amer. Chem. Soc.,* 100:170.

32. Parera, J.; Traffano, E.; Masso, J.; and Pieck, C. 1983. (See ref. 9, p. 101.)

33. Fujimoto, K.; Ohno, A.; and Kunugi, T. 1983. (See ref. 9, p. 241.)

34. Fujimoto, K., and Toyoshi, S. 1980. *Proc. 7th Int. Cong. Catal.*, p. 235. Tokyo: Kodansha.

35. Yang, R. T., and Wong, C. *J. Catal.* 8:154–60.

36. Bond, G. C.; Fuller, M. J.; and Molloy, L. R. 1977. *Proc. 6th Int. Congr. Catal.*, p. 356. London: Chemical Society.

37. Masai, M.; Nakahara, K.; Yabashi, M.; Murata, K.; Nishiyama, S.; and Tsuruya, S. 1983. (See ref. 9, p. 89.)

38. Teichner, S. J.; Pajonk, G. M.; and Lacroix, M. 1983. *In: Surface Properties and Catalysis by Non Metals*. Bonnele, J. P., et al. eds. Amsterdam: Reidel Dordrecht.

CHAPTER 10

Commercial Application of Molecular Sieve Catalysts

Francis G. Dwyer
Albert B. Schwartz

Most zeolitic catalysts are complex composites of two or more components. The role of these components can be directly catalytic, as in the case of the zeolite component or an active metal. Other components can act as stabilizing agents or metal supports or simply contribute to the physical nature of the composite catalyst. During use, these components can and do undergo change, often in the form of an interaction with other components in the catalyst, which can result in a loss in activity and a change in selectivity. In the case of metals, they can migrate from their original locus of incorporation, such as, within the zeolite, to another component of the catalyst, and agglomerate, losing a good portion of their catalytic activity. The catalytic nature of the zeolitic component can also change; for example, there may be a shift in the acid strength distribution. Therefore, catalyst designers must take into consideration not only the composition and state of the catalyst in its initial fresh state but the changes that occur in use and how these changes will affect performance.

COMPONENTS OF ZEOLITIC CATALYSTS

In commercial manufacture, the zeolite component is usually combined with another material or materials before it is formed into the specific particle type for use as a catalyst. These particle forms can be extrudates or spheres for fixed- or moving-bed applications and microspheres for fluid-bed use. These added components are referred to as binders, matrices, or supports, the identification usually dependent on the function intended by their incorporation. Binders are used primarily to impart physical strength to the zeolite catalyst particle so it can withstand the rigors of handling and use in process applications. If maximum catalyst activity is desired, the binder concentration is minimized, while in other applications, it can be employed as a diluent to control catalytic activity. The materials most commonly used are inorganic oxides such as alumina, silica, titania, zirconia, and clays and combinations thereof. Chemical, thermal, and hydrothermal treatments are often used to increase particle strength and develop the desired level of porosity. When such additional properties are incorporated and the zeolite concentration is in a minor proportion, the added component is usually referred to as a matrix. The matrix component is not limited to just contributing to the physical properties of the catalyst particle, but it can be a support for another catalytic function or a catalyst in its own right. Examples of such matrix functions would be as the support for a hydrogenation-dehydrogenation metal or metal compound found in zeolitic hydroprocessing catalysts [1, 2, 3], as a secondary acid function in cracking [4] and hydrocracking [5], or as a scavenger for catalyst poisons such as heavy metals [6, 7, 8]. At the other end of the spectrum where the catalytic contribution of the matrix is to be minimized, silica or sintered forms of alumina, silica-aluminas, and clays have found much use.

In addition to adding components to a zeolite catalyst to effect the desired final product, zeolites can be formed or crystallized from previously formed particles. This technology, pioneered by Engelhard Industries [9], has found application primarily in catalytic cracking of petroleum feedstocks. The advantage of catalysts formed in this manner is that the physical properties desired in the catalyst particle can be attained without any risk of damage to the zeolite component, prior to the in situ crystallization of the zeolite. The main disadvantage is that there is little or no control of the activity or catalytic support characteristics of the matrix since its composition and state are dependent on the nature of the zeolite that is crystallized. For the most part, the matrix component of in situ crystallized zeolite catalysts is essentially inert.

The binder or matrix component must possess good thermal and hydrothermal stability and resistance to chemical attack. It is important that in use it will not change in physical properties, resulting in a degradation of physical strength, or sintering, resulting in encapsulation of the zeolitic catalyst, making it unavailable.

To progress a step further, the zeolite component itself can be a support and contribute substantially to the performance of its cocatalyst. There are numerous examples in the literature in which the zeolite component effectively increases the catalytic activity of a second catalytic component, such as when an active metal is maintained in a high degree of dispersion by ion exchanging it into the zeolite. The zeolite may also interact with a second catalytic component or provide shape and size selectivity [10, 30]. Zeolite shape selectivity can restrict entry of reactants or egress of products, as well as prevent access of catalyst poisons to the catalytic component, and may limit the formation of deactivating by-products within its pore structure.

The literature contains numerous articles citing and discussing the electron deficiency of noble metal catalysts supported on zeolites that results from a donor-acceptor relationship between the noble metal and the host zeolite [12, 13, 14, 20, 21]. In other cases, improved activity has been attributed to improved dispersion caused by the zeolite metal interaction. The spectrum here spans noble metal catalysts [10, 11, 31], Fischer-Tropsch catalysts [17, 18, 23], and other transition metal catalysts. Other metal-zeolite interactions have been reported but with less definition of the mechanism involved. In fact, in some cases, this interaction has been reported to have no catalytic significance at all [31, 32].

CATALYST SELECTION

In the formulation of zeolite-containing catalysts, the choice of the zeolite component is first based on the molecular size and nature of the reactants and products. In such applications as catalytic cracking and hydrocracking, where the reactants are large, high-molecular-weight hydrocarbons, large-pore zeolites such as X and Y are predominantly used. The high acid activity that can be imparted to these zeolites is also an important contributing factor to their use in these applications. The exact ion-exchanged form of the zeolite component is dependent on the product characteristics and stability in use desired. For example, in catalytic cracking, if an olefinic gasoline product with somewhat higher octane number is desired, the hydrogen form of the zeolite would be preferred. If the primary interest is hydrothermal stability, a rare earth exchanged form may be preferred. In applications where shape or size selectivity is the controlling factor rather than the molecular size or accessibility of the reactants, the medium (5–7Å) and small-pore zeolites (<5Å) are the most commonly used. These applications include the use of erionite (<5Å) in Selectoforming [33] to upgrade reformate; the use of ZSM-5 [34–37] and mordenite [38, 39] in dewaxing of petroleum stocks; and aromatics processing, such as xylene isomerization, toluene disproportionation and benzene-ethylene alkylation, and methanol and olefin conversion processes employing ZSM-5 [40–44]. Shape and size selectivity, although important, are not the only basis for zeolite selection. Unique selectivity characteristics and low deactivation rates are equally as important.

In many cases, the zeolite component is not the only catalytic component in the composite catalyst. Often a cocatalyst, which may or may not be zeolite, is incorporated. The catalytic acidity of amorphous matrices in catalytic cracking and hydrocracking should be considered as cocatalysts, as well as the CO combustion promoter in cracking catalyst [45] and the recently introduced octane-enhancing ZSM-5 component [46]. Heavy metal passivating [47, 48, 6, 7, 8] and SOx scavenging agents [49–56], which are incorporated to counteract the catalytic poisoning and environmental emission problems associated with the use of certain petroleum feedstocks, could also be considered cocatalysts in the broadest definition of the term. In hydroprocessing and aromatics processing with zeolite-containing catalysts, the choice of hydrogenation-dehydrogenation component will depend on the characteristics of the feedstock—that is, the nitrogen and sulfur contents—and the degree of activity required. The field of hydrogenation-dehydrogenation components commonly used encompasses Pt, Pd, NiW, CoMo, NiMo, Ni, and Mo.

Another area where cocatalysis has generated considerable interest has been with zeolite containing catalysts for Fischer-Tropsch (FT) synthesis in which the zeolite component increases the activity of the FT catalyst. There are also references in the literature wherein the combination of the FT catalyst and an acid zeolite in the same catalyst can result in a single-stage process to effect FT chemistry and upgrading in the same reactor [57, 58].

A final consideration in catalyst selection is the type of process reactor design in which the catalyst will be utilized. This will not only dictate the catalyst physical form, which may be microspheres, spheres, or extrudates, but also physical properties necessary for effective performance. The physical properties required for a fluidizable microsphere catalyst to be used in fluid catalytic cracking (FCC) may be substantially different from those required for a fluid-bed methanol-to-gasoline process. The high-attrition resistance, the density, and the particle size distribution required by the severity of FCC operation may be relaxed in a less physically rigorous fluid-bed operation and permit some freedom in further tailoring of the physical properties to increase catalytic performance. Similar considerations apply to continuously circulating moving bed systems. In fixed-bed catalytic applications, whether vapor or mixed phase, mass transfer into the catalyst particle is often a controlling performance parameter. In processes with relative low mass and volume flow, the mass transfer can be improved by reducing particle size—that is, smaller diameter extrudate or spheres—until the physical strength is reduced below an acceptable level. Processes in which high mass or volumetric flows exist are not amenable to this approach because the reduction of catalyst particle concomitantly increases the pressure drop across the catalyst bed. This situation has led to the development of shaped particles or extrudates [59–62] such as trilobe and quadralobe extrudates and has stirred interest in the formation of monolithic catalyst forms such as those used in pollution abatement applications. These catalyst forms reduce the length of the diffusion path and correspondingly increase the rate of mass transfer without the increase in the particle drag forces and bed compaction associated with the reduction of the catalyst particle size.

The wide variety of factors in catalyst selection is reflected in the numerous forms in which zeolite-containing catalysts are produced with respect to composition and physical characteristics.

CONDITION AND NATURE OF NEW (UNUSED) CATALYST

The state or condition of freshly manufactured zeolite-containing catalysts varies somewhat depending on the specific application. Fluid catalytic cracking catalysts are supplied to the user in a dried-only state containing 10–15% water. This is possible because the catalyst in this state has sufficient physical strength for handling and loading. Furthermore, it is introduced to the FCC unit by the regenerator, where the catalyst is exposed to a high-temperature oxidizing atmosphere, which activates the catalytic zeolite component and imparts additional physical strength to the catalyst particles. On the other hand, catalysts used in moving-bed catalytic cracking (TCC) are not only fully calcined to give the necessary activation and physical strength but in some cases are also given a mild steam deactivation to improve the catalytic selectivity by reduced coke production.

With extruded catalysts for fixed-bed applications, it is usually necessary to calcine the catalyst at an elevated temperature to effect changes that will give the catalyst particle the physical strength necessary to withstand breaking and attrition in handling. If some alteration in the activity of the catalyst is desired, the calcining atmosphere can be chosen to accomplish this, or such treatment can be done subsequent to the calcination step. These types of treatments can be incorporated to activate, deactivate, or selectivate the catalyst.

The preceding and ensuing discussions encompass the basic theme of this chapter and the entire book: the physical and chemical makeup of the catalyst is altered profoundly during use or by special treatments before use. These alterations have a major effect on the performance of the catalyst, as is manifest by coke formation, selectivity, specificity, stability to temperature, aging, and production rate of the catalyst.

With multifunctional catalysts, especially catalysts containing a hydrogenation-dehydrogenation catalyst, a further pretreatment is performed after the catalyst has been charged to the process reactor. To avoid excessive or unselective metal activity, which often manifests itself in use by high heat release, the metals are reduced and/or sulfided. The exact procedures used for activation, deactivation, and selectivation usually fall in the realm of proprietary information and are not readily found in the open literature.

Finally the state of some zeolite catalysts gradually changes under the operating conditions to which they are exposed. A case in point has been reported for ZSM-5 used in TCC for octane enhancement. Commercial results show that the catalytic chemistry substantially changes from paraffin cracking in the fresh state to olefin isomerization as the catalyst is aged and equilibrated. Similar changes probably occur in many other applications.

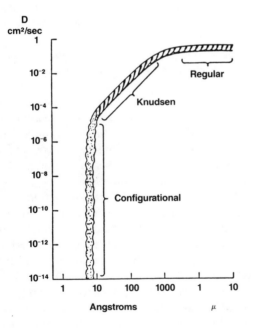

Figure 10.1 Diffusivity and size of aperture (pore): The classical regions of regular and Knudsen and the new regime of configurational diffusion [63].

TRANSPORT OF REACTANTS AND PRODUCTS

Diffusion of reactants and products in and out of an activated molecular sieve matrix-binder composite becomes rather complex. An explanation of different diffusional regimes that may coexist in a composite particle is given by Weisz [63]. The binder or matrix usually has a pore structure with pore openings somewhere in the range of 50 Å to 2,000 Å, while the pore openings of zeolites range from about 3 Å to 10 Å. As depicted in Figure 10.1, the diffusion through the binder or matrix is in the well-known Knudsen regime, while in the zeolite it is in the configurational regime.

ACTIVATION OF CATALYSTS

As a final step in manufacture, zeolitic catalysts are usually heated to a temperature above the temperature of use. An exception is fluid cracking catalyst, which is conventionally added to the FCC in a dried state and calcined in situ as it mixes with the hot, circulating catalyst. The calcination step serves to remove water from the catalyst, drive off other volatile components, and harden the particle to increase its attrition resistance, and it may provide for special conditioning of the catalysts to control its activity and selectivity. Calcination of the fresh catalyst is usually done in air, steam, hydrogen, or nitrogen or combinations of these gases.

Interactions between zeolite and binder or matrix may be evident after calcination. With silica gel matrices, it is possible to encounter pore plugging of the zeolite when low-molecular-weight silicates are used. This can be minimized by increasing the molecular weight of the silicate polymer in which the zeolite is dispersed or by using a silica-metal oxide gel.

Alumina binders may cause an increase in the activity of the zeolite by transport of aluminum from the binder into the crystalline framework of the zeolite. The work of Shihabi [64] demonstrated that aluminum insertion can occur through a soluble Al species by reaction with SiOH groups of highly siliceous ZSM-5. An increase in ion exchange capacity and Brønsted acidity occurs corresponding to the increase in tetrahedrally coordinated aluminum in the framework. The resulting catalysts are active for such reactions as cracking, olefin oligomerization, dewaxing, and conversion of methanol to hydrocarbons. The shape selectivity evident in these reactions confirmed that the active sites generated in this manner are truly intrazeolitic.

When boron is present in the framework of ZSM-5, catalytic activity can be generated by hydrothermal treatment in the presence of alumina [65, 66], which introduces aluminum into the zeolite lattice. Solid-solid exchange of cations from the zeolite to the binder or matrix may also occur. Examples of this phenomenon have been demonstrated in cracking catalysts consisting of the zeolite faujasite, dispersed in an inorganic oxide matrix. Plank [67] has shown that when an alkali metal aluminosilicate, with a silica-alumina mole ratio of at least 3.0, is composited with specific inorganic oxide matrices and then treated in a steam atmosphere, the alkali metal cation irreversibly migrates to the inorganic oxide matrix to form a highly stable catalyst. Had the alkali metal not been trapped by the matrix, it would have reduced the hydrothermal stability of the zeolite.

DEACTIVATION OF CATALYSTS DURING USE

Reversible Deactivation

Essentially all catalysts deactivate over a long period of use. Some types of deactivation are only temporary in the sense that the catalysts can be regenerated to restore all or part of the activity lost.

Reversible deactivation is caused most frequently by carbonaceous deposit on the catalysts due to side reactions. The deposits reduce activity by blocking off pores in the matrix or binder and by covering active sites. Rollmann [68] reported a correlation between the coking tendency of a large number of zeolites and their shape selectivity, as shown in Figure 10.2. Derouane [69] has classified various ways that coke may cause pore blockage, as illustrated in Figure 10.3.

Acidic catalysts may deactivate because of chemisorption of basic compounds containing nitrogen, as well as by compounds containing oxygen or sulfur. In some cases, simple heating of the catalyst in an inert atmosphere to desorb these poisons will restore activity. Otherwise regeneration in an oxygen-containing gas at elevated temperatures is required.

Irreversible Deactivation

Irreversible deactivation occurs most often because of thermally or hydrothermally induced degeneration of the molecular sieve or matrix-binder or both. It is important

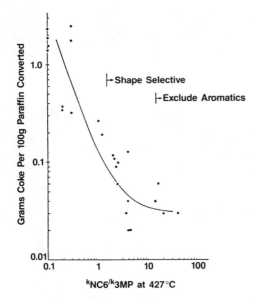

Figure 10.2   Coke yield versus shape selectivity of paraffin conversion for acid zeolite catalysts [68].

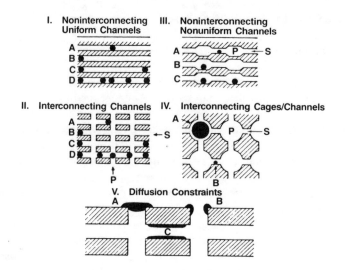

Figure 10.3 Classification of pore blockage effects in zeolites [69].

to understand how the deactivation of the composite catalyst occurs. An example is provided in the work of Chester [70] on the steam deactivation of zeolitic cracking catalysts. The matrices of most cracking catalysts have some catalytic activity although a much lower level than that of the zeolitic component. The rates of steam deactivation of three commercial catalysts are shown in Figure 10.4. The relative stabilities of the catalysts change in different temperature ranges, presumably because of differences in the zeolitic and matrix components. It is postulated that low-temperature deactivation (1100–1350°F) is dominated by matrix changes, while deactivation at higher temperatures (1350–1550°F) is dominated by loss of crystallinity of the zeolite component.

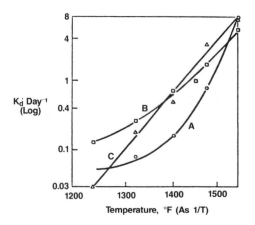

Figure 10.4 Temperature dependence for catalyst steam deactivation: 100% steam, 0 psig for A, B, and C [70].

The hydrothermal stability of zeolites generally increases with increasing silica-alumina ratio. For example, zeolite X, which has a relatively low silica-alumina mole ratio of about 2.5, undergoes irreversible deactivation when it is cyclically hydrated and dehydrated at elevated temperature. Eastwood [71] demonstrated that this was an important factor that affected the activity of zeolite-containing catalyst circulating in moving-bed cracking units. It is believed that this activity loss is caused by hydrolysis of tetrahedrally coordinated aluminum in the zeolite framework and corresponding loss of acid sites originally associated with aluminum.

In dual-function catalysis involving a hydrogenation component combined with an acidic zeolite, deactivation of the hydrogenation component is frequently a problem. When the catalyst particles are bound with an inorganic oxide, the rate of deactivation and loss of selectivity may increase still more rapidly because of migration of the hydrogenation metal to the binder, thereby reducing the intimacy of the metal with the zeolite. Weisz [72] has applied an intimacy requirement between the two catalytic functions, as shown in Figures 10.5 to 10.7, to quantify how close the functions need to be to carry out a multiple-step reaction effectively. Although this criterion was illustrated with a nonzeolitic catalyst, it is just as applicable to zeolite-containing catalysts. The use of a binder, such as alumina, to which the platinum can migrate makes it even more important to apply this criterion in designing and understanding the performance of composite zeolitic catalysts.

Another important cause of catalyst deactivation is the deposition of metal poisons on the catalyst from the feed to the reactor. This is particularly severe in applications for converting heavy hydrocarbon feeds, such as catalytic cracking. In addition to the

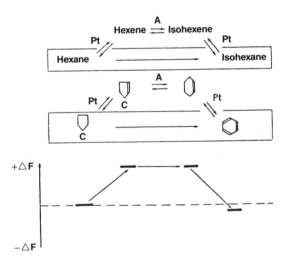

Figure 10.5 Polystep reactions in the catalytic transformation of hydrocarbon structures, as practiced by the petroleum industry.

Note: Paraffin isomerization (above) and aromatization of alkylcyclopentanes are carried out over catalysts that contain both acidic sites (A) and platinum (Pt). The free-energy changes in the reaction sequence are qualitatively similar and involve a high-energy intermediate [72].

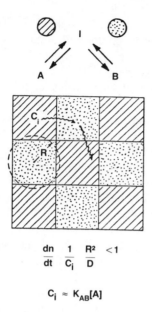

$$\frac{dn}{dt} \frac{1}{C_i} \frac{R^2}{D} < 1$$

$$C_i \approx K_{AB}[A]$$

Figure 10.6 Intimacy criterion applied to the two-step reaction A to B, catalyzed by geometrically separate catalytic regions, with an intermediate I required to travel by diffusion from one type of catalyst to another [72].

sulfur and nitrogen compounds in the feed, nickel, vanadium, and iron are commonly deposited on the cracking catalyst, usually zeolite Y in a silica-alumina gel or clay matrix, in quantities totaling as much as 1% by weight. Physical plugging of the pores of the matrix and zeolite easily occurs with large deposition of metals, which are usually in the form of oxides or sulfides on the catalyst surface. Nickel and iron act

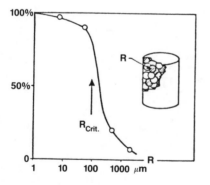

Figure 10.7 Early demonstration of the application of the intimacy criterion for the polystep reaction of n-heptane isomerization over a mixture of highly porous platinum- and acid-bearing particles.

Note: The approach to theoretical (equilibrium) conversion (ordinate) depends critically on the component particle size expressed by their radius (R) [72].

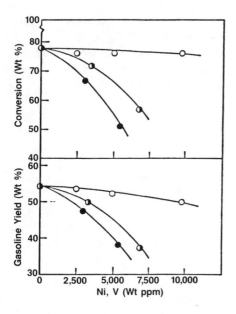

Figure 10.8 Effects of contamination by Ni and V on conversion and yield of gasoline [73].
Note: Catalyst: MRZ-260, Steam deactivation: 100% steam, 770°C 6 hr; ASTM MAT: Reaction temp.
482°C, 16 WHSV, 3 C/O.

as cocatalysts, creating undesirable dehydrogenation activity. Although vanadium is not as active a dehydrogenation catalyst as nickel, it has sufficient mobility to migrate to the zeolitic component of the catalyst where it reacts with the zeolite and destroys its crystallinity and porosity. Recent work by Matsuda [73] shows the effects of nickel and vanadium poisoning on the performance of cracking catalysts (Figure 10.8).

Sodium is another metal poison commonly found in heavy hydrocarbon feeds to cracking units. Sodium can migrate from the matrix to zeolite and neutralize acid sites, thereby reducing activity. It also reduces the thermal and hydrothermal stability of the zeolite, accelerating its deactivation at the high temperatures of the reactor and regenerator in cracking units. Sodium in the feed can be minimized by thorough desalting of the crude oil or by use of a guard chamber to trap out sodium or other metals. In cases where the feed is pretreated to hydrogenate and remove sulfur and nitrogen, metals are partially removed prior to subsequent reactions where the feed contacts the zeolitic catalyst.

RESTORATION OF CATALYST ACTIVITY

Regeneration

Carbonaceous deposits on catalysts can be removed by burning in an oxygen-containing gas. Sulfur and nitrogen deposits will also be removed, although part of the sulfur may be oxidized and remain on the catalyst surface as a sulfate salt, especially if a transition metal is present. Care has to be taken to avoid overheating of catalyst by controlling oxygen partial pressure, gas flow rate, and temperature. In composite catalysts, it is not unusual to have different burning kinetics for the coke on the zeolite and the coke on the binder-matrix. The larger are the catalyst particles, the greater is the probability of having higher intraparticle temperatures than measured in the bulk gas phase due to diffusion and heat transfer rate limitations.

Reactivation

In some process applications, catalyst activity can be at least partially restored by desorbing part of the carbonaceous deposit at elevated temperatures in an inert gas stream or in H_2. This is especially effective for removal of basic nitrogen compounds, which are chemisorbed on the surface of the zeolitic component. After several such treatments, the reactivations will lose effectiveness, and the catalyst will have to be oxygen regenerated.

Rejuvenation

Oxygen regeneration alone may not be effective enough for restoring the hydrogenation activity of platinum that has aggregated on the surface of the zeolite or migrated to the binder. The platinum can usually be redispersed by oxygen regeneration, followed by treatment with low partial pressures of chlorine, as has been practiced for several years with platinum-alumina reforming catalyst. Low concentrations of water are provided with the chlorine to improve control of the redispersion and avoid corrosion of the reactor and auxiliary equipment.

Chemical Treatment

Recent advances have been made in controlling metal poisons deposited on cracking catalyst by injecting materials into the cracking units that will react with the metal poisons on the surface of the catalyst and convert them to more inert compounds.

Antimony, usually in the form of an organometallic compound, has been used effectively [74] to passivate the hydrogenation activity of nickel. Tin compounds are claimed [75] to be effective for passivating vanadium.

The zeolitic component may deactivate because of migration of alkali or alkaline earth metals from the binder to the zeolite. Also, alkali or alkaline earth metals, which were originally "locked" in small cavities of the zeolite, may gradually diffuse into large intracrystalline framework openings and ion exchange with the acid sites. One approach to reactivating this type of used catalyst is to treat the catalyst with a solution of an ammonium salt to replace the accessible alkali metals with ammonium ions. After washing, drying, and calcining, the active sites should be restored. Rejuvenation treatments for metal-supported zeolite catalysts are discussed by Ward [76] and Reichle [77].

FUTURE DIRECTION

The level of sophistication in catalyst design has been directly proportional to the quality of the analytical techniques available to define the catalyst and its chemistry. Recent advances in electronics have spawned analytical tools that allow extensive observations and evaluations at the atomic level. The advances in surface science, although they have found only limited application with highly porous commercial catalysts, exemplify this new technological capability. In addition, equally significant advances have been made in techniques that reveal more about the bulk properties of the catalyst such as nuclear magnetic resonance, X-ray and electron diffraction, extended X-ray absorption fine structure, and electron microscopy. By interrelating highly sophisticated chemical and physical characterization of catalysts in both the fresh, unused state and in the deactivated, used state with their catalytic performance, catalyst formulations and preparational procedures will evolve that will continue to advance the science of catalysis.

REFERENCES

1. Sullivan, R. F., and Scott, J. W. *ACS Symposium Series 222*, pp. 293–313. Las Vegas, Nev.: ACS.
2. Voorhies, A., Jr., and Smith, W. M. 1964. *Advances in Petroleum Chemistry & Refining*, pp. 8, 169. New York: Interscience.
3. Choudhair, N., and Saral, D. N. 1975. *IEC Prod. Res. & Dev.* 14:74.
4. U.S. patent 3,140,249 (1964); U.S. patent 3,140,253 (1964).
5. U.S. patent 3,620,964 (1971).
6. U.S. patent 4,101,417 (1978).
7. Maselli, J. M., and Peters, A. W. 1984. *Catal. Rev. Sci. Eng.* 26:525–54.
8. Ritter, R. B., et al. 1985. "Improvements in FCC Catalyst Technology for Light Hydrocarbon Technology." NPRA Annual Mtg.
9. U.S. patent 3,367,886 (2-6-68) "Synthetic Zeolite Contact Masses and Method for Making the Same;" U.S. patent 3,367,887 (2-6-68) "Solid Catalysts;" U.S. patent 3,657,154 (4-18-72) "Microspherical Zeolitic Cracking Catalyst;" U.S. patent 3,663,165 (5-16-72) "Zeolitic Catalyst and Preparation."
10. Kubo, H.; Arai, H.; Tominaga, H.; and Kunugi, T. 1972. *Bull. Chem. Soc. Japan* 45:607–12.
11. Kubo, H.; Arai, H.; Tominaga, H.; and Kunugi, T. 1972. *Bull. Chem. Soc. Japan* 45:613–16.
12. Chubin, G. D., et al. 1976. *Proc. Int. Congr. Catal., 6th* 2:668–76.
13. Vedrine, J. C., et al. 1977. *Proc. Int. Vac. Congr., 7th* 1:481–84.
14. Vedrine, J. C., et al. 1978. *J. Chem. Soc., Faraday Trans.* I. 74:440–49.
15. Trengler, A., et al. 1978. *Acta. Phys. Chem.* 24:319–25.
16. Ballivet-Thatchenko, D., and Coridurier, G. 1979. *Inorganic Chem.* 18:558–64.
17. Nagy, J.; Van Eenoo, M.; and Derouane, E. G. 1979. *J. Catal.* 58:230–37.
18. Madhusudhan, C. P.; Patel, M.D.; and Good, M. L. 1979. *Inorganic Chem.* 18:2384–89.
19. Lehn, J. M.; Sauvage, J. P.; and Ziessel, R. 1980. *Nouv. J. Chim.* 4:355–58.
20. Weber, R. S.; Boudart, M.; and Gallezot, P. 1980. *Stud. Surf. Sci. Catal.* 4:415–20.

21. Blackmond, D. G., and Goodwin, J. G., Jr. 1981. *J. Chem. Soc. Chem. Commun.* 125–26.
22. Ganzerla, R., et al. 1981. *J. Organomet. Chem.* 208:C43–45.
23. Scherzer, J., and Fort, D. 1981. *J. Catal.* 71:111–18.
24. Landau, M. V., et al. 1976. *Kinet. Katal.* 17:1281–87.
25. Jackson, P. F., et al. 1980. *J. Organomet. Chem.* 190:C1–C4.
26. Bandiera, J. 1980. *J. Chim. Phys. Phys-Chim. Biol.* 77:303–10.
27. Tsybulevskii, A. M., et al. 1973. *Khim. Teklinol. Topl. Masel* 18:3–6.
28. Khudiev, A. T., et al. 1979. Neftekhim protsessov im Yu. G. Mamdealieva, Akad. Nauk., Az SSR 10:66–74.
29. Rasko, J.; Felian, B.; and Solymosi, F. 1979. *Geterog. Katal.* 4th pt. 1:67–72.
30. Chen, N. Y., and Weisz, P. B. 1967. *Chem. Eng. Symp. Ser.* :63, 86.
31. Dufaux, M.; Gelin, P.; and Naccache, C. 1980. *Stud. Surf. Sci. Catal.* 5 (Catal. Zeolites):261–71.
32. Bogomolov, V. N., et al. 1980. *Phys. Status Solidi A* 62:43–51.
33. Chen, N.Y.; Maziuk, J.; Schwartz, A. B.; and Weisz, P. B. 1968. *Oil & Gas J.* 66:154.
34. Chen, N. Y.; Gorring, R. L.; Ireland, H. R.; and Stein, T. R. 1977. *Oil & Gas J.* 75:165.
35. Ireland, H. R.; Redini, C.; Raff, A. S.; and Fava, L. 1979. *Hydrocarbon Proces.* 58:119.
36. Smith, K. M.; Starr, W. C.; and Chen, N.Y. 1980. *Oil & Gas J.* 78:75.
37. Graven, R. G., and Green, J. R. 1980. Cong. of Australian Inst. of Pet., October.
38. Bennett, R. N.; Elkes, G. J.; and Wanless, G. J. 1975. *Oil & Gas J.* 73:69.
39. Hargrove, G. K.; Elkes, G. J.; and Richardson, A. H., 1970. *Oil & Gas J.* 77:103.
40. Meisel, S. L., and Weisz, P. B. 1982. Advances in Catal. Chem. II Symp., Salt Lake City, May.
41. Fagan, F. N., and Weisz, P. B. 1983. Japan Pet. Inst., Tokyo, May.
42. U.S. patent 3,960,978 (1976).
43. Garwood, W. E. 1983. *ACS Symposium Series 218*, p. 383. Las Vegas, Nev.: ACS.
44. Tabak, S. A., and Krambeck, F. J. 1985. *Hydrocarbon Proces.* 72, September.
45. U.S. patent 4,064,039 (1977); U.S. patent 4,072,600 (1978).
46. Anderson, C. D.; Dwyer, F. G.; Koch, G.; and Niiranen, P. 1984. *Proc. IX Ibero-American Symp. on Catal.* 1:247. Lisbon.
47. U.S. patent 4,025,458 (1977); U.S. patent 3,711,422 (1-16-73) "Cracking Catalyst Restoration with Antimony Compounds;" U.S. patent 4,321,129 (1982).
48. Dale, G. H., and McKay, D. L. 1977. *Hydrocarbon Proces.* 56:97.
49. U.S. patent 4,469,589 (9-4-84) "Catalyst and Process for Conversion of Hydrocarbons;" U.S. patent 4,472,267 (9-18-84) "Catalyst and Process for Conversion of Hydrocarbons;" U.S. patent 4,495,305 (1-22-85) "Catalyst for Conversion of Hydrocarbons;" U.S. patent 4,495,304 (1-22-85) "Catalyst for Conversion of Hydrocarbons."
50. Thiel, P. C., et al. 1985. *Davison Catalagram:* no. 71.
51. Byrne, J. W.; Speronello, B. K.; and Leuenberger, E. L. 1984. *Oil & Gas J.* :101.
52. Byrne, J. W. 1984. "New Development in FCC SOx Catalyst Technology." NPRA Annual Mtg.
53. Blanton, W. A. 1982. *Oil & Gas J.* :62.
54. U.S. patent 4,115,250 (1978); U.S. patent 4,071,436 (1978); U.S. patent 4,166,787 (1979).
55. U.S. patent 4,311,581 (1982); U.S. patent 4,341,661 (1982).
56. McArthur, D. P.; Simpson, H.D.; and Baron, K. 1981. *Oil & Gas J.* :55.
57. U.S. patent 4,298,695 (1981); U.S. patent 4,354,963 (1982).
58. U.S. patent 4,361,503 (1982).

59. U.S. patent 3,857,780 (1974); U.S. patent 3,966,644 (1976).
60. de Bruijn, A., et al. 1981. *IEC Process Res. Dev.* 20:40.
61. U.S. patent 4,342,643 (1982).
62. U.S. patent 4,441,990 (1984).
63. Weisz, P. B. 1973. Zeolites—New horizons in catalysis. *Chem. Tech.* 3:498.
64. Shihabi, D. S.; Garwood, W. E.; Chu, P.; Miale, J. N.; Lago, R. M.; Chu, C. T–W.; and Chang, C. D. 1985. *J. Catal.* 93:471.
65. Chang, C. D.; Hellring, S. D.; Miale, J. N.; and Schmitt, K. D. 1985. *J. Chem. Soc., Faraday Trans.* I. 81:2215.
66. Chu, C. T–W.; Kuehl, G. H.; Lago, R. M.; and Chang, C. D. 1985. *J. Catal.* 93:451.
67. Plank, C. J., and Rosinski, E. J. U.S. patent 3,391,088 (7-2-68) "Catalyst Prepared by Steaming High Silica Alkali Metal Aluminosilicates in a Matrix."
68. Rollmann, L. D. 1979. *J. Catal.* 56:140.
69. Derouane, E. J. 1985. *Catalysis by Acids and Bases*, p. 224. Imelik, et al., eds. Amsterdam: Elsevier.
70. Chester, A. W., and Stover, W. A. 1977. *Ind. Eng. Chem., Prod. Res. Dev.* 16:285.
71. Eastwood, S. C.; Oleck, S. M.; and Schwartz, A. B. U.S. patent 3,407,148 (10-22-68) "Minimizing Deactivation of Aluminosilicate Catalysts due to Changes in Hydration Level."
72. Weisz, P. B. 1973. *Science* 179:436–37.
73. Matsuda, T.; Ogata, M.; Yoshida, S.; and Nishimura, Y. 1985. *Int'l Chem. Eng.* 25:340.
74. McKay, D. L., and Dale, G. H. 1977. Passivate metals in FCC feeds. *Hydrocarbon Proces.*
75. English, A. R., and Korvalczyk, D. C. 1984. Tin passivates vanadium. *Oil & Gas J.*: 127.
76. Ward, J. W., and Clark, D. E. U.S. patent 3,835,028 (9-10-74) "Hydrocracking Process with Rejuvenated Catalyst."
77. Reichle, A. D.; Pine, L. A.; Ward, J. W.; and Hansford, R. C. 1974. *Oil & Gas J.* :137.

CHAPTER 11

Multifunctioning Catalysts

Emmerson Bowes

There can hardly be a better example of a catalyst support serving as more than a platform for the active catalytic component than in a multifunctioning catalyst where, for example, a metal is combined with an acidic support. The first demonstration of cooperative action between different catalytic entities in polystep catalytic reactions was in studies carried out mainly in the 1950s of hydrocarbon reactions over transition metals, especially nickel and platinum on oxide supports. It was shown that there were physically separate sites, each of which catalyzed separate reactions that the other did not effect. True intermediate chemical species were shown to be formed on one site which were transported to the other. Such intermediates could be in very low concentration and not always detected. Speculation on the possibility of cooperative action between different catalyst components by way of intermediate reaction products had previously been subject to other explanations. Multifunctional catalysts are sometimes defined in a very broad sense [1] in which all the different functions embodied in an industrial catalyst are recognized. By such definition, almost all catalysts fall into the net of multifunctional catalysts. For the purpose of this chapter, multifunctional or polyfunctional catalysts are defined as catalysts containing two or more types of distinct catalytic sites, each of which facilitates a distinctly different step in an overall polystep reaction scheme. The definition of multifunctional catalysts is specific and relies on that of P. B. Weisz [2]. The mechanisms and kinetics of bifunctional catalysts also were reviewed by J. H. Sinfelt [3].

Following Weisz, where the two successive reaction schemes

$$A - X \rightarrow B - Y \rightarrow C \tag{11.1}$$

take place over two different catalysts in successive zones and where the conversion is high in each stage, the combination of the two catalyst zones would be expected to give similar overall conversion. This he defines as the trivial case of polystep chemical reaction. Catalysts for such reactions will not be described here since no cooperative action between the different catalytic sites is necessary.

When, however, the conversion in the first reaction step is severely limited for reasons of thermodynamic equilibrium, then the consecutive reaction can only lead to negligible overall conversion. If, for example, n-hexane is passed over a dehydrogenative catalyst to form olefin at 435°C at 30 atm partial pressure of hydrogen, the equilibrium concentration of olefin is about 0.02%. The subsequent skeletal isomerization of the olefin on a catalyst having an acid function yields no more than 0.02% of product. The conversion can be improved by repeating the process over and over again. The concentration of olefin always remains the same, but the paraffin composition changes as new n-paraffins are dehydrogenated and some of the isomerized olefins are rehydrogenated to isoparaffins. Thus the n-olefin is effectively removed as the acid site continues to isomerize fresh n-olefin until the overall composition finally reaches the thermodynamic equilibrium composition for the temperature, pressure, and hydrogen concentration in the reactors. Of course, the number of reactors in line to achieve the desired result would be prohibitive. When, however, the hydrogenative and the acidic catalysts are combined in one bed, either as an intimate mixture of separate particles or on the same particle, there is a remarkable increase in conversion. Weisz shows that the overall rate constant can be made large by appropriate choice of the two forward rate constants. The conversion of $A \rightarrow C$ is greater than the product of the conversions attainable in separate successive steps, and this is Weisz's definition of the nontrivial polystep reaction. The distance between the hydrogenative site and the acid site is crucial to the effectiveness of the combination of sites. The intermediate B molecules must diffuse over that distance, and Weisz derived expressions relating diffusion and reaction rates. One expression useful in catalyst design is

$$P_B > 2.3 \times 10^4 \frac{T}{273} \frac{dN}{dt} \frac{R^2}{D} , \qquad (11.2)$$

derived from a more general

$$\frac{dN}{dt} \cdot \frac{1}{Beq} \cdot \frac{R^2}{D} < 1 , \qquad (11.3)$$

where P_B is the partial pressure of the intermediate [atm], Beq is the concentration at equilibrium [moles/cm^3], dN/dt is the overall reaction rate [moles/sec.cm^3], T is the reaction temperature [°K.], and D is the diffusivity of the medium [cm^2/sec.], and R is the catalyst particle size [cm]. Weisz illustrates the usefulness of 11.2 after substituting $D = 2 \times 10^{-3}$ cm^2/sec., typical of silica-alumina, and $dN/dt = 10^{-6}$ moles/sec.cm^3, with a graph showing intimacy requirement in terms of particle size versus partial pressure of intermediate. There is a mine of information in Weisz's publication and it should be required reading for catalyst designers and evaluators alike.

If the partial pressure of an intermediate can be estimated, the required intimacy of the two catalytic sites can be calculated. This process in turn suggests the constraints that may have to be applied to forming a dual-functional catalyst. Can it be formed by mixing two particles? Is the degree of intimacy required attainable by size reduction, or must one catalyst component be added to the other in solution to obtain the required intimacy? It also follows that the size requirement limits the heterogeneity permissible in a mixed catalyst. Intimate mixing of fine particles on a commercial scale is difficult, and special attention may be required where a dual-functional catalyst is made from an acidic component and a matrix on which it is desired to deposit a transitional metal.

Once a satisfactory dual-functional catalyst has been formed and the desired dispersion of one component with respect to the other achieved, it is necessary to maintain the relationship between the two sites. This relationship contains spatial and qualitative components. In a well-dispersed platinum-alumina catalyst, the metal is in the form of small clusters of <20 A, below the level of detection by X-ray diffraction methods, with particles down to 5–10 Å as detected by electron microscopy. Migration of the metal on the surface to form larger clusters reduces its activity relative to the acid site. Relative enhancement of the acidic site results in the accumulation of carbonaceous material and a faster aging rate. In a catalyst made up of a separate acidic component and a binder, migration of the metal to the binder may result in agglomeration or too great a separation between acid and metal sites. The nature of the support is of paramount importance. For a given support, high surface area is desirable, although this is an empirical observation. What really matters is more likely to be discontinuities in the surface due to the packing of the greater number of support particles that give rise to the surface area. Too high a surface area, however, results later in loss of the smallest particles when the catalyst is exposed to higher temperatures in service than it was in preparation. Noble metal dispersions are more complete and more stable on alumina than on silica and on high alumina content zeolites than on high silica zeolites. These observations imply some affinity between the metal and the surface, though clear demonstration of bonding has not been forthcoming. Equally important, however, is the affinity of the support for oxidized species or chloro compounds formed in the regeneration and rejuvenation of these catalysts that affect redispersion after normal use or plant upsets. Interesting observations have been made of coclustering in bi-metallic catalysts, which is also affected by the support by Sinfelt and Cusamanno [4], Sinfelt [5], and Burton and Garten [6].

Acid sites deactivate by hydrothermal processes or depletion of acid-enhancing components such as chlorine. The balance of activities between sites has to be controlled while on stream by the controlled addition of water or halogen compounds to reactor feeds.

CATALYTIC-REFORMING CATALYSTS

The most important and widely used dual-functional catalysts are those employed in the catalytic reforming of petroleum naphthas. Catalytic reforming is a fixed-bed process using platinum, and optionally one or more modifiers, on an acidic support operating at high temperature and moderate to low pressure with recycle of hydrogen-rich gas. Ciapetta [7] in 1961 summarized some ten years of laboratory, pilot plant, and engineering studies leading to various catalytic-reforming processes. Thirteen such processes were developed in the United States between 1949 and 1956. In 1971, Ciapetta [8] comprehensively reviewed catalytic naphtha reforming over the 1960s covering properties of the catalysts and hydrocarbon reactions. From 80,000 B/SD in 1950, U.S. capacity had grown to over 4.7 million B/SD by the end of 1970 with metallic platinum as the (de-)hydrogenation component and a halogenated alumina or a silica alumina as the acidic component. By the end of 1970, there was some 5.5

million barrels per day of catalytic-reforming capacity outside the Eastern Bloc countries according to a *World Petroleum* report [9]. As of 1985, that total was over 8 million barrels per day, down from 1980 but still exceeding that of any other catalytic process, including cracking.

The availability of high octane gasoline from catalytic reforming spurred the development and manufacture of efficient high-compression-ratio automobile engines. In the 1970s, new environmental requirements leading to control of exhaust gas emissions and eventually the use of lead-intolerant catalytic converters sharply reversed this trend in engine design. The new engines had lower octane requirements and ran on unleaded gasoline. New regulations restricted the amount of lead in other gasolines, which meant that refiners had to maintain or increase the clear (without lead) octane number of gasolines. Overall demand for gasoline was reduced as a result of the OPEC price increases and the popularity of small-engined cars. Today, however, the strains on the refiners are growing as lead is phased out by regulation and the proportion of cars on the road using no-lead gasoline increases as the car population ages. Catalytic reforming is the only process producing economically a gasoline fraction with a clear research octane number of 100 or more. In Europe, reforming accounts for 60% of the gasoline pool, and there is surplus capacity so that octane improvement is likely to be obtained by increasing reformer severity. In the United States, more catalytic reforming may be required, as well as isomerization and other processes. The time is ripe for the development of reforming processes capable of handling wider boiling range and less pure feed stocks. Perhaps the catalysts will incorporate new versions of zeolitic or novel structures with controlled acidity.

A great deal of research and development on platinum reforming catalysts carried out in the early 1950s led to a good understanding of the process and provided the basis for future catalyst development [10, 11, 12, 13, 14]. The catalyst was, and has remained essentially, platinum metal (platinum 0.35–0.7% weight) on an acidic support. Significant improvements have been made, however, by incorporating additional elements. The first major change came with the introduction of the platinum-rhenium catalysts in 1967. Rhenium addition (platinum 0.35–0.4% weight, rhenium 0.2–0.4% weight) has no effect on the basic dual-functional reactions, but it reduces the aging rate. Other elements used in reforming catalysts as promoters include germanium, iridium, and tin, all generally in amounts of about 0.2–0.6% weight on catalyst. All of them increase the stability of the catalyst by reducing coke deposition, which gives the benefit of longer on-stream times or use of more severe conditions. Platinum-iridium catalysts are claimed to be significantly more active than conventional platinum or other bimetallic catalysts. Bimetallic catalysts have permitted designers to go to lower pressures (from 400 to 100–200 psig), which favor higher yields of aromatics. They are now being operated successfully at high severity with continuous withdrawal and regeneration.

How the second metal functions is still unclear. There is the possibility of interaction of the support with rhenium, germanium, and tin oxides, of stabilization of some intermediate oxidation states by alumina, and of alloying or clustering of metals. It must be considered, however, that since the buildup of coke is very slow, it is the result of either an infrequent event or the net effect of a reaction that is almost but not quite complete. Either way, the second metal may be more efficient than platinum in catalyzing the removal of the intermediate involved or promoting an independent pathway to drain it off.

While silica-alumina was used in some processes, the support was predominantly high-surface-area alumina. The so-called support has a catalytic function that makes it as important as the metal(s) it carries. Eta alumina, derived from beta alumina trihydrate, was favored initially because of its high acidity but has been displaced by gamma alumina obtained by calcining alpha alumina monohydrate (boehmite). Both aluminas were used extensively in commercial units, but the eta alumina suffered from relatively poor mechanical strength, and it suffers initially a rapid loss of surface area from about 400 m^2/g to 200–300 m^2/g. Loss of surface area is the result of the coalescing of the smallest alumina crystallites with larger crystallites. For an average surface area of 400 m^2/g, the average crystallite would have an approximate diameter of only 80 Å, with many crystals much smaller and too near the size of a crystallite of well-dispersed platinum for stability. Just as we are finding that alumina can migrate into and out of zeolite frameworks, it would not be surprising to find that the growth of alumina crystallites is by transport of ions or molecular entities. Gamma alumina is more stable under hydrothermal conditions and has better mechanical properties. A distinct advantage of alumina over other supports is its relative ease of being formed by extrusion into various shapes with good physical strength. The shapes of alumina-based reforming catalysts are usually cylindrical extrudates or spherical particles. Spheres may be formed from gel dropped into oil, as is done for silica-alumina, or formed by spheridizing an extrudate or pellet.

High-purity aluminas (<500 ppm impurities) are required, containing less than 100 ppm of alkali metals, low in platinum poisons such as arsenic and antimony, and of surface area of about 180–200 m^2/g for good dispersion of metal and thermal stability. Research on other supports has been extensive and valuable in elucidating the degree of dispersion of platinum, adsorption phenomena, and mechanism of the reactions, but none provides as consistently high dispersion of metal and stability in use and regeneration as does alumina. The high surface area of alumina is the result of the small size of the crystallites. The pores are the voids between these otherwise nonporous (except to ions) particles averaging less than 200 Å in diameter. The metal particles grow on a very rough surface made by close packing of spherulites and other shapes in contact, probably in the niches where crystallites meet but rarely on a perfectly flat surface. The (111) and (110) faces are preferentially exposed by eta and gamma alumina, respectively. The surface presents a face to the impregnation liquors of oxygen and hydoxyl groups, with aluminum present as both octahedral and tetrahedral ions, which strongly sorbs many metal salts and thereby lessens migration during drying. When the metal is generated by heat and reduction, the smallest crystals will result from the simultaneous growth of the largest number of nuclei, a process promoted by the highest dispersion during ion exchange or impregnation. The interfacial energy between the metal and the support may influence the form of metal crystals, as well as location. There is a recent review by G. C. Bond and R. Burch [15] of literature on strong metal-support interactions (SMSI) and in the same volume one on structural characterization of surface species and surface sites by Zecchina, Garrone, and Gugliel-minotti [16].

Alumina has Bronsted acidity due to hydroxyl groups and Lewis acidity where an electron-deficient aluminum atom is exposed by loss of water from two adjacent hydroxyls. These are considered to be the active catalytic sites. The acidity is developed to a maximum at calcining temperatures of about 550°F, especially in the complete absence of alkali metals, but it is insufficient for hydrocarbon processing. Acidity is therefore adjusted in the course of manufacture and use by the addition of chlorine compounds. Gamma alumina requires more chloride than eta alumina, and the amount on fresh catalyst usually corresponds with the stoichiometric amount in the chloroplatinic acid used in manufacture. There is about 0.4% chlorine content in 0.35% platinum catalyst and 0.7% in 0.6% platinum catalysts. During on-stream and rejuvenation periods, chlorinated compounds are added to maintain acidity and to redisperse platinum, respectively. The halogen content of bimetallic catalysts must be maintained carefully at an optimum level to maintain desired selectivity. Initially these catalysts contain about 1% chlorine. Too much chlorine results in increased hydrocracking reactions, which consume hydrogen and produce propane and butane. Excessive amounts for long periods lead to cracking and coking.

The reversibility of the reaction of chloriding of alumina is essential to the success of acidity control of the support, making alumina well suited for its dual role as cocatalyst and carrier.

HYDROISOMERIZATION

Although the isomerization of n-paraffins in the reformer process is used as the example of dual-functional catalysts, the reformer does not efficiently isomerize or hydrocrack paraffins, especially below heptane. Ideally for maximum octane improvement, the n-paraffins up to and including hexane should be removed from the feed and isomerized at low temperature where equilibrium favors isoparaffins. Hydroisomerization is the classical example of dual-functional catalysis and is the subject of many publications and patented processes, but in practice it is difficult to achieve at attractively low temperatures. The requirements for a strong acid and active hydrogenative function have led to the use of platinum on highly chlorided alumina or on zeolites. The highly chlorided aluminas are made by addition of aluminum chloride or carbon tetrachloride. They are active at low temperatures but are highly corrosive and sensitive to water. Ethyl aluminum chloride has been reported by Franck and Le Page [17] to combine with 85% of the surface hydroxyls on platinum-impregnated alumina to give a catalyst active at 300°F. It is not, however, dual functional in that the catalyst operates as well initially without platinum, which functions to reduce aging. This may well be the case in other highly chlorided catalysts. Indeed, it has also been shown that some zeolite catalysts behave as Friedel-Crafts type acids. Carbonium ions are formed directly by hydride abstraction from the paraffins in a concentration in excess of that which would result from the paraffin-olefin equilibrium. Addition of a noble metal reduces the concentration by establishing that equilibrium [20]. The olefin may block the direct path by being preferentially absorbed at the acid site. The zeolite catalysts compensate for a higher operating temperature by being more tolerant of adverse conditions. Both faujasite and mordenite have been used, but the latter operates at a lower temperature and C5–C6 feeds are converted to near equilibrium at 480°F. Here the mordenite acts as the support, although other materials may be added as binder. It is necessary to disperse the platinum thoroughly throughout the zeolite. This can be accomplished by ion exchanging the ammonium form with the platinum ammine cation and carefully calcining the catalyst. In general, metals ion exchanged into zeolites are initially atomically dispersed, but reduction causes migration to the outside of the crystallite or on to the binder. Very high silica-alumina zeolite surfaces behave like silica, and metal interactions with it are unlikely. Zeolites with high alumina content have sufficient external alumina to provide sites for interaction with cations or to serve as points of strong sorption.

Hydroisomerization of higher molecular weight n-paraffins is also of interest as an alternative process to catalytic dewaxing. The studies and patents in the field are on a variety of metals (platinum, palladium, nickel, and others) on zeolites such as faujasites, Linde L, zeolite beta, and mordenite and as such are beyond the scope of this chapter. The search for the correct balance between hydrogenative and acid function, dispersion of the metal, and its stability still goes on. When the third dimension of the zeolite surface is added, together with the size and shape selectivity factors and the strength of acid sites of different zeolites, there appears to be much scope for further research.

HYDROCRACKING CATALYSTS

Hydrocracking is a reaction that simultaneously (de-)hydrogenates and breaks carbon-carbon bonds. In petroleum processing, the carbon-to-sulfur, -nitrogen, and -oxygen bonds are also broken. The feedstocks are from a wide range of refinery intermediate products, such as aromatic cycle oils, thermal and coker gas oils, and heavy gas oils, to make products ranging from liquid petroleum gas, gasoline, to middle distillate products. The hydrocracking and isomerization of paraffins are mechanistically the same as on reforming catalysts, but the process is carried out at lower temperatures (500°–850°F) rather than the 930°F of reformers, and the objective is to reduce aromaticity of the products, not increase it. Paraffins are cracked via an olefin intermediate, randomly from the third carbon atoms. Alkyl aromatics are dealkylated and naphthenes cracked by single-ring opening. Aromatic rings are progressively hydrogenated and cracked, and saturation of nitrogen compounds precedes denitrogenation.

Hydrogen must be added to the process, the pressure must be increased (800–3000 psig), and the catalyst must contend with recycle gases containing ammonia and hydrogen sulfide, light hydrocarbons, as well as hydrogen. In single-stage units, the feed is restricted to fairly low sulfur and nitrogen content. In two-stage units, the first stage at 650–800°F is used to reduce the concentration of nitrogen compounds, which are stripped out as ammonia, and to a lesser extent remove sulfur. The second stage can then be operated at lower temperature, commonly in the range 500–700°F. The use of dual-functioning catalysts and high pressures results in very long on-stream times stretching into years.

The catalysts for the first stage are typical of those used in hydrodesulfurization

(HDS) processes. Nickel-molybdenum-alumina is usually chosen over the equivalent cobalt catalyst since nitrogen compounds are the most objectionable in hydrocracking. Little hyrocarbon conversion takes place other than hydrogenation of unsaturates.

In the second stage, the catalyst is tailored for the feed and desired products. The hydrogenation component may be a platinum or palladium or nickel, molybdenum, or tungsten. Frequently a zeolite provides the acid component, a stabilized Y-zeolite being the most frequently used. The supports are metal oxides, often gamma alumina calcined to 550–600°F to give surface areas of about 150–180 m²/g or silica-alumina. Other supports described include silica-zirconia-titania and alumina-titania. Pore size does not seem to be as important in hydrocracking as in HDS, where much attention has been paid to optimizing the pore size distribution. Yan [20], however, reported that a nickel-tungsten-rare-earth–exchanged X-type zeolite was ineffective for hydrocracking a wide-range boiling feedstock with recycle to extinction. Catalyst aging and hydrogen consumption were high, and a buildup of polynuclear ring aromatics was observed, due, it was believed, to steric hindrance at the pore mouth of the zeolite. Addition of an amorphous silica-alumina to the catalyst composition prevented the accumulation of large-ring compounds, and severity could be reduced.

An excellent review of the design and preparation of hydrocracking catalysts has been done by Ward [18]. In this review, Ward also discusses reaction mechanisms and the unit processes. He points out that hydrocracking is now the second largest catalytic use of zeolites. Franck and Le Page [19] presented a pragmatic approach to selecting and optimizing hydrocracking catalysts for maximizing middle distillates from heavy gas oils. Their work gives good insight into the nature and variety of feedstock species and how they adsorb on the different sites and hydrocrack.

SHAPE-SELECTIVE HYDROCRACKING

A special case of hydrocracking is the shape-selective cracking of normal paraffins in reformer gasoline to increase octane number (Selectoforming). Here the acid support has an additional function of segregating only those molecules with a cross-section small enough to enter the eight-membered oxygen ring that is the effective opening into the natural zeolite, erionite. The hydrogenation function is provided by nickel. It is known that nickel migrates out of a zeolite on calcining and reduction. It is evident, therefore, that the shape selectivity operates on the olefins, selecting only the n-olefins. Presumably the n-paraffins that enter the zeolite either do not react or are prevented from coking the catalyst by the action of nickel on the outside of the zeolite. This process is used commercially where and when the economics are favorable for converting principally pentane and hexane to propane.

REFERENCES

1. Schuit, G. C. A., and Gates, B. C. 1983, September–November. *Chemtech*, pp. 556, 693.
2. Weisz, P. B. 1962. *Adv. in Catal.* 13:137–90.
3. Sinfelt, J. H. 1964. *Adv. in Chem. Eng.* 5:37–74.

4. Sinfelt, J. H., and Cusumano, J. A. 1977. *Advanced Materials in Catalysis*, pp. 1–31. Burton, J. J., and Garten, R. L. eds. New York: Academic Press.
5. Sinfelt, J. H. 1983. Bimetallic catalysts. *Exxon Monograph*.
6. Burton, J. J., and Garten, R. L. 1977. *Advanced Materials in Catalysis*, pp. 33–65. New York: Academic Press.
7. Ciapetta, F. G. 1961. *Petrol./Chem. Eng.* 33:C–19.
8. Ciapetta, F. G. 1971. *Catal. Reviews* 5(1):67–158 (6).
9. Report. 1970. *World Petroleum*, 16:29.
10. Haensel, V., and Donaldson, G. R. 1951. *Ind. Eng. Chem.* 43:2102.
11. Ciapetta, F. G. 1953. *Ind. Eng. Chem.* 45:159.
12. Ciapetta, F. G., and Hunter, J. B. 1953. *Ind. Eng. Chem.* 45:147.
13. Ciapetta, F. G., and Hunter, J. B. 1953. *Ind. Eng. Chem.* 45:155.
14. Hettinger, W. P., Jr.; Keith, C. D.; Gring, J. L.; and Teter, J. W. 1955. *Ind. Eng. Chem.* 47:719.
15. Bond, J. C., and Burch, R. 1983. *Catalysis*, vol 6, pp. 27–60. London: The Royal Society of Chemistry.
16. Zecchina, E.; Garrone, E.; and Guglielminotti, E. 1983. *Catalysis*. vol 6, pp. 90–143. London: The Royal Society of Chemistry.
17. Franck, J. P., and Le Page, J. F. 1980. New horizons in catalysis. *Proceedings 7th International Congress on Catalysis*, Tokyo. Amsterdam: Elsevier.
18. Ward, J. W. 1976. *Preparation of Catalysts III*, p. 587. Poncelet, P.; Grange, P.; and Jacobs, P. A. eds. Amsterdam: Elsevier.
19. Franck, J. P., and Le Page, J. F. 1980. New horizons in catalysis. *Proceedings 7th International Congress on Catalysis*, Tokyo. Amsterdam: Elsevier.
20. Yan, T. Y. 1983. *I & EC Process Design & Development* 22:154.

About the Contributors

ROBERT L. ALBRIGHT

Robert L. Albright holds a B.S. degree in chemistry from Elizabethtown College and a Ph.D. degree in organic chemistry from the University of Illinois. In 1958, he joined Rohm and Haas Company and has worked primarily in four areas: process design and development, design and synthesis of crosslinked polymers, the physical chemistry and mechanism of formation of porous organic polymers, and technical consulting. Made a Research Fellow of the Rohm and Haas Company in 1982, Albright's research emphasis has been primarily synthetic with the use of mechanistic studies to provide understanding in order to guide the synthetic approach and to optimize design. He currently directs a group working on the design of new polymers and on the design and the development of improved manufacturing processes for many kinds of molecules. He has authored nine publications and four patents.

ALFONSO L. BALDI

Alfonso L. Baldi holds both a B.S. degree in chemistry and a M.S. degree in metallurgy from the University of Pennsylvania. He has forty years' experience in research, development, and troubleshooting in the field of metal treatment and corrosion. An inventor, he holds more than sixty U.S. patents pertaining to metal treatments, one of which is a process to provide high surface area on metals. He has also developed numerous diffusion coating processes as well as masking and stripping compounds that are unique and being used throughout the industry.

For the past twenty-two years, Baldi has been with the Alloy Surfaces Company, where he is currently Chief Scientist and Vice President of Research and Development of this wholly owned subsidiary of MATEC Corporation. He is the author of several papers in the field of metal treatment.

ALFRED J. BIRD

Alfred Bird has been engaged in research with Johnson Matthey Ltd. at their Technical Research Center in Sonning, England, since 1954. His areas of research have been primarily, but not exclusively, fuel cells, automotive exhaust fumes abatement, and liquid-phase catalysts in general. He was recently given responsibility for the liquid phase (slurry) type catalyst development group at Sonning. Bird is widely recognized as one of the world's foremost experts on carbon and catalysts supported on carbon. His experience encompasses laboratory and plant scale preparation and use.

EMMERSON BOWES

Emmerson Bowes received a B.A. degree from Liverpool Technical College and a M.R.S.C. degree from Cambridge College. His initial association was with Ellesmere Port at Lobitos Oilfields, where he successfully pioneered the liquid chromalographic analyses of all refinery streams that are broadly used in industrial and academic research. He joined Mobil Research and Development Corporation in England at Croydon and then transferred to Mobil at Paulsboro, where he was Senior Research Engineer and where he developed the first low-aging-rate xylene isomerization catalyst. After a six-year interlude with Mallinckrodt in Erie, Pennsylvania, he returned to Mobil at the Princeton Research Laboratories as Research Associate. He has been active in the development and application of ZSM-type zeolites. He is the author of many publications and patents.

JEAN-PIERRE BRUNELLE

Jean-Pierre Brunelle received his M.S. degree from Lille University and graduated from *Ecole Nationale Superieure des Petroles et Moteurs* (E.N.S.P.M.). He joined the Rhône-Poulenc company in 1974. He was involved first in refining and automotive catalysts for Procatalyse and then in several catalytic processes for Rhône-Poulenc. Since 1983, Brunelle has been responsible for the Catalysts, Carriers, and Ceramics Materials Department of the Research Center in Aubervilliers and is one of the recently nominated Research Associates of Rhône-Poulenc.

FRANCIS G. DWYER

Francis G. Dwyer received his B.Ch.E. from Villanova University and both his M.S.Ch.E. and Ph.D. in Ch.E. as a Mobil Fellow from the University of Pennsylvania. In 1953, he joined Mobil Research and Development Corporation, where his career has been in process and catalyst research and development. He has been associated with most phases of petroleum and petrochemical catalysis and has also worked in auto exhaust catalysis, intraparticle diffusion in catalysts, and intracrystalline diffusion in zeolite catalysts. He is currently a Senior Scientist and Manager of Catalyst Research and Development at Mobil. Dwyer has authored more than thirty publications and over thirty U.S. patents in the areas of petroleum and petrochemical processing, catalyst manufacture, and catalyst characterization.

IGNAC JOSEPH JAKOVAC

Ignac Joseph Jakovac received his B.S. degree in chemistry and biochemistry, his M.S. degree in organic chemistry, and his Ph.D. degree in organic chemistry from the University of Toronto. He joined Rohm and Haas Company in 1980 as Senior Scientist and has carried out research in catalysis with a primary focus on porous polymers. In 1983, he moved into the process development group in plant technical services and, in 1984, into marketing. Jakovac is currently Marketing Manager in the

Fluid Process Chemicals Group, with responsibilities in the special applications area, which includes ion exchange catalysis.

SARGIS KHOOBIAR

Sargis Khoobiar obtained his B.S. degree from Abadon Institute of Technology and both his M.S. and Ph.D. degrees from the Illinois Institute of Technology. He has had twenty-five years' experience in petroleum research, and of primary interest is the fact that he discovered the phenomenon of H_2 spillover. As Director of Catalysis Research at Halcon Corporation, he was involved in the exploration and development of new processes, as well as existing processes and catalyst sales. At present, Khoobiar is a private consultant.

PATRICE NORTIER

Patrice Nortier graduated from the *Ecole Normale Superieure de Paris* where he later become *Professeur Agrege* in Physics and Chemistry. In 1983, he joined Rhône-Poulenc company and became involved in research on catalyst carriers for the abatement of automotive exhaust gas. Since 1985, Nortier has been Senior Research Engineer supervising the Alumina Carriers and Adsorbant Group.

REGIS POISSON

Regis Poisson obtained his Ph.D. degree in electrochemistry from the *Ecole Nationale Superieure de Chimie de Strasbourg*. In 1971, after post doctoral studies in the Federal Republic of Germany (Munich Technical School) and Canada (Montreal University), he joined the Rhône-Poulenc company. He first worked on rare earth chemistry, later joined the Catalyst Carrier Research Group, and initiated research on synthesis of powder for advanced ceramics in 1978. In 1981 he was offered a position in the management of chemical research at Rhône-Poulenc. Poisson has been Research Manager of the Minérale Fine Division since its creation in 1985.

ALBERT B. SCHWARTZ

Albert B. Schwartz has a B.S. degree in chemical engineering from the University of Pennsylvania. He joined Mobil Research and Development Corporation in 1945 after a brief period with Anthracite Industries Laboratory. He has held a number of technical and management positions in research and development that have been primarily related to various aspects of catalyst synthesis, including development and applications in petroleum and petrochemical processes. His present position is Senior Scientist and Science Advisor. He holds over fifty-five U.S. patents and has published several papers.

About the Author

ALVIN B. STILES

Alvin B. Stiles received his B.Ch.E. and M.S. degrees from Ohio State University. He began his career with E.I. du Pont de Nemours at their then relatively new plant near Charleston, West Virginia. For the ensuing forty-two years, his activities were essentially related to catalyst research and development on laboratory, semi-works, and plant scale fabrications and use. He had major or complete responsibility for catalysts used for synthesis gas production, ammonia, alcohols, Nylon intermediates, acrylonitrile, and formaldehyde, as well as for other operations, including total and selective oxidation, selective hydrogenation, reductive coupling, ammoxidations, and oxidative dehydrogenations.

Upon retiring from du Pont, Stiles was appointed Research Professor at the University of Delaware where he and colleagues organized the Center for Catalytic Science, of which he is an Associate Director.

He is the author of many articles, one previous book, and over sixty patents.

INDEX

Acceptor support, spillover effect on, 215
Acetylene
  carbon black manufacture from, 112
  hydrogenation of, 120
Acid function, 234, 255
Acidification, of aluminate, 22
Acidity, of porous organic polymers, 189
Acrylonitrile, 160
Agglomeration, 1
Alcogel, 11
  as coalescing control, 95
Alcohol(s), dehydration of, 50, 192–193
Alcoholate hydrolysis, 24
Alfol alcohols, 13
Alite, 83
Alkaline earths, 80–84
Alkylaromatics, hydrodealkylation of, 121
Alkylation
  with graphite intercalates, 121
  reductive, with charcoal catalysts, 123
Alumina(s)
  as active catalyst, 49–50
  alpha, 11–13, 14
  amphoteric nature of, 11, 41–44
  Baymai, 24
  in catalytic-reforming catalysts, 253–254
  chi, 18
  as cocatalyst, 51–52
  crystalline species of, 11–13, 30
  defined, 14
  delta, 18
  electrical conductivity of, 206–209
  eta, xv, 18
  exothermicity of, 41
  flash, 25
  forming of, 25–29
  gamma, xv, 12, 18, 49
  hardness of, 13
  in honeycomb, 93
  hydrogen spillover effect on, 226

  kappa, 18
  melting point of, 11
  morphology of particles of, 29–32
  physicochemical properties of, 11–14,
    40–44
  point of zero charge of, 42
  porosity of, 13, 32–40
  preparation of, 13, 19–25
  structures of, 14–19
  as support, 46–49, 57
  surface models of, 44–46
  texture of, 29–40
  theta, 18
  transition, 18–19
  uses of, 13, 44–52
  wettability of, 40–41
Alumina binders, in zeolitic catalysts, 238,
  241
Alumina carriers, 53
Alumina gels
  extrusion of, 13, 27, 29
  preparation of, 22–24
  qualities of, 11
Aluminates
  acidification of, 22
  alkaline earth, 83
Aluminum oxides, 14
Aluminum oxyhydroxide, 14, 16–18
Aluminum salts, neutralization of, 22–24
Aluminum trihydroxides, 14–15, 31, 32–36
Amberlite polymers
  chemistry of, 176–178
  in MTBE synthesis, 195–197
  structure of, 162–165, 167, 168, 192,
    193
Amberlyst polymers, 192, 193, 194–197
p-Aminophenol, production of, 123–124,
  135–136
Ammonia formation, with graphite
  intercalates, 121